1992

The New Zealand Bed and Breakfast Book

Homes   Farms   Guest Houses

Compiled by J. and J. Thomas

Moonshine Press

Copyright ©1991. Janete and James Thomas

Published by Moonshine Press. 1991
27 Marine Drive, Mahina Bay,
Eastbourne, New Zealand
Telephone 04-562-8990, Fax 04-568-4679

ISBN 0-9597827-7-x
ISSN 0114-2232

Drawings by Gerald Bull

All information in this guidebook has been
supplied by the hosts. Information about the
homes listed is subject to change without notice.
Readers are asked to take this into account
when consulting this guide.

8 STAY PAGE

WHEN YOU HAVE STAYED AT 8 B&BS YOU CAN BE IN THE DRAW FOR 3 WEEKS **FREE** B&B FOR TWO

(More details over the page)

- You have to stay only 8 nights to be in the draw.

- The 8 STAY PAGE must be signed by the host at each place you stay.

- Send in your 8 STAY PAGE when it is full, to be in the draw for 3 weeks free B&B.

8 STAY PAGE

More Information

- Entries will be drawn on 21 December 1992 and the winner will be notified by mail immediately.
- Entries must be on the 8 STAY PAGE from *The New Zealand Bed and Breakfast Book.*
- Each 'box' must have the name and signature of the host and the date of stay.
- If you stay at the the same place more than 1 night the host simply signs and dates the 8 STAY PAGE again.
- Each person can have their own 8 STAY PAGE, eg a couple can fill in two 8 STAY PAGES.
- Every entry <u>accompanied by a comment form</u> will receive a gift voucher for a free *New Zealand Bed &Breakfast Book.*

The Prize

- The prizewinner will be given vouchers entitling them and a partner to stay 1 night and have breakfast at any 21 B&Bs they choose in *The New Zealand Bed and Breakfast Book.*
- The stays can be any time between 1st March 1993 and 31 October 1993. They need not be consecutive.

Complete the following sentences:

W_____ is the capital city of New Zealand.

Mount C_____ is the highest mountain in New Zealand.

Post your completed entry to:
The New Zealand Bed and Breakfast Book
Eight Stay Lucky Draw
P O Box 41022
Eastbourne, New Zealand

Name..

Address...

....

From letters on our file

Everyone we stayed with was helpful and made us feel welcome. Our vacation was a great success mostly due to our hosts and hostesses where we stayed.

SALT LAKE CITY, UTAH, USA

"I would certainly use the book again if I am lucky enough to return to New Zealand and will recommend it to friends. My only criticism – all the people were so hospitable that I chatted for hours and got very tired."

BROCKENHURST, HAMPSHIRE, ENGLAND

"We were delighted with your publication and the high standard of accommodation."

ASHFORD, KENT, ENGLAND

"Your book helped make our holiday brilliant. All of our hosts were lovely and we wouldn't have found them without your help.

DETROIT, MICHIGAN, USA

"Our farmstay holiday was tremendously successful. The hospitality extended to us was outstanding. All in all it was a wonderful experience and we are looking forward to planning another."

TAUPO, NEW ZEALAND

"I would like to say how much better your kind of accommodation is than motels."

KINGS LYNN, NORFOLK, ENGLAND

"Since discovering The New Zealand Bed and Breakfast Book my husband and I have used it regularly on our trips away from New Plymouth and we have been really pleased with both the accommodation and great hospitality offered."

NEW PLYMOUTH, NEW ZEALAND

5

New Zealand Regions

Northland

Great Barrier Island

Gisborne and District

Auckland

Waikato, Coromandel Peninsula, King Country

Bay of Plenty

Taranaki, Wanganui

Hawkes Bay

Manawatu

Wairarapa

Wellington

Nelson, Marlborough

Christchurch and District

Westland

Timaru, Oamaru District

Dunedin and District

Southland

Stewart Island

Contents

Introduction

The popularity of B&B in New Zealand has doubled each year since we first published *The New Zealand Bed and Breakfast Book*. The reason for this amazing growth is quite simply that the hosts are such wonderful people. The hosts who are listed here are homeowners who want to share their love of the country with travellers. Each listing has been written by the host, and you will discover their warmth and personality is obvious in their writing. Ours is not simply an accommodation guide but an introduction to a uniquely New Zealand holiday experience.

Any holiday is remembered primarily by the people one meets. How many of us have loved a country simply because of one or two especially memorable individuals encountered there? Bed and Breakfast offers the traveller who wants to experience the feel of the real country and get to know the people to do just that.

Bed and Breakfast in New Zealand means a warm welcome into someone's home. Most of the places listed are homes, with a sprinkling of private hotels and guesthouses. Remember that Bed and Breakfast hosts cannot offer hotel facilities. Therefore please telephone ahead to book your accommodation and give ample notice if you require dinner. Most of our B&Bs do not have credit card facilities.

Guarantee of Standards

Many B&Bs belong to national associations, which inspect the property, and guarantee the standard of facilities. The *NZ Association of Farm and Home Hosts* represents private homeowners; the *NZ B&B Hotels Federation,* and *Historic B&B Inns of NZ* represent the more commercial B&Bs. Hosts that display a *KiwiHost* logo have taken part in a special workshop which trains them in communication, customer relations and visitor industry skills. The symbols are shown on each listing.

We expect that all B&Bs in *The New Zealand Bed and Breakfast Book* will offer excellent hospitality. We ask you to let us know if you stay at one that does not come up to your expectations so that our very high standard can be maintained.

Tariff

Most hosts will charge rates which are fairly consistent throughout the country. Some rates vary because of facilities or location and these are shown in each listing. The prices listed will apply for the year 1992. There will be no extra costs to pay unless you request extra services. Some offer a reduction for children. Unless otherwise stated this applies to age 12 and under.

Self-Contained Accommodation

Many homes in towns and on farms can offer separate self-contained accommodation. In almost every case linen and food will be provided if required. The tariff will vary depending on your requirements, so check when booking.

Campervans

For those who get to know the country by camping or motor-home, Bed and Breakfast offers wonderful advantages. You will see in many listings the word 'campervans'. These homes have suitable facilities available such as laundry, bathroom, electricity and meals if necessary. The charge, usually for up to four people, is modest and is shown in each listing.

Finding Your Way Around

A satisfying part of compiling *The New Zealand Bed and Breakfast Book* is that we have been able to change an irritating aspect of most New Zealand guide books. Usually towns are listed alphabetically so that we hop about the country from such places as Akaroa to Auckland to Blenheim for example. This is infuriating to a reasonably well-travelled native like myself, so I imagine the despair of a visitor unfamiliar with place names and local geography.

New Zealand is long and narrow. It makes more sense to me to travel southwards down the islands listing the homes as we come to them. We have divided New Zealand into geographical regions and have included a map of each region. We have simply listed the homes as they occur on our southward journey. In areas such as Southland where we travel across more than down, the route we have taken should be quite obvious.

I picked up a young Japanese hitch-hiker near Wellington and asked him if I should include a list of problems which might arise for a traveller in New Zealand. He emphatically replied, "No. Because New Zealanders are so friendly they make everything OK!"

Whether you are from overseas or a fellow New Zealander, please take the opportunity to stay with New Zealanders in their homes. Chat with your hosts. Enjoy their company. Each host will be your additional personal travel agent and guide. They want to make everything in your holiday OK. We wish you an enjoyable holiday and welcome comments from guests. Please write with compliments or suggestions to:

The New Zealand Bed and Breakfast Book
Moonshine Press
27 Marine Drive
Mahina Bay
Eastbourne

Happy travelling
James Thomas

Northland

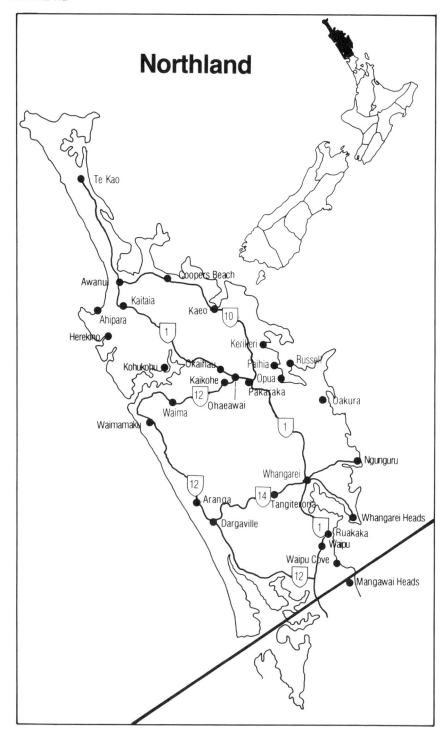

Te Kao, Far North
Tourist Lodge
Address: Te Kao Lodge, Far North Road, R.D. 4, Kaitaia
Name: Irene & Kim Lee
Telephone: (09) 409-7826
Beds: 3 Double, 4 Single, (4 ensuite bedrooms)
Tariff: Double $50, Single $25, Children 1/2 price, 3 Course Dinner $20, Campervans welcome
Nearest Town: Te Kao, 72 km North of Kaitaia

Explore and fish the winterless far North from the most central ensuite accomodation in the North. Over 40 World Game Fishing records have been broken by guests of the Lodge.
The lodge is situated on its own, amongst bush and farms at the South end of Parengarenga Harbour. We are situated 10 kms from Ninety Mile Beach, 10 kms from the East Coast Beaches and only 40 kms from Cape Reinga.
We have full Restaurant facilities with a liquor license pending. Guest lounge with TV and pool table.
Directions: *Continue 72 kms North of Kaitaia - we are approximately 2 kms past Te Kao General Store on the right hand side - we are well sign posted and situated just before a one way bridge.*

Awanui - Kaitaia
Farmstay
Address: Beach Road, Awanui R.D. 1, Northland
Name: Tony & Helen Dunn
Telephone: (09) 406-7494 (Before 8:00 am or evngs)
Beds: 2 Double (2 bedrooms, guest bathroom)
Tariff: B&B Double $70, Single $35, Children (under 10 yrs) 1/2 price, Dinner $20, Campervans $20
Nearest Town: Awanui 9 kms, Kaitaia 16 km

We have a comfortable, modern home, built for the sun and sea, on a hill overlooking the farm, the Aupouri Pine Forest and the Ninety Mile Beach.
"Ninety Mile Angoras" is a property of 40 hectares of rolling sand hill country, presently carrying cattle, sheep and goats.
Ninety Mile Beach, noted for its fishing, is one minute drive away to the West, while a feast of East Coast Beaches lie within thirty minutes easy drive. All have beautiful golden sands and unpolluted waters.
Many local tours and trips are available.
This home is an excellent central point to fully explore the North of New Zealand. Tour buses to the Cape pass the farm and will collect and deliver passengers from the farm gate.
Directions: *From Awanui, drive North approximately 6 kms. Turn left at signs to Ninety Mile Beach. Our farm is on the right, approximately 3 km after turn off, the last farm before the forestry and beach.*

11

Ahipara - Kaitaia
Tourist Lodge
Address: Siesta Guest House,
Tasman Heights Road,
P.O. Box 67, Ahipara
Name: Rolf and Hanna Stump
Telephone and Fax: (09) 409-4565
Beds: 2 Double (2 bedrooms, guest bathrooms)
Tariff: B&B Double $90, Single $60; Dinner $25 each
Nearest Town: Kaitaia 15 km

We are a family of four with two teenage girls, emigrated from Switzerland some 12 years ago to this beautiful country. As well as English we speak perfect German. Our home is especially designed and built as a guest house with the comfort and privacy of our guests in mind. It is situated on a large hillside section, 50 m above sea level. You have a fantastic panoramic view, overlooking the famous Ninety Mile Beach, Ahipara Bay and rocky shore with sandhills to the left. The setting is very peaceful, framed by pine trees and the gentle rolling ocean beyond. The European-style house is solidly built with concrete to offer maximum quietness, faces north and receives all day sun.

Each of the large double guest rooms has natural timber ceilings, comfortable queen-size beds, colour TV, radio and writing desk, has its own bathroom, tea- and coffee-making facilities and sheltered balcony with uninterrupted sea views; even a sea view out of your bed.

Our house is most ideal for couples or anybody wanting to get away from it all and enjoy a clean environment with plenty of outdoor activities. As we will host no more than four people at any one time, we can provide you with the best of service in all aspects. Also we can offer you full board with a first class evening meal, served in our spacious family dining room.

Directions: *Take the road to the west coast from Kaitaia. Drive straight past Ahipara Primary School 1.2 km until you see the beach. Right opposite to the left you see the"Tasman Heights" sign. Follow the tar-sealed road right to the top, then follow the "Siesta" signs.*

All telephone numbers in New Zealand are
being changed, so the numbers listed may not be current.
Ring 018 for directory assistance if you cannot contact your hosts.

Coopers Beach

Beachfront Retreat
Address: The Caber, 8 Braemar Ave,
Coopers Beach, R.D. 3, Kaitaia
Name: Roland R Parsons
Telephone & Fax: (09) 406 0399
Beds: 2 Double, 1 Twin, 6 Single (9 bedrooms, 3 Guest bathrooms)
Tariff: varies by season and room, dinner by arrangement.
Nearest Town: Kaitaia to the North and Mangonui to the South

*Walk out of The Caber across the lawn and sand and swin in the blue Pacific!
This is a unique beachfront home with direct access onto beautiful Coopers
Beach. Large, modern and spacious, the home is fully carpeted with superb
views of the expansive sea. There is a separate lounge, dining room, kitchen,
TV lounge and breakfast room. Beds have blankets, fairydown underlays and
duvets. Bathrooms are adjacent. Most rooms overlook the sea and open onto
decks for you to enjoy the consistently above average high temperatures.
Decor includes natural timbers which combine with comfortable furniture to
ensure an atmosphere of rest and relaxation.
For the computer minded a fast IBM compatible 80386 work station is
available. For the fitness minded, I am preparing a well equipped home
gymnasium. Overseas guests, travellers and mature young adults are very
welcome. I am a bachelor, former Air Force Officer, travelled extensively and
will meet you at Kaitaia Airport or off your coach.*

Kaeo

Homestay
Address: Te Ngaere Beach,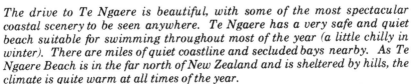
Wainui Bay Road, Kaeo
Name: John and Christine McBain
Telephone: (09) 405 0249
Beds: 2 Double, 2 Single (3 bedrooms, guest bathroom)
Tariff: B&B Double $55 Single $30, Children $12; Dinner $18;
Nearest Town: About 35 kms north of Kerikeri

*The drive to Te Ngaere is beautiful, with some of the most spectacular
coastal scenery to be seen anywhere. Te Ngaere has a very safe and quiet
beach suitable for swimming throughout most of the year (a little chilly in
winter). There are miles of quiet coastline and secluded bays nearby. As Te
Ngaere Beach is in the far north of New Zealand and is sheltered by hills, the
climate is quite warm at all times of the year.
Accommodation - separate one/two bedroom flat with private bathroom or
one bedroom upstairs overlooking the bay (share bath with hosts). Your
hosts are well travelled and have enjoyed the company of guests from many
countries. We are keen botanists and enjoy gardening.
Other attractions – yacht charters available, fishing and diving, sub-tropical
rain forest one hour away by car.*
Directions: *travel north from Kerikeri on Highway 10 for approx 15 km to
Matauri Bay Road (which is well signposted). Turn right onto Matauri Bay
Road and follow the road signs to Te Ngaere Bay. There are few houses at
Te Ngaere Bay, so our house is easily found.*

Herekino, Northland
Farmstay, Self-contained Accom
Address: Tui Inn Farm, Puhata Road, Herekino C M Box 11A
Name: Grant & Tangi Davan
Telephone: (09) 409-3883
Beds: 2 Double, 4 Single (2 bedrooms with guest bathroom)
Tariff: **B&B** $60 Double, $30 Single, children $5, Dinner $15
Nearest Town: Kaitaia (25 km)

Farm Stay Plus - we would like to invite you to stay on our 'life-style' farmlet and experience our friendly hospitality at Herekino near Kaitaia in the subtropical North.

The Tui Inn Lodge is a self-contained accommodation unit, it will sleep up to 8 people, is fully furnished with TV and self contained laundry. Food is available to buy or meals prepared on request, plus barbeque and hangi facilities. The lodge is set in native bush overlooking a large orchard where farm animals freely graze.

We also provide conducted trips, diving, fishing, horse riding, camping and hunting plus 4 wheel drive tours to Cape Reinga and Ahipara gumfields and sand dunes.

Directions: *Take the West Coast road to Herekino from either Kaitaia (25 km) or Mangamuka Bridge (42 km). Tui Inn Farm is well signposted from Herekino. For bookings please phone or write to the above address.*

The standard of accommodation in *The New Zealand Bed and Breakfast Book* ranges from homely to luxurious, but you can always be sure of superior hospitality.

Kohu Kohu
Farmstay
Address: Hawkins Road, Motukaraka,
Kohu Kohu, R.D. 1, Hokianga,
Name: Catherine & John Bawden
Telephone: (09) 405-5534
Beds: 1 Double, 3 Single (2 bedrooms)
Tariff: B&B $50 Double, $25 Single, Children 1/2 price - under 4 free,
Dinner $14
Nearest Town: Kohu Kohu - 8 kms

Motukaraka is a peaceful rural retreat on the Northern side of the picturesque Hokianga Harbour.
Our home is a former schoolhouse recently renovated using natural timber milled on the farm and offering beautiful views of the harbour. We are a family of four with two young children. I am formerly from Ireland, my husband John is a New Zealander and we run a dairy farm.
The location is ideal for walking and tramping, close to the rugged West coast beaches and historic settlements that were once the thriving hub of early New Zealand.
Come and enjoy the hospitality, tranquillity and pace of life that is distinctly Hokianga.
Directions: *2.5 km West of the Northern vehicular ferry terminal, turn right into Hawkins Road, we are 200 metres along the road on the right.*

Kerikeri
Homestay
Address: Bulls Road, RD3, Highway 10
Name: Jetske Zijderveld
Telephone: (09) 4079-220
Beds: 2 Double, 3 Single (3 bedrooms, guests bathroom)
Tariff: B&B Double $55, Single $30
Nearest Town: Kerikeri 5 minutes, Paihia 15 minutes

Our house is warm and sunny. It is nearly new with 3 double bedrooms for guests (one with twin beds) and one small room with a single bed. The house has 2 bathrooms, so you have your own for your use.
We are on a 16 acre farmlet with beautiful rural views on all sides overlooking Waimate North.
Kerikeri is situated in the Bay of Islands and is ideally situated to explore the area. Our house is 5 minutes drive from Kerikeri and 15 minutes from Paihia.
Directions: *On State Highway 10 with a 'Bed and Breakfast' sign outside so it is easy to find. Please phone for further details.*

15

Kerikeri

Homestay
Address: Matariki Orchard,
Pa Road, Kerikeri
Name: David & Alison Bridgman
Telephone: (09) 407-7577
Beds: 1 Double, 2 Single (2 bedrooms, guest bathroom)
Tariff: B&B $60 Double, $35 Single, children $15, Dinner $20,
Campervans $20
Nearest Town: Kerikeri (4 mins), Paihia (20 mins)

David and I would like to welcome you to our 4 bedroom brick home, set in the seclusion and privacy of a small mixed citrus and sub-tropical orchard, with a garden of colourful mature trees and swimming pool. Our family of 4 have left home and we are now interested in meeting and entertaining people from all walks of life.
We are fortunate in having travelled extensively around New Zealand and overseas and look forward to sharing our knowledge and experiences with others.
Kerikeri, the earliest settled area in New Zealand is widely known for its history, culture and many crafts and scenery. We are close to the famous Stone Store, Kemp House and have local sporting and bridge clubs and many scenic bush walks.
Local tours to Cape Reinga and cruises around the Bay of Islands can be arranged. We would love to provide a 3 course dinner of locally grown foods and wine, but if this is not required, there are many restaurants to choose from. Kerikeri supports an airport and a regular bus service. We would be happy to meet you.
Directions: *Turn off Highway 10 into Kerikeri township - turn right into Cobham Road, which runs into Inlet Road and Pa Road is first on the left. We are the 2nd house on the right.*

Kerikeri

Homestay
Address: "The Gables",
Cnr SH 10 and
Te Ahuahu Road,
Puketona, Kerikeri
Name: Margaret Dines
Telephone: (0887) 68623
Beds: 2 Double, 2 single (3 bedrooms, guest bathroom)
Tariff: B&B Double $80, Single $40, Dinner on request,
Nearest Town: Kerikeri 7 mins, Paihia 12 mins

"The Gables" is a charming Country House with beautiful gardens, set in delightful rural surroundings and offering a comfortable and peaceful stay.
We live in an area rich in early colonial history, and we are centrally situated for the beautiful Bay of Islands with its many attractions.
Enjoy a full English style breakfast of your choice from my country kitchen. Vegetarians are catered for.
Come , relax and enjoy.

Kerikeri, Waimate North

Farmstay
Address: "Aspley House", Waimate North, RD3, Kerikeri
Name: Frank and Joy Atkinson
Telephone: (09) 4059-509
Beds: 1 Double, 2 Single (2 bedrooms, each with own bathroom)
Tariff: B&B $50 per person; Dinner $25;
Nearest Town: Kerikeri 10 mins, Paihia 15 mins, Kerikeri Airport 10 mins

At "Aspley House" we provide superior accommodation. Visitors who stay here get a bonus. Guests have the advantage of learning about local history from folk who are both descended from pioneer stock, dating back to the 1820's. The two large twin-bedded rooms have French doors which open on to a large verandah overlooking a small lake and beyond to rolling farmland. The modern bathroom is for guests' use only. When guests are not soaking up the local history or taking in the Bay of Islands activities, the Atkinson's visitors ride on Frank's tractor across some of the 750 acres where he runs Hereford cattle and Romney sheep. Others are just content to stroll around the spacious lawns and landscaped gardens or laze beside an inviting kidney-shaped swimming pool. The three course gourmet evening meals in the formal dining room feature homegrown produce and a good selection of local wines. The family antiques contribute to the charm of this stately and attractive colonial-styled home.
Two pets - Jack Russell terrier and black cat.
We look forward to sharing our home with you.
Directions: *3 km west off SH10 at Puketona Junction.*

Please let your hosts know if you have to cancel.
They will have spent time preparing for you.

17

Paihia
Homestay
Address: 31 Selwyn Road,
Paihia, Bay of Islands
Name: Bill and Bunny Lind
Telephone: (09) 402-7182
Beds: 3 Single (2 bedrooms)
Tariff: B&B Double $55, Single $35,
Continental breakfast only - "Kiwi" Style

We are a retired couple who enjoy meeting people from all walks of life. Our family are grown up and we now have only one daughter here who is a hostess on the cruise ships in our lovely bay. Our special interests are outdoor bowling and china painting.

We are only a two minute walk from the beach and a five minute walk from all the shops and restaurants. The departure points for all tours and cruises are within the five minute walk.

Our home is a modern 2-storey townhouse with a spacious open plan living area and a sea and bush outlook. We have one single bedroom downstairs and one twin room upstairs. The bathroom is on a shared basis, with one toilet downstairs and one upstairs.

Being non-smokers ourselves we thank you for not smoking in the house.

Although we have Continental breakfast only it is of a very generous proportion and variety.

Paihia can offer many lovely walks in bush and beach. We love our town and enjoy sharing it with others.

Directions: *Turn left at the Post Office, then the first turn right which is Selwyn Road. We are the last house on the right.*

Paihia
Homestay
Address: 6 Moana Avenue, Paihia
Name: Patricia Beaufoy
Telephone: (09) 402-7201
Beds: 3 Single, (2 bedrooms, guest bathroom)
Tariff: B&B $50 Double, $30 Single - self-contained flat sometimes available.
Nearest Town: Paihia

Two storeyed modern home, spacious, split-level, open plan in central Paihia. Outstanding views over the waterfront, wharf, town, to the islands in the bay to Russell. Lovely beaches, swimming, boating, bus tours, cruises, shopping, restaurants all within short walking distance of 5 mins.

I enjoy meeting people from other countries and would make you very welcome. Cooked breakfast is provided.

Directions: *Turn left at the Post Office into Williams Road, then the first turn on the right into Selwyn Road. Continue along to the Bounty corner. Turn left into Bayview Road, Moana Ave is a few metres along on the right. The house is the third on the left. I am happy to meet the bus in Paihia.*

Paihia, Northland

Guesthouse
Address: The Totaras, 6 School Road, Paihia, Bay of Islands
Name: Frank & Christine Habicht
Telephone: (09) 402-8238
Beds: 2 Double, 1 Single (1 bedroom, 1 self-contained apartment, 2 guest bathrooms)
Tariff: B&B Double $80, Single $60, (reductions for longer stays), Dinner $15. Above rates apply to "NZ B&B Book" holders only.
Nearest Town: Paihia

In 1982 Christine my wife and our two sons Florian and Sebastian moved from Berlin to the beautiful Bay of Islands. We built and operated with success a Motel in Paihia.

Since December 1990 we enjoy life from a hill-top residency and want to share our happiness with you. We are overlooking Paihia harbour, historic Waitangi, Russell and various smaller islands. The view from all rooms, sundeck and terraces are simply stunning. All guest areas have separate entrance, decor and furnishings are of best quality and taste. English / German library. We are in the centre of township within walking minutes to safe beaches, wharf (ferry ride to Russell 15mins), restaurants and shopping centre. A 5 minute bushwalk also leads to town and a coastal track. In summer you are welcome to enjoy our pool and should you be in a hurry, steps will also take you downtown in no time.

We arrange all tours and provide courtesy car from Paihia Wharf (bus terminal). A rich German breakfast is served in our conservatory, which is always at your leisure. Besides travelling and meeting people my life has always been devoted to photography. My book "Young London" was published in the 'sixties.

For bookings and directions please phone or write.

Paihia

Farmstay, Homestay
Address: "Wairoa" Overseas Visitor Farm Home Stays, PO Box 36, Bayly Road, Waitangi, Paihia, Bay of Islands
Name: Dorothy Bayly
Telephone: (09) 4027-379
Beds: 1 Double, 2 Single (2 bedrooms, guest bathroom)
Tariff: B&B Double $76, Single $38, Dinner $38; Children $28
Nearest Town: Paihia

My two storeyed farm home is built on the sea front set in gardens with tennis court, overlooking historic Russell. Situated 5 minutes from the tourist town of Paihia, through Waitangi Golf Course.
Bedrooms have sea views. Electric blankets on beds.
Enjoyable farm walks, lots of bird life.
Private beach. Tennis raquet and balls provided.
"Wairoa" Farm was bought by my father-in-law in 1929. This coastal farm plus another undeveloped 1000 acre block purchased by us 30 years ago was developed by my husband.
We farm Romney sheep and Angus-cross cattle, dairy beef bulls for the American market, also Cashgora goats.
My married daughter and husband and family live on the farm in the old homestead built in 1838. My daughter trains and rides show jumping horses.
TV, tea and coffee making facilities and laundry are available for guests.
We will arrange deep-sea, line fishing, sailing trips and bus tours. If you wish to dine at one of the fine restaurants in Paihia we will book for you.
Please pre-book to save disappointment. We can also meet the bus in Paihia for a small charge. Looking forward to your stay.

Paihia, Bay of Islands
Homestay
Address: Puketona Road, Paihia, Bay of Islands
Name: DL & MA Ogilvy
Telephone: (09) 402-7041
Beds: 2 Double, 1 Single (3 bedrooms, guest bathroom)
Tariff: B&B $70 Double, $35 Single, $15 Dinner
Nearest Town: Paihia

Our small holding (10 acres) is conveniently situated five miles from Paihia in the Bay-of-Islands and provides ready access to beaches, historical places, deep sea fishing, local tours and a number of golf courses including the picturesque Waitangi International.
We graze a few sheep and cattle and have 500 assorted fruit trees. Our homemade jams and preserves are served with meals.
Our comfortable Lockwood house is set in park like grounds with a large lawn and a variety of flowering trees and shrubs. The atmosphere is quiet and peaceful.
We have a wide variety of interests, are well travelled and enjoy the company of local and overseas guests. We do request that our guests be non-smokers.
Directions: *We can be found on the Paihia - Kerikeri road and the "Lily Pond Orchard" sign is at our gate.*

Paihia
Homestay
Address: Puketona Lodge, Puketona Road, Paihia

Name: Heather and Maurice Pickup
Telephone and Fax: (09) 4028-152
Beds: 1 Double, 2 Single (2 bedrooms, guest bathroom)
Tariff: B&B Double $55, Single $45, Children $20, Dinner $16.50
Nearest Town: Paihia

We are a semi-retired couple of English / NZ origins who lived in America for a number of years.
Our modern home features native woods and is spacious and comfortable. The guests' bedrooms are large and have access to outside verandah. There is a separate bathroom and shower for guests.
We are situated on a 10 acre property that we hope to develop into a farmlet. We have lovely rural views and are close to beaches, golf course and bush walks. Tour buses to Cape Reinga, etc pass the gate.
We are 5 minutes from Haruru Falls, 10 minutes from Paihia, 15 minutes from Kerikeri.
We are on the main Paihia-Kerikeri Road, but as there are no street numbers, please phone for directions.
Our interests are gardening, ceramics and crafts.
A cooked breakfast is provided or continental if preferred. Dinner available on request and vegetarians are welcome. Non-smokers preferred.

21

Russell, Bay of Islands
Homestay
Address: Titore Way, Russell, Bay of Islands
Name: Morrell & Diana Folley
Telephone: (09) 403-7658 **Fax:** (09) 403-7388
Beds: 1 Double, 2 Single (2 bedrooms, guest bathroom)
Tariff: **B&B** $67 Double, $35 Single, children under 12 1/2 price, $20 Dinner
Nearest Town: Russell

Overlooking the historic town of Russell with million dollar views of the Bay and Pacific, our home is set in a tranquil cul-de-sac with bush and beach walks starting from the property. There is a dinghy in our secluded beach, free for guests to use, and we also have available a 21ft cabin cruiser for light tackle fishing or picnics around the islands.
A couple of comments from our visitors' book "One hundred percent better than the Auckland hotel I paid a fortune for". Another summed up her feelings with "Making new friends in such a beautiful place is what I'd hoped my vacation would be".
Breakfast is cooked or continental, Dinner is three course and wine is served with the meal. (Seafood a speciality).
We are the proprietors of NZ Host Homes Ltd, and are therefore able to assist with ongoing accommodation and also have major credit-card facilities.

Russell
Homestay
Address: Wellington Street, Russell
Name: Kay Bosanquet
Telephone: (09) 403 7843
Beds: 2 Double, 1 Single, 1 twin
Tariff: B&B Double $77, Twin $77, Single $44

My home overlooks Russell Bay with magnificent water and bush views. Born and bred in Northland I take great pride in showing my guests NZ's first capital. I love every type of fishing and frequently escort my guests out game fishing. I am a national doll collector and I love the world coming to stay with me.
Meals are usually served on the terrace. Although I will serve all meals if requested I have found my guests like to explore and sample the different fish restaurants that abound in Russell.
We have several lovely walks handy, as well as golf, bowls, diving, cruises and yacht charters.
I also belong to Russell RSA, bowling, gamefishing and yachting clubs and if my guests wish to meet our locals I take them to whichever club interests them.
All I ask of my guests is to completely relax and use my home as theirs.
Directions: *by car - take Opua car ferry to Russell and you will be met.*
By bus - choice of Northliner right to Russell or Intercity Services to Paihia, then ferry to Russell where you will be met.
By plane - to Kerikeri and you will be met by bus to Paihia ferry.
Please phone and I will meet buses, ferries, etc.

Russell

Homestay
Address: Robertson Street, Russell
Postal: (PO Box 203)
Name: Dudley and Sharyn Smith
Telephone: (09) 403-7200 (Fax 403-7537)
Beds: Private facilities in self-contained unit. Sleeps 4
Tariff: B&B Double $75, Single $65, Children $20; Campervan Facilities $25

Our new home is situated on an elevated section in the historic town of Russell. We have magnificent views of the town and Russell Harbour.
Our home has a large basement flat with its own shower, toilet and coffee-making facilities. This area has excellent views and good parking. As our kitchen, dining area and lounge is all open living it becomes very easy for guests to make themselves at home.
We operate an 11.5 metre charter boat for big game and light tackle fishing and would imagine our guests to be people who like the sea and perhaps intend to go fishing with us.
Directions: *Please phone when you arrive.*

Russell

Homestay
Address: Jacks Bay, No. 1 RD, Russell, Bay of Islands
Name: Marie C. Graham
Telephone: (09) 4037-322 before 9 am and after 5.30 pm; (09) 4041-582 from 10 am to 4 pm
Beds: 4 Single (2 bedrooms, guest bathroom)
Tariff: B&B Double $65, Single $35; Campervans $20 (no more than 4 people); Dinner $15 per person
Nearest Town: Russell 16 km

My house is situated approximately 16 km from Russell on a metal road, just above the Jack and Jill Resort. Near the beach with lovely views of the sea and islands.
A quiet situation and very peaceful.
I am a farmer's widow and live alone with one corgi dog who is very gentle and loving and lives inside.
Guests have separate bathroom and toilet facilities. I work part time for social welfare so some days I am out during the middle of the day.
Directions: *To reach my place you turn off the Opua–Russell road at Oronga Bay onto a metal road, follow the road to Jacks Bay. It is well signposted. I am on the left side of the road just after the entrance to the camp – my house is painted green and white.*

Russell
Homestay
Address: Major Bridge Drive, Te Wahapu, Russell
Name: Eva and Denis Brown
Telephone: (09) 4037-431
Beds: 1 Double, 1 Single (1 Bedroom, guest bathroom)
Tariff: B&B Double $60, Single $35, Child half price; Dinner $17
Nearest Town: Russell, 7 km by car or 20 minutes
rowing by our faering rowboat.

Our wooden house is near a quiet beach in a sheltered bay. We recommend walking shoes to our guests because our parking area is on the top of the hill and our house is by the water. A footpath leads down through a tunnel of native ferns, kanukas and manukas.

We provide a 15-foot rowboat free for fishing or crossing to Russell, the historic first capital of New Zealand. It is a small village with a museum and historic buildings, tourist boats, yacht charters, gourmet restaurants and the visitors' centre of the Bay of Islands Maritime and Historic Park.

Beach walks start from our door, and many bays, Maori pas, kauri forests and historic sites are only a short drive or sail away from our house.

Dinners may be arranged and special diets are catered for. Breakfasts range from muesli, fresh fruit and wholemeal bread to eggs and bacon to order.

Please phone ahead (in the evening) as we only have one guest room. We can pick up guests at the ferry on the Russell wharf or at the Te Wahapu stop of the Northliner bus.

Russell
Self-Contained
Accommodation
Address: PO Box 54,
Te Wahapu, Russell
Name: Carole Titus Hotchkiss
Telephone: (09) 4037-076, or 4037-854
Beds: 1 Queensize and 1 Queensize sofa bed in lounge (guest bathroom)
Tariff: B&B Double $85, Single $65, Dinner $20
Nearest Town: Russell 6 km

We are Americans who fell in love with the Bay of Islands at first sight and have been residents for 10 years now. We built our California-style home atop a ten acre estate of the most spectacular views of the Bay and are happy to offer our first class separate guest house to visitors who wish the ultimate in comfort and independence. Suitable for long term or overnight, this residence has it all. Your views range from quiet bays to the active panorama between Paihia and Russell, and cruise liners often moor in front of us on their visits to the Bay of Islands. You can either be private and independent, or as involved with us as you wish, although my husband is often away as he commutes to LA to fly the 747-400 for United Airlines. We feature cholesterol conscious menus and offer "happy hour" on the terrace at sunset. There is fishing, golf, swimming, cruising the waters, or walking the beaches or bush tracks. The historic town of Russell is just minutes away by car and offers attractions to charm all tastes. Please write to PO Box 54, Russell or phone well ahead.

Opua, Bay of Islands
Homestay
Address: Oromahoe Road, Opua, Bay of Islands
Name: Pat & Don Jansen
Telephone: (09) 402-8099
Beds: 1 Double, 2 Single, (2 bedrooms, guest bathroom)
Tariff: Double $55, Single $35, Children 1/2 price, Dinner $15
Nearest Town: Paihia 5 km

We are a semi retired couple who enjoy meeting people and sharing our home and surroundings with them.
We have a new home situated on a quiet peaceful site surrounded by native bush and enjoying sea and rural views. Both guest rooms open onto a deck.
Our interests are gardening, sailing and fishing. We offer personal tours by arrangement.
Opua is a small seaside town, one hour's drive North of Whangarei. Drive North on State Highway 1 continuing on to the Opua Paihia Road at Kawaklawa. Detailed directions available when booking.
Bus stop 2 minutes drive. Russell car ferry 6 mins. Paihia 5 km, 6 mins.
The area has beautiful bush and coastal walks, boat trips to explore the bay, a superb golf course and gourmet restaurants. We look forward to meeting you.

Russell
Self-contained Accommodation
Address: Wairoro Park, Aucks Road, PO Box 53, Okiato, Russell
Name: Yan and Beryl Boerop
Telephone: (09) 403-7255
Beds: 1 Double, 3 Single (2 bedrooms, guest bathroom, 3 self-contained chalets)
Tariff: B&B Double $68, Single $68
Nearest Town: Russell

Wairoro Park is a 160 acre (60 ha.) coastal estate in central Bay of Islands. Two thirds is native bush and on the remainder we breed pedigree Limousin cattle. The property includes a private sandy beach and grouped around it we have built three A frame holiday chalets. Each chalet is fully self-contained with private shower, bath, colour TV, fully equipped kitchen and large lounge with sundeck. Upstairs there are two separate bedrooms, one with a king size double bed, the other with three singles. At the beach you will find a choice of boats including motor, sail and rowboat plus a kayak and surf sailer. Just behind the beach is a large lawn with garden furniture, a trampoline and a covered barbeque pagoda to cook your freshly caught fish.
We came to New Zealand some 20 odd years ago as refugees from the European rat race and we enjoy having the time and the opportunity to meet and get to know many different people.
Wij spreken Nederlands.
Wir sprechen Deutsch.

Okaihau, Bay of Islands

Farmstay
Address: Wiroa Road, R.D. 1, Okaihau
Name: Neville & Shennett Clotworthy
Telephone: (09) 401-9371
Beds: 4 Single (2 bedrooms, guest bathroom)
Tariff: B&B $60 Double, $30 Single, children
half price, $20 Dinner, Campervans $20
Nearest Town: Kerikeri 11 kms, Okaihau 8 kms.

We have sheep, cattle and a horse stud on our 280 acre farm and as our home is sited 1000 feet above sea level, we have fantastic views of the Bay of Islands. Next to the house we have a native bush walk, complete with resident Kiwis. The Okaihau Golf Club is only 1 km away. Having travelled overseas we understand the needs of tourists. Puketi Kauri Forest, Hokianga area, Kerikeri, Kaikohe and Paihia are only minutes away.
We have both descended from families that settled in Northland last century and our special interests are farming, genealogy, Northland history and we are involved in Equestrian sports in the North.
Directions: *8 kms from State Highway 1, take the Kerikeri Road, 500 metres South of Okaihau, and we are the 3rd house on the left, past the golf course. / 9 kms from State Highway 10. Take Wiroa Road at the Kerekeri intersection and we are the first house on the right past the bridge.*

Pakaraka, Bay of Islands, Central

Farmstay
Address: Pakaraka, SH1, RD2, Kaikohe
Name: Ken and Glenis MacKintosh
Telephone: (09) 404-1040
Beds: 1 Double, 3 Single (2 bedrooms, 2 guest bathrooms and toilets)
Tariff: B&B Double $70, Single $36, Dinner $28 3-course, Children half price
Nearest Town: Kawakawa

We have a beautiful 51 acre property with historic stone walls, sheep, cattle, pigs and goats.
Ken trains dogs - you can enjoy watching and help shift the Romney sheep and the bulls. Maybe try your hand at shearing a sheep or goat. Take a farm walk to see the historic Pouerua Mountain. We are centrally situated only 15 minutes to Paihia, Kerikeri, Kaikohe, golf, bowls, beaches, shopping, tours, Ngapha Springs, Kawakawa Vintage Rail train ride and only one hour from Kaitaia or Whangarei. The "Romney Northwool Trials" are in progress on our farm. The "Murray Grey Bull Trials" are also grazed on our farm. Our cats are named "Monkey" and "Governor-Grey" - you will understand why when you meet them.
You can enjoy the summer with a dip in our swimming pool. We have a pool table, TV, video. A cosy warm home in winter. Horse rides can be arranged.
Skin-care and beauty treatment by appointment (in-home clinic). In-home shopping: Environmentally safe products / skin-care, personal care gifts, perfumes, etc. Catalogues and price list available.
Directions: *Easy to find, SH1. 10 minutes north of Kawakawa. 1 km south Pakaraka-Kerikeri junction*

27

Kaikohe
**Homestay +
Campervan Park**
Address: Waima Lodge,
Main Road, Waima,
South Hokianga.
Postal: RD 3, Kaikohe
Name: Dennis and Pearl Horne
Telephone: (09) 405-3836 (evenings preferred). Fax (09) 405-3836
Beds: 1 Double, 1 Twin (ensuite bathrooms)
Tariff: B&B Double $70, Single $40; Dinner $25
Nearest Town: Kaikohe 26 km, Opononi 26 km, Rawene 17 km

*We have a lovely old kauri homestead set in 4 acres of orchards and gardens
by the Waima river and mountains. We enjoy cooking and will be serving all
our home-grown fruit and vegetables. We enjoy meeting people from all
over the world and to show them the beauty and local history of the area.
We are situated within a short distance of most of Northland's attractions,
such as the Waipoua kauri forest, Opononi beaches, Kaitaia and the Bay of
Islands. We are ideal as a touring base.
We have no children but 2 friendly dogs and 2 cats.*
Directions: *Our house is on State Highway 12 about midway between
Kaikohe and Opononi. Look for signs and our store and tea rooms.*

Waimamaku
Guest House
Address: Solitaire Guest House, SH12, Waimamaku, South Hokianga
Name: Betty and Lloyd White
Telephone: (09) 405-4891
Beds: 2 Double, 4 Single (4 bedrooms, guest bathroom)
Tariff: B&B Double $50 + GST, Single $30 + GST, Dinner $15 + GST;
Campervans
Nearest Town: Kaikohe 70 km

*Our home is a restored colonial style Kauri homestead situated in the
Waimamaku Valley, 6 km north of the Waipoua Kauri Forest, close to the
Hokianga Harbour and west coast beaches. We have an adult family all
way from home and having travelled ourselves we enjoy meeting people
and sharing experiences while offering a little piece of Kiwi hospitality.
Accommodation is two rooms with double beds and two rooms each with
two single beds. Guests share showers (2) and toilets (2) facilities. We have
30 acres of farmland bordered by two rivers which make a pleasant before
or after dinner walk.*

Kamo, Whangarei
Homestay
Address: 1 Ascot Avenue,
Kamo, Whangarei
Name: David & Ruth Flower
Telephone: (09) 435-0234
Beds: 1 Double, 1 Single (2 bedrooms, share guest bathroom)
Tariff: **B&B** $50 Double, $25 Single, children 1/2 price, Dinner $15,
Campervans welcome
Nearest Town: Whangarei (4 km North)

*We are a couple whose grown-up family has flown the nest, allowing us to
welcome guests to our comfortable home. The large lounge invites relaxation
or a game of pool if you wish.*
*Double bedroom has a ranchslider opening onto a deck, with table and chairs.
Double bed with 'Woolrest' sleeper and electric blankets on all beds for winter
nights. We offer a sparkling swimming pool for summer swims; a sauna
room any time - great for relaxing those travel weary bodies.*
Our outlook is rural and city views.
*There is parking, power supply, downstairs shower and toilet for
campervans. Laundry has an electronic washing machine and a drier.*
*David is an electrical contractor and Ruth a teacher, enjoying her green-house
plants and gardens. Both are keen NZ and overseas travellers.*
Member of Lions International.

Kamo, Whangarei
Self-Contained Accommodation
Address: Dip Road, Kamo, Whangarei (PO Box 4041, Kamo)
Name: Jock and Corin Elliot
Telephone: (09) 435-1427
Beds: 1 Double, 1 Single in self-contained unit (guest bathroom)
Tariff: B&B Double $50, Single $35, Children half-price
Nearest Town: 8 km north from Whangarei City Centre

*Our home is situated on the outskirts of the city of Whangarei amidst two
acres of ground. We have a large garden which provides us with a plentiful
supply of fresh, organically grown vegetables and fruit. We share the property with three sheep, a dozen free-range hens – their handsome lord and
master and a hive of bees. A native bush reserve runs along our eastern
boundary.*
*Guests are accommodated in a self-contained unit which has a double and
single bed, its own bathroom and cooking facilities and opens through glass
doors directly onto a private area of the garden.*
*If you play golf the nearest course is five minutes' walk away and a thirty
minute drive will take you to a variety of beaches and the deep sea fishing
base at Tutukaka. And, if you enjoy sailing we can arrange to take you out
on the harbour – weather and tides permitting!*
Directions: *Travel north via State Highway 1 to the Kamo traffic lights at
the intersection of Kamo Road and Three Mile Bush Road. Take the left turn
into Three Mile Bush Road and after 1.1 km turn right into Dip Road. A further 1.1 km and you will see our name on the right at the entranceway.*

Whangarei
Homestay
Address: Bukit Landing, Manganese Point Rd, Whangarei
P O Box 351, Whangarei
Name: Nelson and Jean Williams
Telephone: (09) 436-2304
Beds: 1 King, 1 Double, 2 Single (3 bedrooms, 2 guest bathrooms)
Tariff: Dinner Bed &Breakfast $66 per person per day
Nearest Town: Whangarei

Bukit Landing sums up all that is best in a New Zealand vacation. The gentle waves of the Pacific lapping at the doorstep, the lush greenery of native bush and more peace and good food than you can probably imagine. Bukit Landing is for those who wish to sidestep cities and overcrowded resorts, and enjoy the tranquillity and outdoor life of this beautiful coastal setting. Sailing, fishing, wind-surfing, swimming, golf, tennis, bush walks, and gazing at the sunset.... these are the things that occupy the time of our guests.

This seclusion and privacy, though is only 16 kilometres from the city of Whangarei and only a two hour drive or 40 minute flight from Auckland. The Bay of Islands is less than a one hour drive away. Transport to and from the airport is complimentary.

The personal attention of your hosts, Nelson, Jean and Sally Williams will ensure that you get exactly the vacation you wish. Advice on the tides and the right bait from Nelson, windsurfing lesson from Sally and the fish you catch cooked to perfection by Jean. A windsurfer and four metre boat with sails and outboard motor are yours to use at no extra charge.

A stay a Bukit Landing includes two meals a day - lunch extra. All are the delicious creations of the Cordon Bleu talents of Jean & Sally, and accompanied by excellent New Zealand wines. And there's nothing like a balmy evening on the patio, watching the sun go down across the bay and enjoying one of Nelson's barbecue dinners.

A maximum of six guests can be accommodated at Bukit Landing, staying in three pleasantly appointed double rooms, all with a view, on the upper storey of the lodge. The upper storey is totally dedicated to guests and also includes two bathrooms, patio area and large lounge and dining area.
Directions: *For reservations please telephone.*

Whangarei
Farmstay
Address: 59 Pukenui Road, Whangarei
Name: Patricia and Owen Flower
Telephone: (089) 488-080
Beds: 4 Single (2 bedrooms, guest bathroom)
Tariff: B&B $50 Double, $35 Single, children 1/2 price, $15 Dinner
Nearest Town: Whangarei

Our comfortable home is situated on a secluded twelve acre block with panoramic views of the town, countryside, native bush and coast. We have a variety of farm animals and our own vegetable garden and orchard. We are five minutes by car from the town centre and within walking distance to such tourist attractions as the "Kiwi House" and Whangarei Heritage Museum and park. We are within a half hour drive to some of Northland's most beautiful beaches where you can enjoy swimming, fishing and surfing. There are two guestrooms available and you have your own bathroom and toilet facilities.
Cooked and continental breakfasts are available and you are welcome to join us for dinner.
Directions: *Transport can be provided to and from bus / plane at no charge.*

Whangarei
Farmstay
Address: Lowe Road, Marua, RD1, Hikurangi, Northland
Name: Rob and Ngaire Futcher
Telephone: (09) 433 8055
Beds: 1 Double, 2 Single (2 bedrooms, guest bathroom)
Tariff: B&B Double $50, Single $35; Dinner $20; Children half price
Nearest Town: Whangarei 22 kms

Our home which we can offer you is located in a peaceful rural setting with bush views and walks. We have available a very warm clean cosy accommodation with own bathroom and Kent fire in winter and electric blankets. Summer we have a large deck and nice pool for cooling off after hot travelling. The house is surrounded by nice gardens. We have recently fully redecorated. The house is situated on our dairy farm which we have workers, but anyone wishing to see or know the workings of a farm we can show you. We are very well located if you're travelling further north from Whangarei or returning from Bay of Islands - just turn off at Hikurangi. Alternatively when leaving our place a lovely drive is to take the coast road to Whangarei; beautiful beaches for swimming, surfing and deep sea fishing all so close. We are available to pick anyone up from Whangarei or airport. We are in our late 30's with no children and we welcome families or single travellers. We are non smokers ourselves but we don't mind smokers in our home.
Directions: *Take Highway 1 north from Whangarei. Turn right into Hikurangi bypass to township. First road on right after Hotel is Valley Road. After one way bridge second road on right is Lowes Road. We are second house on left up Lowes Road. 7 km from town. The road is all tarseal.*

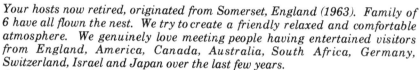

Whangarei
Homestay
Address: Tamaterau Bay,
R.D. 4, Whangarei
Name: Roy & Rae Atkin
Telephone: (089) 436-2265
Beds: 1 Double, 2 Single (2 bedrooms, share bathroom)
Tariff: B&B $50 Double, $25 Single, children 1/2 price, Dinner $15
Nearest Town: Whangarei (15 mins)

Your hosts now retired, originated from Somerset, England (1963). Family of 6 have all flown the nest. We try to create a friendly relaxed and comfortable atmosphere. We genuinely love meeting people having entertained visitors from England, America, Canada, Australia, South Africa, Germany, Switzerland, Israel and Japan over the last few years.

Our home is on the Northern side of Whangarei harbour, with the water at the bottom of our garden and lovely views from our deck. We are in a country area which includes bush-walks and a domain with tennis courts, changing sheds and a safe swimming beach. An 18 hole golf course is within walking distance from our house, again with wonderful views to be enjoyed while you play, and a friendly club to relax in after. A small boat is available for fishing and canoes for young ones. We prefer non-smokers.

Whangarei, Northland
Homestay
Address: Nga Ruru, P O Box 296, Whangarei
(Please phone or write in advance for bookings.)
Name: Helen Murgatroyd
Telephone: (09) 433-8922
Beds: 1 Double, 1 Single (1 bedroom, guest bathroom)
Tariff: Double $70, Single $35, Dinner $15, Campervans $20
Nearest Town: Whangarei (28 kms North of Whangarei 6 mins from State Highway 1)

Nga Ruru is the place to come when you need a break from hectic travel and want to relax in peaceful surroundings.

I will prepare healthy meals to your liking by prior arrangement. Enjoy the beauty of fresh flowers inside and out in the garden.

Nga Ruru is a large country house set in restful and peaceful native bush surroundings, a large established garden surrounds the house with an inground swimming pool.

Bounding the property is a 300 acre wildlife native bush reserve which gives ample scope for walking and relaxing.

Directions: *Nga Ruru is situated 28 kms North of Whangarei and a 45 minute drive further North takes you to the beautiful Bay of Islands. Day trips to local areas of interest can very easily be taken from this central location. Please phone for directions from State Highway One to Nga Ruru.*

Whangarei

Homestay
Address: "Kotare", 37 Kotare Cres, Maunu,
Name: Lynne and Alan   Whangarei
Telephone: (09) 438 5595
Beds: 1 Double, 4 Single, (3 bedrooms, 2 guest bathrooms)
Tariff: B&B Double $60, Single $40, Dinner $15
Nearest Town: 3 minutes from town off SH 14

Our spacious, modern two storey 4000 sq ft home includes three guest bedrooms, separate bathroom-toilet facilities. Double bedroom could also accommodate two children on folding beds. Laundry facilities available. Furnishings are comfortable and relaxing. Large outdoor decks on the house provide quiet cool access to the courtyard, garden and barbeque area. Our spa pool/sun room completes this welcoming, friendly home.

Our large kitchen / day area is available for tea and coffee making. Meals are prepared from local foods, and you dine with us in our separate dining room. Picnic baskets are available at moderate rates.

The section backs onto native bush sheltering numerous native birds including the beautiful native pigeon and kingfisher (Maori name - Kotare). Watch and listen in the early morning or evening.

Your hosts have travelled extensively throughout New Zealand. Alan is a professioal photographer with a residential studio.

We are 30-40 mins from Whangarei Heads,Tutukaka, Bay of Islands.

Courtesy car to/from bus or plane - no charge.

Your privacy is respected.

Ruakaka

Farmstay + Self-Contained Accommodation
Address: Doctor's Hill Road, Ruakaka
Name: Vince and Joyce Roberts
Telephone: (09) 432-7842
Beds: 1 Double, 1 Single (1 bedroom, guest bathroom)
Tariff: B&B Double $50, Single $25, Children $10, Dinner $15
Nearest Town: Ruakaka

We live on a dry stock farm overlooking Ruakaka and State Highway 1.

Our family home includes a visitor's bedsitter with its own bathroom, kitchenette and fridge, a ranchslider leads onto lawn and views of the entrance to Bream Bay and surrounding islands.

The racetrack, squash courts, golf course, good restaurants, beaches and Refinery Visitors Centre are a short drive from our home.

We offer magnificent views of the coast and lovely native bush to trek in or by arrangement we will take you.

We have been dairy farmers most of our lives and have a grown up family of four children.

Vince has recently obtained his Owner/Trainer licence to train our own racehorses.

I work in Whangarei city which is half an hour's drive away, so we do ask you to phone in the evening for bookings however passing callers are welcome.

We enjoy meeting visitors and helping them to enjoy their holiday.

Ngunguru, Whangarei

Homestay
Address: 4 Pine Rd, Ngunguru,
R.D. 3, Whangarei
Name: Jo La Krapes
Telephone: (09) 434-3916
Beds: 1 Double (1 bedroom with guest bathroom)
Tariff: B&B Double $68, Single $40, Dinner $25, Campervans $20 per couple
Nearest Town: Whangarei

Do as much or as little as you like in this quaint seaside resort of Ngunguru
situated 25 km / 15 miles from Whangarei. Take the Dinghy and gather
Cherrystone Clams and Pipi's (I will even make chowder for you) or for the
more energetic drag the net for herring. If you are lucky you may even catch
a Flounder.
There is a 9 hole golf course and tennis courts adjacent and an 18 hole golf
course 20 minutes away. I have a membership to both clubs. Ten minutes
away is Tutukaka - the deep sea anglers base and gateway to World
renowned Poor Knights Islands for Scuba diving.
Barbeque, refrigerator/freezer, ice and electric blankets available to guests.
Guests are invited to join me for a cocktail before dinner. Please make this
your home away from home. Non smokers preferred.
Directions: *Take Tukukaka turn off at Whangarei. Advisable to phone first*
mornings or evenings - otherwise I may be on the golf course.

Whangarei Heads

Homestay
Address: Manaia Gardens,
R.D. 4, Whangarei
Name: Audrey & Colin Arnold
Telephone: (09) 434-0797
Beds: 1 Double, 2 Single (2 bedrooms, guest bathroom)
Tariff: B&B Double $40, Single $20, Children 1/2 price, Dinner $15,
Campervans $20
Nearest Town: Whangarei - 31km on the Whangarei Heads Road.

We have two cabins in the garden with shower and toilet in one and toilet only
in the other. You can make tea and coffee and even cook a light meal, but we
would also enjoy your company in the evenings.
We live beside the sea in a bush setting. We grow our vegetables, keep hens,
and run a few cattle on our small farm. We know how important warm and
comfortable beds and a friendly welcome are to travellers.
We charge $10.00 to meet buses or planes as it is quite a way.
There is a 20% discount for backpacker style.
Often we are outside during the day so the best times to phone are evenings or
before 8:30am.
Directions: *Take the Whangarei Heads Road. We are 31 km from the*
Whangarei Yacht Basin bridge and 1.5 km past Taurikura. Ours are the only
buildings in the bay. Look for the rock wall in front.

Dargaville

Bed & Breakfast Inn
Address: "Kauri House Lodge",
Bowen Street, Dargaville
Name: June and Doug Blaxall
Telephone: (09) 439-8082
Beds: 2 Double, 2 Single (3 bedrooms all with private facilities)
Tariff: B&B Double $98.50–$104.50, Single $74.50–$77.50; Dinner $20
Nearest Town: Dargaville

Have you every wondered what it would be like to live in a stately home in the country? Here is your chance! Kauri House was built early this century for a millionaire and his large family. Only the best materials were used and we believe the house represents a beautiful example of craftmanship of that era. All the rooms are furnished in antiques with kauri (especially mottled kauri) being our special interest.
We have been hosting for 18 years and enjoy sharing our home and lifestyle. Our three guest rooms all have their own ensuites. We have a billiards room, library and swimming pool. Also a 'run-off' for those with time to explore it. It's 100 acres with 35 acres of native bush. Kauri House sits sedately on 8 acres of gardens and trees overlooking the township of Dargaville, which is close to the Ocean Beach that's 100 km long. Also Kaiiwi lakes, our summer playground and enroute to the Far North via Waipoura Forest that personifies NZ before man changed it. Booking is absolutely essential.

The standard of accommodation in *The New Zealand Bed and Breakfast Book* ranges from homely to luxurious, but you can always be sure of superior hospitality.

Dargaville
Farmstay
Address: Prouds Road,
cnr Highway 12,
Aranga, Dargaville
Name: Geoff and Carol Powell
Telephone: (09) 439 0444
Beds: 1 Double, 3 Single + cot, (2 bedrooms, guest bathroom)
Tariff: B&B Double $60, Single $35, Children half price, free up to 4 years;
Campervans $15.

We invite you to come stay with us on our beautiful bush-clad 200 acre dairy farm, for a peaceful, relaxing holiday stop. Located only 8 km south of the spectacular Waipoua Kauri Forest, we are only 43 km north of Dargaville on SH 12.
Activities available include milking 130 cows, trips to Kai Iwi Lakes, which are good for swimming and trout fishing, only 25 minutes drive away.
Trounson Kauri Park has night bush walks, kiwi spotting and glowworms, and is only 15 minutes drive away. Also wild west coast beaches and spectacular bluff walkways with bush and sea views, only 10 minutes away.
Our rooms are big and have lovely views of surrounding farmlands from big windows and our house is a large farmhouse. Best time to ring is about 9 o'clock-10 o'clock in the mornings (but try ringing anytime as you may catch us in).

Dargaville
Motel / Lodge
Address: Awakino Point Lodge, State Highway 14, Dargaville
Postal: P O Box 168, Dargaville
Name: June Birch
Telephone: (09) 439-7870
Beds: 3 Double, 5 Single (3 self-contained units with own bathrooms), electric blankets; cot and highchair available
Tariff: B&B $70 Double, $57 Single - $13 each extra person per unit. No special rates for children, babies free of charge. Campervans welcome.
Nearest Town: Dargaville

This unique country lodge is situated on a 5 acre farmlet surrounded by attractive gardens, orchard and aviary.
We can be found just two minutes drive from Dargaville township, 1.5 km along State Highway 14.
The Lodge has three motel units, one and two bedrooms sleeping up to 5 people in queen, double or twin beds. One unit has kitchen, log fire and bath providing extra comfort during winter months.
Breakfast can be either delivered to your unit on a trolley or taken with your host and other guests in the family dining room.
There are plenty of good restaurants in Dargaville and prices are reasonable but should you wish to take dinner with your hosts please ensure its pre-arranged.
High standards at moderate rates combined with friendly hospitality awaits you.

Tangiteroria
Farmstay
Address: State Highway 14, Private Bag, Tangiteroria, Northland
Name: Doug & Irene Bamber
Telephone: (09) 433-2671
Beds: 2 Single (1 bedroom, guest bathroom)
Tariff: Dinner, Bed & Breakfast $70 per person
Nearest Town: Whangarei 32 km, Dargaville 25 km

We are situated on the main highway between Whangarei and Dargaville. Our 11 year old house is on a hill overlooking the district. Lovely farm views can be seen and our home captures the sun all day long. Private bathroom facilities are available. Please feel free to wander over our 520 acre farm where we raise drystock and a few coloured sheep for spinning wool. We are happy to collect visitors from the bus or airport depot for a small extra fee. Come and enjoy our hospitality and enjoy a real home grown meal. Please phone prior to arrival and we will give directions of how to reach us.

Waipu, Northland
Farmstay
Address: "Barachel Orchard", Glenmohr Road, Waipu
Name: Tom & Sylvienne McClelland
Telephone: (09) 432-0656
Beds: 1 Double + 2 single stretcher beds (1 bedroom, guest bathroom)
Tariff: **B&B** $50 Double, $30 Single, children 1/2 price, $12.50 Dinner, Campervans welcome
Nearest Town: Waipu - 10 kms North

Our property is about half way between Auckland and the Bay of Islands, just 5 minutes off State Highway 1. We chose an elevated sunny position to build our large house in 1986, among some of our 2,000 Macedamia nut trees. Missing your pets? You'll love it here! Our menagerie includes the usual and unusual, furred and feathered, as well as coloured sheep and beef calves. We're within 15 minutes of delightful beaches and the area has much of historical interest. Our own native bush guarantees plenty of wild birdlife and a small river forms part of the boundary.
Tom is a chartered accountant (I'd rather be sailing!) and presently our 'cash crop'. Sylvienne - ex-arty, now farmy - dabbles in all sorts. Both recent immigrants from Auckland city. Our grown up family of nine includes two sons permanently residing in the U.S.A.
We cater for vegetarians and carnivores and prefer non-smokers. Extra accommodation available in caravan.
Directions: *Please phone.*

Waipu Cove

Farmstay + Self-Contained Accommodation
Address: Cove Road, Wiapu
Name: André and Robin La Bonté
Telephone: (09) 432 0645
Beds: 2 Double, 3 Single (SCA + 2 bedrooms, guest bathroom)
Tariff: B&B Double $55, Single $30, Dinner $15, Children under 12 yrs $15
Nearest Town: 10 km south of Waipu on Cove Rd, 50 km south of Whangarei via SH 1

My wife and I are Americans who became residents of New Zealand in 1985. We built a modern home with separate guest accommodation on a 36 acre coastal "lifestyle" farmlet by the edge of the sea.

Sleep to the sound of the ocean in either the separate apartment with private kitchen and bathroom facilities, queen-size sleeper and oversize single bed or in the guest bedrooms, with double or two single beds and private bathroom. No smoking please.

We have expansive views of the Pacific Ocean and offshore islands. Fish or explore our 850 ft of shoreline with its limestone rock formations and tidepools or just sit and relax under the mature pohutukawa trees that grace the shoreline. A ten minute walk along the shore takes you to the beautiful white sand beach of Waipu Cove, a ten minute walk inland takes you into native bush, streams and a swimming hole fed by a small waterfall.

We have 20 head of Devon stud cattle grazing the pasture, dozens of water fowl living on or around our 2.5 acre pond, marine fish in our salt water aquariums and wild birds that enjoy being hand fed. Glow worm caves, deep-sea fishing, scuba diving and golf are all available locally.
Directions: *Please phone*

Some homes share the bathroom, others have bathrooms
exclusively for guests – they are indicated in the listing.

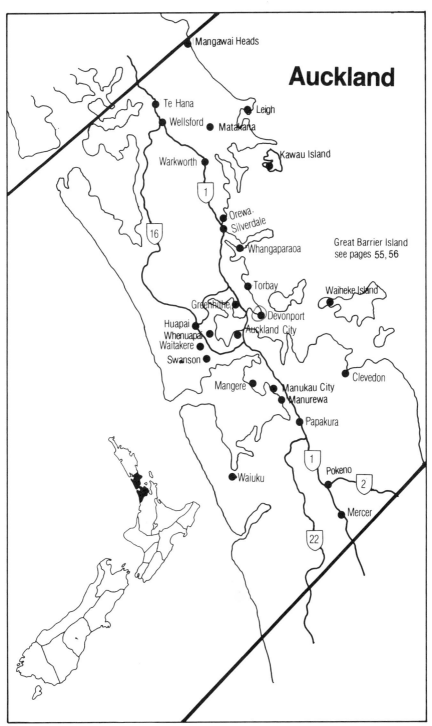

Auckland

Mangawai Heads

Te Hana

Leigh

Wellsford

Matakana

Warkworth

Kawau Island

16

1

Orewa
Silverdale

Whangaparaoa

Great Barrier Island
see pages 55, 56

Torbay

Waiheke Island

Greenhithe

Devonport

Huapai

Auckland City

Whenuapai

Waitakere

Swanson

Clevedon

Mangere

Manukau City

Manurewa

Papakura

1

Waiuku

Pokeno

2

Mercer

22

Mangawhai Heads
Studio Unit
Address: Milestone Cottage,
Moir Point Road, Mangawhai Heads,
R.D. 2, Kaiwaka, Northland
Name: Ian Milestone & Gail McConachy
Telephone: (09) 431-4018
Beds: 1 Double, 1 Single (1 bedroom with guest bathroom)
Tariff: B&B $70 Double, $40 Single, Dinner available
Nearest Town: Mangawhai (Kaiwaka on State Highway 1)

The bed and breakfast unit is adjacent to the house. The bedroom and bathroom is situated upstairs and has a private deck with outdoor furniture overlooking the garden of native and exotic plants.

The interior has a sarked gable roof with a double bed, single bed, table and chairs, TV, fridge and tea/coffee making facilities. The ensuite bathroom features a leadlight window, toilet, handbasin and shower shub. The property extends to a sandy beach on the estuary - only 2 minutes walk. Other local facilities within a 5 minute walk include shops, restaurant, take-aways, "lookout" and an 18 hole Golf links.

For breakfast we serve a fresh fruit platter using a variety of local and imported fruit, toast and cereal. At present our price is $35 per person (B&B incl). For an additional cooked breakfast of fish etc we charge an extra $5. We also provide dinner the nights the restaurant is closed from $10 - $20 per person.

Te Hana, Wellsford
Farmstay
Address: Te Hana, RD5, Wellsford
Name: George and Olga Yuretich
Telephone: (09) 423-7237
Beds: 1 Double, 2 Single (2 bedrooms)
Tariff: B&B Double $55, Single $35; Dinner $15; Children half price
Nearest Town: 8 km north of Wellsford, 1 hour north of Auckland and 1 hour south of Whangarei on SH 1

We are a farming family of 1st generation Kiwis of Yugoslav descent. We have four daughters all of whom have now left home. We enjoy all sports, craft and outdoor life especially meeting people and sharing our hospitality with others.

Our home is a large, modern open-plan farmhouse set in two acres of garden with 20 acres of native bush as a backdrop.

Enjoy a touch of rural New Zealand in our area. We offer a variety of bush walks. A beautiful coastal walk along the cliff-tops of Mangawhai and back along the seashore. Ocean surf beaches 30 minutes away offer swimming, fishing, surfing, and lazing.

Lake Tomarata (fresh water) 20 minutes away for swimming or trout fishing. Matakohe Northland Pioneer and Kauri Gum Museum is 45 minutes away. Dargaville Waipoua State Forest with its magnificent kauri trees – 1 hour away. Forty minutes to the Kawau Island ferry.

Pottery and crafts.
Directions: *Please phone.*

Te Hana, Wellsford

Farmstay
Address: "The Retreat",
Te Hana, RD5, Wellsford
Name: Tony and Colleen Moore
Telephone: (09) 423-8547
Beds: 1 Double, 2 Single (2 bedrooms, guest bathroom)
Tariff: B&B Double $55, Single $30 Dinner $15

"The Retreat" is a kauri homestead built in 1867 for a family with 12 children. It faces north and we look out over farmland including the eight acres where we graze black and white sheep. Colleen is a spinner and weaver and produces goods from the wool which are sold from the house.
Guests have a choice of twin or double bedrooms and use of their own bathroom.
Creating a garden to compliment the house is an ongoing source of enjoyment and a large herb garden and perennial borders are features that visitors can appreciate.
We have travelled extensively overseas and in New Zealand and are keen to promote our scenic and historic places — especially local ones.
Directions: *"The Retreat" is on State Highway 1, 6.5 km north of the Wellsford Post Office. You will see the weaving sign by our entrance.*

Warkworth

Homestay
Address: 17 View Road, Warkworth
Name: Ina & Trevor Shaw
Telephone: (09) 425-8667
Beds: 1 Double, 1 Single (extra single available on roller bed), 2 ensuite bathrooms)
Tariff: B&B $44 Double, $24 Single, $12 Children, $15 Dinner
Nearest Town: Warkworth, Auckland city 67 km

Our home overlooks the very picturesque town of Warkworth set on the Mahurangi River, one hour North of Auckland. The ferry for Kawau Island leaves from near here. There is a Marine Park with skin diving, snorkelling, together with safe sandy bays and surf swimming close by. There are two local golf courses as well as a variety of walks available. You may view a Kauri Park and Museum in Warkworth.
We offer a self-contained bedsitter. It includes an ensuite shower and separate guest toilet. The guest room has its own outdoor entrance and car park. There is a kitchen unit in the room, suitable for a small amount of cooking. Also available is a separate single bedroom with shower and toilet under the main floor if needed.
We really enjoy guests in our home and we have used this type of accommodation extensively overseas. Trevor is a journalist, Ina retired college teacher who is currently working towards art exhibitions. We both belong to the golf club and could introduce guests to the local courses. If necessary we are willing to bring guests by car from Auckland, a one hour drive.
Directions: *next door to the hospital on the hill.*

Matakana, Warkworth
Homestay
Address: "Amberleigh Country Lodge" Matakana Valley Rd, P O Box 145, Matakana, Auckland North
Name: Pam & Roy Hayward
Telephone: (09) 422-7059
Beds: 2 Double, 3 Twin
Tariff: B&B $80 Double, $45 Single - full tariff including 4-course dinner, "Happy Hour", wines, teas, picnic lunches - by prior arrangement
Nearest Town: Warkworth 9 kms. Easy 1 hours drive from Auckland

You will find "Amberleigh" to be a unique and wonderful experience for our maxim, extending over 20 years in the visitor service, has always been to treat all guests as being very special. Our house in yours - you are one of the family.

The property of several acres is nestled in pleasant, park-like surroundings with extensive lawns, landscaped gardens, a backdrop of native bush where even kookaburras abound and a bush walk. One thing is certain - this rural environment is conducive to complete relaxation and wellbeing. One can expect a zest for eating and meals are indeed a speciality. Breakfast is normally taken on a spacious back verandah overlooking the lily pond or you can have an early morning cuppa and breakfast in bed if you so desire. Dinner is always a notable event, held in a charming old-world atmosphere of gracious living. Special menus are no problem - just tell us. Complimentary wines are provided. Lunches or a picnic hamper can also be arranged for excursions to nearby Mansion House on Kawau Island or to the beautifully rugged Tawharanui Peninsula with its incredible beaches and scenery. The area is a most interesting one, steeped in history and culturally active in most arts and crafts. There is a wealth of interest in places to visit.

Directions: *If you are travelling by car, take the Leigh turnoff from SH1 at the northern end of Warkworth and at Matakana Township turn left up Matakana Valley Road past the general store and Post Office and only a few hundred yards along on the righthand side, opposite the Pony Club and tennis courts you will see the "Amberleigh" entrance sign. Drive up the tree-lined drive and park directly outside the main lodge.*

Warkworth
Address: Martins Bay Road,
13 km east Warkworth
Name: Rod and Rosalie Miller
Telephone: (09) 425-5612
Beds: 2 Single
Tariff: B&B, Double $55, Single $35, Children 1/2 price, Dinner $15;
Campervans $20

We live on a 314 acre coastal farm overlooking Kawau Bay, Mahurangi Heads and river in the Hauraki Gulf, approximately 80 km north of Auckland. We farm sheep, poultry, deer and cattle. We live in a private setting with plenty of open space, close to good safe beaches and seaside shopping centre, 13 km from Warkworth on sealed road.
Our family home is 45 years old, comfortable, warm and relaxed with open fireplace, woodstove and beautiful views. Farm walks and natural bush reserves on property with tracks to view N.Z. flora.
Family member commercial pilot and flying instructor. Scenic flights both local and Hauraki Gulf available.
The guest room has two single beds. Family meals available.
Directions: *Please phone.*

Leigh
Homestay
Address: 10 Ferndale Avenue,
Leigh, North Auckland
Name: Joan & Ken Helliwell
Telephone: (09) 422-6099
Beds: 3 Single (2 bedrooms, extra beds on request, guest bathroom)
Tariff: B&B $55 Double, $35 Single, Dinner $15, Campervans $5 per person.
Nearest Town: 23 km East of Warkworth

Leigh is a seaside fishing village 70-80 minutes drive North of Auckland, situated on the cliffs above the Leigh Cove. It offers facilities for boating, including a ramp and anchorage within the small harbour. The village community has an interdenominational church, a hotel, general store, "takeaway" food store, garage and dairy. Within 5 minutes car travel are sandy swimming beaches, excellent underwater diving, a good surfing beach, tidal flats as well as deep water and rocky shore coastline, coastal and country walks, and the Marine Reserve.
Our home is in the village. We are retired school teachers living in the family home with a large, well laid out garden. We have a small boat, and weather permitting, will be happy to share this with our guests.
We have travelled overseas extensively, enjoying other people's hospitality, and would be glad to offer a warm "Kiwi" welcome to our guests.

Kawau Island
Self-contained Accommodation
Address: Kawau Island Holidays,
Vivian Bay, Kawau Island
Postal: Private Bag, Warkworth
Name: Penelope & Ken McCormack
Telephone: (09) 422-8835
Beds: 1 Double, 1 Single (1 bedroom,
guest bathroom)
Tariff: B&B $140 per couple,
24 hour stay - 3 meals and snacks inclusive
Nearest Town: Warkworth

Vivian Bay, Kawau Island is only a 45 minute ferry ride from Sandspit, 10 km from Warkworth. With a safe, sandy beach at the front entrance, our guests enjoy swimming, snorkeling, fishing (dinghies are free), beachcombing - some even relax and do absolutely nothing. For the more energetic, there are easy bush walks (we provide hamper lunches if desired) during which you are likely to see more wallabies than people. Visits to historic Mansion House and fishing trips can be arranged. Two modern chalets, each accommodating only two guests, have en-suite bathrooms, sun decks, TV, refrigerators etc, for your comfort and convenience.

With fresh fruit and vegetables from our garden and fish from the bay, our menus can tempt the most dedicate weight-watchers - for Japanese guests we offer sushi, sashimi and limited conversation in their language.

Our interests include gardening, music, ham radio and the comfort of our guests. We have two friendly Shetland collies, six cats and an almost-tame wallaby.

Red Beach, Orewa
Homestay
Address: 54 Walton Street,
Red Beach
Name: Helen and John Bassett
Telephone: (09) 426-6963
Beds: 2 Double, (guest bathroom)
Tariff: B&B Double $50, Single $30; Dinner $15
Nearest Town: Orewa

Recently retired, we live 2 km from State Highway 1 and 100 metres from a good beach. Orewa 5 km, Auckland 30 km and Waiwera thermal pools 10 km.

We have a recently-built house on a large, private section, peaceful and quiet. We are happy to help with local sightseeing and to share our local knowledge.

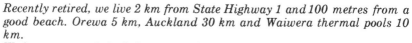

44

Silverdale
Farmstay + Self-Contained Accommodation
Address: RD2, Silverdale
Name: Ute Engel
Telephone: (09) 426-6175
Beds: 1 Double, 4 Single (3 bedrooms, guest bathroom)
Tariff: B&B Double $50, Single $30, Children half price; Dinner $15
Self-contained, semi-detached flat Double $70 Single $40
Nearest Town: Orewa 6 km, 40 km north of Auckland

If you wish to experience the peace and tranquility of New Zealand country living, then my home is for you. It is situated in rolling farmland country, 2 km off Highway 1.

My wooden home is cosy, modern, inviting and unusual and I pride myself in providing an atmosphere of friendliness and warmth. The self-contained flat is luxurious and spacious. On the 4 acres surrounding the house I raise a variety of animals, including sheep, goats, ducks, hens and peacocks. I love my animals some of which are pets.

I was born in Germany and have lived in many European countries and Australia. I love gardening, swimming and walking as well as cooking. I provide tasty vegetarian and meat dishes and delicious desserts. In winter I spin my own black, white or dyed wool, angora and mohair fibre. I do massages, facials and Reiki, and offer colour analysis and herbal consultations.

It is my pleasure to provide details of local attractions — beaches, boating, fishing, bushwalks, horse-riding, golfing and hot pools.

I have travelled extensively and enjoy meeting visitors from all over the world. Whether you are touring New Zealand on holiday or seeking a quiet and harmonious retreat from daily life, I welcome you into my home.
Directions: *Please phone.*

Silverdale, Auckland

Farmstay
Address: "Mt Pleasant", Pine Valley Road, Silverdale, Auckland
Name: Bob & Molly Crawford
Telephone: (09) 426-4280
Beds: 1 Double, 1 Single
Tariff: **B&B** $30 per person, children 1/2 price - discount for 2 nights or more. $15 Dinner, $5 Cooked breakfast
Nearest Town: Orewa 13 kms, Auckland 36 kms

The homestead is a large early colonial home furnished throughout with antique colonial furniture. We offer a comfortable and peaceful stay on our 328 acre beef farm looking out to our 120 acres of native bush. Only 25 minutes to Auckland, 10 minutes to beaches, or enjoy a stroll around the farm and its animals, or explore the native kauri bush and feel free to participate in farm activities.
Being close to Auckland and beaches many activities are available within easy distance e.g., harbour cruises, fishing trips, golf, practice ski slope, tennis courts, gymnasium, squash courts, swimming pool etc. As we have a 4 year old son, children are welcome and having travelled overseas on several occasions all nationalities are welcome although we only speak English.
Enjoy a breakfast of your choice, with evening meal available, if desired, and adequate notice given.
Directions: *Turn off SH1 at Dairy Flat, between Caltex Service Station and Falloons Vege Store, Pine Valley is 2nd road on right, our entrance 1st on left. Please ring if possible.*

New Zealand is known as the friendliest country in the world and
our hosts will live up to that reputation.

Whangaparaoa Peninsula
Homestay
Address: 13 Glenelg Road, Whangaparaoa
Name: Paul & Nancy Evans
Telephone: (09) 426-7167
Beds: 1 Double, 1 Single (2 bedrooms, guest bathroom)
Tariff: B&B $55 Double (B&B), $35 Single, Dinner $15
Nearest Town:

We have beautiful sea and islands view from our modern, large, 3 bedroom home.
A double bedroom and a single bedroom are available for our guests with their own bathroom and toilet.
The solar heated swimming pool is adjacent to the guests bedrooms where breakfast can be enjoyed on the surrounding sundeck. A spa pool is also available for guests use.
Your hosts, Paul & Nancy, have travelled extensively over many years, so our guests, either "Kiwis" or overseas visitors, can relax in their company and swap yarns.
Paul and Nancy are non-smokers and would prefer that their guests appreciate the seashore aromas that abound from the nearby beach by following their example.
Directions: *Arrangements can be made for transportation by the Shuttle Service to the Hibiscus Coast. Late arrivals can be collected from the Auckland Downtown Terminal. Please phone.*

Whangaparaoa Peninsula
Homestay
Address: 1249 Whangaparaoa Road, Fisherman's Rock, Whangaparaoa, Auckland
Name: David and Audrey Eades
Telephone: (09) 424-5316
Beds: 1 Double, 2 Single (2 bedrooms, guest bathroom)
Tariff: B&B Double $50, Single $28, Dinner $12
Nearest Town: Orewa 10 km

Our home is situated towards the end of beautiful Whangaparaoa Pensinsula – 50 km north of Auckland.
We can be reached from the airport via Auckland by buses which pass our door. (More information given on request.)
Close at hand is the 'Gulf Harbour Marina' and a choice of ocean beaches, headland walks, shops, churches, restaurants and golf course are all within easy reach. A 20 minute drive away are the Waiwera thermal pools.
Our children are now overseas and we have room to offer you a comfortable stay. The double room which is upstairs has separate bathroom facilities, the single room (2 beds) is on the ground floor.
We really enjoy meeting people and will do all we can to make your stay with us a happy time. Visitors from abroad are very welcome. Guests may have dinner with us by arrangement.

Torbay

Homestay
Address: 23 Auld Street, Torbay,
North Shore, Auckland
Name: Colleen and Maurie Gray
Telephone: (09) 473-9558
Beds: 1 Double, 2 Single (2 bedrooms, guest bathroom)
Tariff: B&B Double $65, Single $35, Children half price; Dinner $15
Nearest Town: Browns Bay

Our spacious modern home has been designed with guests' comfort in mind. We enjoy sharing the beautiful sea views, luxurious living and rambling garden. We have created a restful atmosphere and plenty of outdoor living area for the warmer days. A grand-piano graces the large lounge and we have a huge open-fireplace. We enjoy the outdoors, swimming, sailing, barbecues and are located within a few minutes walk of a beautiful beach. Torbay offers sandy beaches, safe swimming, cliff-top walks, a choice of restaurants. Easy bus-ride to Auckland city.
I enjoy preparing attractive, wholesome meals so you're welcome to dine with us. We have two Persian cats who will love to meet you too!
A smoke-free home.
Directions: *Turn right as you leave the Northern motorway at East Coast Bays exit. Turn left into East Coast Road. Proceed to Browns Bay turnoff and turn right. Pass Browns Bay, travel along Beach Road, past picturesque Waiake Beach. Turn right at Torbay Service Station and you're in Auld Street.*

Greenhithe

Rural Homestay
Address: 177 Upper Harbour Drive,
Greenhithe
Name: Ned and Therese Jujnovich
Telephone: (09) 413-9270
Beds: 4 Single (2 bedrooms,
2 guest bathrooms)
Tariff: B&B Double $60, Single $40; Dinner $20
Nearest Town: Glenfield 5 km, Auckland city 15 km

Ranch-style home nestling above the upper harbour set in 10 acres of pasture and native bush to the water's edge – the air is alive with bird song.
Warm wood fires in the winter, swimming pool in the summer months.
Every modern convenience, and just 15 minutes from Auckland city.
You can do a spot of native birdwatching, swim or just relax in the tranquil surroundings. And you can take in the sights of Auckland city too.
Your hosts Ned and Therese Jujnovich have travelled extensively in New Zealand and overseas. With their family of five, all grown up – they especially welcome overseas guests.
Local sightseeing easily arranged. Greenhithe is a handy starting-off place to the Bay of Islands being just north of Auckland.
Directions: *From Auckland – over the Harbour Bridge – turn left at Tristram Avenue, right at Wairau Road, continue to Greenhithe turnoff (left turn). Continue 2 km to 177 Upper Harbour Drive – 177 is at the end of right of way. Transport from city terminal available on request.*

Devonport, Auckland

Homestay B&B+ Self -contained accommodation
Address: Karin's Garden Villa, 14 Sinclair St, Devonport, Auckland 9
Name: Karin Loesch
Telephone: (09) 445-8689
Beds: 1 Double, 3 Single (3 Bedrooms, 1 guest bathroom)
Tariff: B&B $65 Double, $35 Single, children 1/2 price, Dinner $15
Nearest Town: Devonport - 15 minutes by ferry from downtown Auckland
or 20 minutes drive across bridge

Directions: _From the Airport_ use the very reasonable shuttle buses for door
to door transport; your bike travels free.
Driving North cross Harbour Bridge, take Takapuna-Devonport turnoff, turn
right at T-intersection. Before Devonport, turn into Old Lake Road on left, go
past Narrow Neck Beach, first road on right after the Vauxhall shopping
centre.
Southbound leave Motorway at Takapuna-Northcote exit, turn right at lights,
go through Takapuna towards Devonport, and then before Devonport turn
into Old Lake Road, then as above.
Please, if possible, book in advance, before 10:00 am or after 6:00 pm.
_Our Victorian-Edwardian villa, once a horse farm, shares large lawns with old
fruit trees at the end of a quiet cul-de-sac. It's airy, light and comfortable, 5
minutes' stroll to bus, local shops, golf course and tree-lined Cheltenham
Beach. 3 minutes' drive to the charming centre of historic Devonport. Here
you will find an excellent range of eateries (Thai, Mexican, seafood, etc.), a
real German bakery (watch the Schwarzwaelder Kirschtorte - it puts on
pounds!), waterside pubs. Superb shops (also one for the cyclists), cinemas
and lively panoramas of harbour, city and gulf from adjoining parks and
beaches._
_Karin comes from Hamburg and Tony is a native Kiwi who, from time to
time, has business in Asia. With our two school-age children, Martina and
Stefan, we travel worldwide, are multilingual and enjoy meeting and helping
travellers and tourists._
_You will love your breakfast in our new dining-room or on our sunny
verandah with Karin's home-made muesli. Guests are welcome to join in the
family barbeque, relax in the garden under the pear and apple trees (not
however a good idea when they are ripe!), or help themselves to tea and
German style coffee anytime and to use the kitchen and laundry. At your
request, Karin will make typical German dishes._
We look forward to meeting you!

49

Devonport, Auckland
Homestay
Address: "Devonport Villa",
21 Cheltenham Road, Devonport
Name: Jackie Cozby
Telephone: (09) 445-2529, Fax 445-7623
Beds: 4 Double, 3 Single (4 bedrooms, 2 guest bathrooms)
Tariff: B&B $80-$100 Double, $50-75 Single
Nearest Town: Devonport - 15 mins by ferry or car to Auckland city

This lovely Victorian villa with its antiques and teddy bears wraps around a swimming pool and is just one block from Cheltenham Beach. Breakfast is very special - homemade muffins and muesli, fresh fruit salad, fresh orange juice, eggs, excellent coffee and teas. Quiet, pretty bedrooms have firm beds, feather duvets and comfortable charm.
Devonport is a delightful old-world seaside village just across from downtown Auckland. A magic place close to inner city excitement, it offers its own excellent variety of restaurants and shops, lovely beaches, golf and the best view in Auckland from the top of Mount Victoria.
Directions: *From the Airport take the shuttle direct or city bus to the ferry which we will meet. Driving North across the bridge follow Devonport signs, past shops to waterfront, turning left to the last street. Southbound take Takapuna-Northcote exit left, turn right and follow main road south as above. Please call ahead if possible to avoid disappointment... See you soon!*

Devonport
Homestay
Address: 2 Grove Road, Devonport
Name: Joyce and Harry Mossman
Telephone: (09) 445-9437
Beds: 5 Single (3 bedrooms, guest bathroom)
Tariff: B&B Double $60, Single $40; Meals by arrangement;
Children are welcome
Nearest Town: Devonport – 20 minutes across harbour from Auckland city
Transport: Available by "Super" Shuttle Bus direct from airport

Adjacent to lovely Cheltenham Beach. Twenty minutes by road or relaxing ferry ride across harbour to city. Fifty minutes to International Airport.

Large, clean, comfortable home in quiet area with a sea view, shade trees and spacious lawn.

Facilities have private shower, toilet and handbasin and own entrance.

One minute walk onto beautiful, safe beach (swimming, sailing, walking). Two minutes' walk to shops and bus stops. Short walk to golf course, bowling and croquet club, squash, rugby, soccer and sailing. Pleasant walks to North Head Maritime Park and Mt Victoria with unexcelled extensive views of Waitemata Harbour, city and Auckland Harbour Bridge and Hauraki Gulf.

Other meals in addition to bed and breakfast by arrangement. Complimentary tea / coffee is provided. Restaurants handy.

We supply an escort service by private car for business, sightseeing, pleasure and places of interest. Mobile mini-camper available.

Our interests and activities are people, travel, tourism, family, swimming, camping, boating and fishing, photography. We have a background of farming, navy and building.

There is no other marine suburb which offers so much in such a small picturesque area.

A warm welcome is assured by your hosts. We regret no animals. Reservations are advisable to avoid disappointment.

Huapai
Homestay
Address: "Foremost Fruits",
45 Trigg Road, Huapai, Auckland
Name: Evelyn and Gerry Brown
Telephone: (09) 412-8862
Beds: 1 Double, 2 Single (2 bedrooms, guest bathroom)
Tariff: B&B Double $55, Single $35, Children half price; Campervans $20
Nearest Town: Huapai/Kumeu 2km, Auckland City 30 mins

"Foremost Fruits" is situated in the heart of New Zealand's wine producing area on a small orchard, growing apples, peaches, pears and plums but specialising in growing hothouse table grapes. Guests will be warmly welcomed by your hosts who have extensive overseas Bed and Breakfast experience. Our aim is to provide accommodation plus those little extras appreciated by travellers. Our guest accommodation, including tea / coffee making facilities, consists of 2 bedrooms with a separate guest bathroom. A small TV lounge adjoins the rooms. Breakfast is of Continental style which includes our own orchard grown fruit. Within easy driving are several restaurants with fares ranging from A La Carte to take-aways. It is our pleasure to provide details of local attractions including golf course, wineries, riding school, beaches, etc. Non smokers by preference.
Directions: *from Auckland take the northwestern motorway heading for Helensville, Highway 16. 1 km past Huapai township, turn left into Trigg Road, homestead 500 metres on left hand side of road (sign posted).* ——

Whenuapai

Homestay
Address: 89 Totara Road,
Whenuapai, Auckland
Name: Gary & Robyn Langstone
Telephone: (09) 416-8333
Beds: 2 Single (1 bedroom, guest bathroom)
Tariff: B&B $55 Double, $30 Single, Dinner $15, Campervans $20
Nearest Town: Whenuapai 2 km, Auckland City 25 km

Our home is spacious and comfortable, situated in 3 acres of parklike grounds, on the shores of the upper harbour - we even have our own historic 110ft derelect boat hull.
The property offers fishing and boating from the edge of the garden - dinghy and gear are available. Hot pools, beaches, forest, golf courses, farms, vineyards and all that Auckland City offers are within 5 to 30 minutes drive.
Part of our business activities include a glasshouse where we hydroponically grow vegetables - previously we farmed cattle and own a vineyard.
Our household now consists of your hosts, an adult son (currently at Auckland University), a pet goat, two outdoor dogs and two cats.
Guests have a twin bedroom, private bathroom and private sitting room - which could double as an extra bedroom for two.
Directions: *North West Motorway from Auckland to end. Then Highway 16 for almost 3 km, right into Brighams Creek Road, about 2 km and left into Totara Road.*

Whenuapai

Homestay
Address: 13 Bristol Road, Whenuapai, RD2, Kumeu
Name: Laura and Peter deLeon
Telephone: (09) 4168 701
Beds: 1 Double (own facilities), 2 Single (share bathroom)
Tariff: B&B Double $55, Single $30, Dinner $15, 10% discount for weekly stays. Meals available with family if required. Breakfast $7
Nearest Town: Henderson 10 kms, Auckland 25 mins

We are semi-retired, having sold our Consulting Engineering Practice to concentrate on developing the extensive gardens on the property.
We have wide and varied interests having travelled extensively, and are lovers of outdoor activities such as as bushwalking etc.
Our three adult sons have left home which leaves us with a few empty beds and vacancies at the dinner table, which we like to have filled. Overseas and NZ visitors can be assured of a warm welcome.
Our home is an English styled modern house sited on 1.4 ha of land in a horticultural area, which grows mainly flowers and tomatoes in glasshouses, and grapes are also grown in the area, which provides us with many fine wineries within a 10 km radius of our home.
Directions: *Coming from Auckland - take the Northwestern motorway (SH 16). Continue past end of motorway towards Kumeu, then take first right (Brighams Creek Road) past Whenuapai bus depot. Turn left into Totara Road, just before Whenuapai Village, then 1st left into Dale Road. Bristol Road is second right. Our property is about 1 km on the right hand side, (look for sign.*

Waitakere
Farm / Self-contained Accom
Address: Greenmead Farm, 115 Bethells Road, Waitakere
(R.D. 1, Henderson, Auckland)
Name: Averil & Jon Bateman
Telephone: (09) 810-9363 {Fax (09) 801-9122}
Beds: 4 Single (2 bedrooms with guest bathroom)
Tariff: Self-contained cottage - $55 Double, $10 for each extra guest; Meals available with the family if required, Dinner $20, Breakfast $7, children's meals 1/2 price
Nearest Town: Henderson 16 km (Auckland city 30 mins drive)

We live a mile from the sea in a 100 year old home in the Waitakere Ranges. We breed Simmental cattle and grow globe artichokes. A large garden and orchard surround the main house and guest cottage. There are old roses and an extensive organic vegetable garden. We handmilk a house cow and keep chickens and bees.

Visitors have sole use of the cottage which has two bedrooms, each with two single beds (linen provided). A cot is available. The parlour has colour TV. The well equipped kitchen / dining room has cooking facilities covering everything from microwave to wood range, including an electric oven and hot plates. You are welcome to eat with us if you do not feel like cooking.

The area has spectacular scenery for people who enjoy walking. There are caves to explore at the black sand beach and a track to the cliff tops, with superb views, or to Lake Wainamu lying hidden behind the dunes. There are many bush tracks where large Kauris and waterfalls can be seen. There is a golf course in the valley and it is only a ten minute drive to local vineyards for an afternoon of wine tasting.

The cottage provides a cosy retreat. Travellers using Auckland Airport find 'Greenmead' a relaxing place to stay, in the countryside yet close to Auckland City.

Directions: *15 minutes by car from Lincoln Road turnoff on the NW Motorway out of Auckland. Please phone for detailed directions. We can collect visitors using public transport from either Waitakere Rail Station or from the bus at Ranui*

Swanson, Auckland
Self-contained Accom
Address: 148 Christian Road, R.D. 1, Henderson, Auckland 8
Name: Mac & Val McMillan
Telephone: (09) 833-9872
Beds: 2 Double (1 bed & bed-settee), (1 bedroom , guest bathroom)
Tariff: **B&B** $50 Double, $30 Single, Children 1/2 price, Dinner $15, Campervans $20
Nearest Town: Henderson (7 km), Auckland (25 km)

We offer a self-contained motel-type unit, with double bed and bed settee, kitchen and bathroom, situated on a 10 acre farmlet with a large landscaped garden. A swimming pool is alongside the unit.
We are successful breeders of dairy goats and kune-kune pigs, keep poultry and have three cats, a German Shepherd dog and a rainbow lorikeet. Pets welcome.
Our property has magnificent rural views of which the Waitakere Ranges are a feature and is only 400 metres from the Waitakere Centennial Park with its famous walking tracks, kauri trees, native bush and birds. Thirty minute drive to West Coast beaches and Muriwai gannet colony and 45 minutes to Parakai Hot Springs.
Henderson is well equipped with shops and has a variety of restaurants and is well-known for its vineyards and orchards. The farmlet is within a 30 minute drive of approximately 20 vineyards.
Our interests include sport, classical music, gardening, animals, travel.
Directions: *Please telephone.*

Swanson
Homestay
Address: 26 Knox Road, Swanson
Name: Colleen Sherwood
Telephone: (09) 8337-007 (home), 5794-189 (work)
Beds: 1 Double, 1 Single (2 bedrooms)
Tariff: B&B Double $60, Single $35; Children half price; Dinner $20
Nearest Town: 6 kms north of Henderson on Swanson Road

This is a large comfortable home situated on half an acre of attractive garden and fruit trees of many varieties. A feature of the house are views from all rooms, of Redwood Park Golf Course, and surrounding bush. A wide variety of native birds live in the garden where plants have been grown as a food source for them. A conservatory with spa pool runs the length of the house and is used for growing orchids, and palms and other exotic plants.
A paved area is used for BBQs or relaxing in the privacy of an enclosed garden. Guest accommodation is spacious with tea making facilities available and TV. Non-smokers preferred.
Golf is on the doorstep as No.1 green adjoins the drive. Green fee players are welcome on this course.

Hosts: interests are fishing, dining out, theatre, golf, rugby, good wines. There are a wide variety of restaurants in the area. Tourist features of the area are: scenic drive at the base of Waitakeres, ARA bush walks, West Auckland vineyards, western beaches. 10 minutes to Auckland on NW Highway.

As I work in Auckland please ring in the evening for bookings, or my business number or leave a message on the answerphone.

Directions: *from NW motorway turn off at Lincoln Road - follow through to sign - at traffic lights - Swanson - continue down Universal Drive, turn right at traffic island into Swanson Road to the township. Knox Road is on your right past Railway Station. Signs show Redwood Park. No. 26 is last house in the street on the right.*

Our B&Bs are mostly private homes.
Most do not accept credit cards.

Great Barrier Island
Homestay
Address: Arum Lodge, Medlands Beach
RD1, Great Barrier Island
Name: Chris and Colin
Telephone and Fax: (09) 429-0362
Beds: 1 Double, 2 Single (2 bedrooms,
guest bathroom)
Tariff: B&B Double $65, Single $45,
Dinner $20
Nearest Town: Auckland

Great Barrier is a semi-tropical island paradise of clear blue waters,clean white sandy beaches, unspoilt native bush and beautiful harbours. Charter fishing and diving trips, horsetreks, bushwalks, visits to hot pools, old gold and silver mines and 9 hole golf can be arranged. Transport is available for scenic tours. Rental cars can be hired and buses meet all passenger boats and most plane flights.

Luxury air-conditioned passenger boats leave from downtown Auckland and Great Barrier Airlines operates 2 flights daily from Auckland Airport domestic terminal.

Our new home which has beautiful rural and sea views is 200 metres from Medlands Beach where there is excellent swimming fishing and surfing.

We offer country-style accommodation which is shared within our home. Lunch and dinner can also be provided. We welcome those who wish to experience the charm of the island and who want to enjoy the simple life.

Great Barrier Island
Homestay + Self-Contained Cottage
Address: Tryphena, RD1, Great Barrier Island
Name: "Crosswinds Homestead"
Telephone: (09) 4290-557
Beds: 1 Double, 2 Single (2 bedrooms, guest bathroom)
Tariff: Double $70, Single $49, Dinner $20; Children half price
Nearest Town: Auckland City 53 nautical miles SW

A visit to the Auckland area is not complete without a trip out to Great Barrier Island. 'The Barrier' is unique with its rugged terrain, native bush, regenerating kauri forests, picturesque harbours to the west and long white surf beaches to the east. We invite you to share our homestead for that special break away from it all. The homestead commands views of Tryphena Harbour, Coromandel Peninsula, Channel Island, a large valley of native bush to the north east and Rangitoto and Tiri-tiri Islands in the distance. We know you will be comfortable with us and we would also like to help you enjoy the many activities 'Barrier' has to offer. Beach and sea related, fishing, tramping, tours, social activities, golf, picnics, or just relaxing.
We are non-smokers and also have an old English sheepdog, very beautiful but not allowed in guests' rooms. Our main interests are our homestead, garden, hens/animals, 'the Barrier', and our guests' happiness. We have been in transport related businesses and still have an interest in the small business scene. A full range of transport is available to Gt Barrier - air, fast catamarans, launches and an 80 year old traditional scow. Bev and Terry would like to hear from you. Phone (09) 4290-557

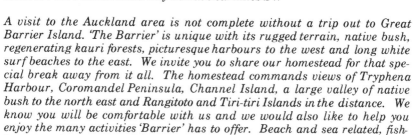

Waiheke Island
Homestay
Address: 'Far Horizons',
21 Great Barrier Road,
Palm Beach, Waiheke Island
Name: Marion Bridge
Telephone: (09) 727-799
Beds: 2 Double, 1 Single (2 bedrooms)
Tariff: B&B $50 Double, $30 Double bunk, $20 Single, children 1/2 price, Dinner $10
Nearest Town: Auckland

Join me in my unique style small home set on a headland with panoramic sea views and all day sun.
Both doubles have a view of the sea from your bed. The main bedroom has ranchsliders to the deck and to a garden courtyard with barbeque. The small bedroom sleeps 3 in a comfy double bunk and single bed. This room is more suited to a younger couple or family. The bathroom is shared.
The open plan living/kitchen area has a spacious deck. There are many walks and water activities all around, sandy beaches or rocky coves. Kayaks and small rowing dinghy available. Peaceful rural atmosphere - dog, cat, chickens. I teach part-time locally. I look forward to meeting you and sharing

the pleasure of my lovely island.
Directions: *Catch a fast ferry from the Downtown Ferry Terminal, Pier 2, opposite Downtown, behind Cin Cin Restaurant. For ferry times ring Auckland (09) 393-918 or 728-305, 728-823 or my number. The passenger ferries take 35 minutes to arrive at the wharf at Matiatia. Buses and taxis meet the ferries. Car ferries leave from Auckland (Gulf Trans) and Half Moon Bay, Bucklands Beach (Subritzky). Best times to ring me ar early mornings or evening. I can meet most ferries.*

Waiheke Island
Homestay
Address: 49 Great Barrier Road,
Enclosure Bay, Waiheke Island
Name: Alan Ramsbottom & Lois Baucke
Telephone: (09) 72-6629, After April 92 372 6629
Beds: 1 Double, 2 Single (2 bedrooms, guest bathroom)
Tariff: **B&B** $60 Double, $35 Single, Dinner $15
Nearest Town: Auckland

Waiheke Island is different. A unique lifestyle, superb scenery, yet only 35 minutes from downtown Auckland.
Our new home sits on a low ridge on over an acre of land running down to the sea. A garden path takes you to secluded rockpools and clear deep water.
Warm and comfortable, the house and garden take advantage of the dramatic views of the Northern Coast of Waiheke Island, with Coromandel Peninsula and Great Barrier Island beyond.
We provide an excellent continental breakfast and if requested, dinner, though there are good restaurants on the island. Tea or coffee is always available. Lois and I enjoy the outdoors and the Arts, and are non-smokers.
Explore the island; (we have 2 bicycles), its beaches and hills, its acclaimed vineyards, its varied crafts, its golf course, or just relax. We can give you a tour (nominal charge).
We enjoy our island hideaway and its mild climate and welcome you to experience it with us.
Directions: *Passenger ferry from Ferry Buildings, Downtown Auckland, approx every 2 hours. Also vehicular ferry and plane services. We can meet you from any, but please phone first if you plan to visit us.*

Waiheke Island

Homestay +
Self-Contained Accommodation
Address: 223 Ocean View Road,
Little Oneroa, Waiheke Island
Name: Waiheke Punga Lodge
Telephone: (09) 726 675
Beds: 2 Double, 2 Single (3 bedrooms, guest bathroom)
Tariff: B&B Double $60, Single $30,Dinner $15
Nearest Town: Auckland 35 mins

Wonderful Waiheke Island 'the jewel of Auckland' is a must for all travellers and Punga Lodge waits to welcome you. Perhaps we should let previous guests tell our story.

"Beautiful, everything an island holiday should be", Ailsa Swanson.

"If you think you can find better hosts than Jo and Peter, try - but we're sure you won't find them" - Beatrix and Stephan, Austria.

"Just the kind of people and place I was looking for but didn't expect to find" - Karen, Scotland.

We have all day sun - our spacious decks overlook tree ferns and native bush. We are surrounded by beautiful beaches, fine vineyards, quality arts and crafts. We provide meals to suit, but interesting restaurants are only a walk away. The magic of this island continues through all seasons. Warm welcome awaits.

Directions: *'Quickcat' ferry from downtown Auckland - 35 minutes of superb harbour cruise - $5 taxi to the door - Buses meet all ferries or a 25 minute walk.*

Waiheke Island

Farm & Homestay, Guest House
Address: Hauraki House, 50 Hauraki Road,
Sandy Bay, Waiheke Island
Name: Gladys Hurley
Telephone: (09) 72-7598
Beds: 2 Double, 2 Single (3 bedrooms
plus folding bed & cot)
Tariff: **B&B** $45 Double, $35 Single,
Dinner (by experienced chef $20)
Nearest Town: Auckland

The Island is 35 minutes from Queen St Ferry Buildings by big Catamarans. The smooth crossing is fascinating.

The spacious house decorated with old Kauri furniture, provides a gracious atmosphere with incredible views of the Hauraki Gulf.

On Bus route, with stop outside; or courtesey car.

The Island has an interesting history and a permanent population of 7,500. It offers many beautiful beaches and water sports, including good fishing. Golf and Bowls are also available.

The climate: warmer and drier than Auckland.

Where else in the world can you visit an Island like this on the door-step of a city the size of Auckland?

Be our welcome guest!

Freemans Bay, Auckland City

Guest House +
Self-Contained Apartment
Address: 65 Wellington Street,
Freemans Bay, Auckland 1
Name: Freeman's Travellers' Hotel
Telephone: (09) 765-046
Beds: 2 Double, 17 Single (12 bedrooms)
Tariff: B&B Double $56, Single $38, Triple $66
Serviced apartment: B&B 2 persons $74, 3-$94, 4-$104, 5-$114

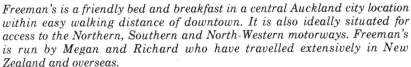

Freeman's is a friendly bed and breakfast in a central Auckland city location within easy walking distance of downtown. It is also ideally situated for access to the Northern, Southern and North-Western motorways. Freeman's is run by Megan and Richard who have travelled extensively in New Zealand and overseas.

Their aim is to create a haven for travellers and to this end are assisted by a garden with a small swimming pool, a barbeque and a conservatory. There is a laundry and a guest lounge with a telephone, a fridge, tea and coffee, a television, and a piano. Breakfast provides a number of choices including freshly-ground coffee. The relaxed atmosphere arises in part from independence being valued as much as friendliness.

Megan and Richard are pleased to assist in planning stays in Auckland and New Zealand and, in particular will undertake to book cars and campervans at the best possible rates. Early reservations are recommended.

Directions: *From the Airport, Supershuttle to Freeman's door.*
From the Railway and Bus Stations, phone for pick-up.
From the south, exit SH1 at Nelson St, first left, first left.
From the north, exit SH1 at Cook St, first right, first right.

St Mary's Bay, Auckland City

Address: St Francis de Sale Street, St Mary's Bay
Name: Leigh
Telephone: (09) 786-034 Bus, 762-676 Home
Beds: 4 Single (2 bedrooms)
Tariff: B&B $60 Double, $40 Single, Dinner $20, Children half price

My home is situated in St Mary's Bay, walking distance to the Central Post Office and Auckland Harbour. This is one of the first settled areas in Auckland and is very charming in character.

My home is very spacious in Tudor style, with covered decks facing north across the harbour, and set in pleasant surroundings.

We have in our vicinity Westhaven Marina, wonderful restaurants and BYOs, good library, tennis courts, swimming baths, markets and beaches.

You may have dinner at home or if you prefer, only bed and breakfast.

I enjoy meeting people from other countries and would make you very welcome to our city and home.

Directions: Please phone.

Grafton, Auckland City

Homestay
Address: 17A Carlton Gore Road,
Grafton, Auckland 1
Name: George and Janette Welanyk
Telephone: (09) 774-319
Beds: 1 Double, 1 Single (2 bedrooms)
Tariff: B&B Double $60, Single $40
Nearest Town: Auckland Central

When visiting New Zealand we invite you to stay with us in our home which is within walking distance of the city, shops, parks and other attractions. We are situated in a quiet inner city area of Auckland. Our house was built in 1925 and is large, comfortable and furnished with antique furniture.
The facilities for guests include a private sitting room with colour television and video. Breakfast is inclusive and evening meals are by arrangement.
Your hosts have travelled extensively overseas and welcome visitors.
Personal travel plans to any part of New Zealand can be arranged prior to your arrival.
Directions: *Please telephone.*

Parnell, Auckland City
Guest House, Small Hotel
Address: 36 St Stephens Avenue, Parnell, Auckland 1
Name: Ascot Parnell
Telephone: (09) 309-9012
Beds: 6 Double, 8 Single (9 bedrooms, all with phone, private facilities and heating)
Tariff: B&B Double $88 plus GST, Single $64 plus GST; Children $10 plus GST, reduced winter rates
No meals provided, about 30 restaurants in walking distance
Nearest Town: Aucland city centre - 2 km

The Ascot Parnell is an historic mansion restored to its former elegance, yet combined with modern comfort.
It has nine guest rooms. This intimacy makes it possible for the guests to enjoy a friendly service and personal attention. A delightful gourmet breakfast is served in a dining room which shows the beauty of this lovely home. Throughout the day free tea, coffee and juice are served in the lounge. Upon request a minibus from the airport stops in front of the house. The tidy, comfortable guest rooms are individual in character. Each room has its own bathroom, direct dial telephone, heating and electric blankets. Smoking restrictons apply.
The lovely garden of the Ascot Parnell displays many of the trees, bushes and flowers native to New Zealand. Although the Ascot Parnell is a quiet place to stay in, it is nevertheless very close to the city centre (2.5 km) and within walking distance to many tourist attractions such as Parnell Village or the Auckland Museum.

Mt Eden, Auckland City
Guest House
Address: 83 Valley Road, Mt. Eden
Name: Bavaria Guest House
Telephone: (09) 689-641 **Fax:** 689-665
Beds: 8 Double, 2 Single (10 bedrooms all with private facilities and phone)
Tariff: B&B Double $69 + GST, Single $40 + GST, Children $10 + GST; reduced winter rates

Bavaria Guest House was originally an old villa which has been completely modernised and refurbished. It is situated in the heart of Mt Eden's residential area. Our establishment comprises double, twin, single and family rooms all with own bathroom and heating. Five rooms have queen size beds and balconies with sunny northerly aspect. All are friendly and tastefully decorated. During the day we serve free tea and coffee in the generously designed sunny guest lounge/breakfast area which opens out to a northfacing private sundeck. There is ample off-street parking available.
We are located only 3 km from the city centre and 15 minutes from the airport. The bus stop is nearby, so are restaurants, shops, banks, post office and famous Eden Park. A scenic walk leads up to magnificent Mt Eden, an extinct volcano. Your hosts Rudi and Ulrike from Germany are happy to assist you with your travel plans and endeavour to make your stay a pleasant experience.

Mt. Eden, Auckland City
Homestay
Address: 811 Dominion Road, Mt. Eden,
Name: David Fitchew & Bryan Condon
Telephone: (09) 694-284. Fax: (09) 697-238
Beds: 2 Double, 1 Twin (3 bedrooms, 2 guest bathrooms)
Tariff: B&B Double $55 Single $35 includes cooked breakfast, fresh muffins daily. Tea & coffee always available

Your hosts Bryan and David welcome you to their turn of the century home. Centrally located on Dominion Road which is an extension of Queen Street city centre. The bus stop at the door, only 10 minutes to city and 20 minutes to airport, shuttle bus from airport. Easy walking to Balmoral shopping area (banks, excellent restaurants, cinema).
We have operated a bed and breakfast on a farm in Digby County, Nova Scotia, Canada. Our home reflects years of collecting and living overseas. Dogs to welcome you.
Directions: *from north-south motorway, Greenlane off ramp, continue on Greenlane, to Dominion Road. Turn left and we are 7 blocks on your right to 811 (between Lambeth and Invermay and across from Landscape Road).*

Remuera, Auckland City
Homestay
Address: 18 Darwin Lane,
Remuera, Auckland 5
Name: Tony & Joanna Greenhough
Telephone: (09) 524-6281
Beds: 2 Double, 2 Single (2 bedrooms, guest bathroom)
Tariff: **B&B** $60 Double, $35 Single, campervans welcome
Nearest Town: Auckland central

We have lived in this idyllic spot for 25 years. It is secluded, sunny and sheltered, and away from the traffic, intimately overlooking the waters of the Orakei Basin.
In this tree filled environment you are only 10 minutes from central Auckland via parks or waterfront drive. There are also buses to the city or we are able to assist with transport.
Guest facilities include off-street parking, guest bathroom, and own sitting room with colour television. Evening meals are available by arrangement. We would also be pleased to assist you with your Auckland itinerary prior to your arrival.
Directions: *From the airport, take the door to door shuttle minibus. By car take Greenlane exit from southern motorway. For detailed directions please telephone.*

Remuera, Auckland City
Guest House
Address: Remuera House, 500 Remuera Road, Remuera, Auckland 5
Name: Ray King
Telephone: (09) 524-7794
Beds: 3 Double, 7 Single (10 bedrooms)
Tariff: **B&B** $56 Double, $38 Single
Nearest Town: Auckland 6 km (10 mins by car, 15 mins by bus)

For connoisseurs of old-world character, Remuera House is worth a stay. Situated in an exclusive area. Built in 1901, the last year of Queen Victoria's reign, the two-storey house is full of interesting memorabilia, the breakfast room being a feature with paintings, antiques etc.
The large foyer and lounge are panelled in native timbers. Remuera House

62

offers quietness, off-street parking, TV lounge with tea/coffee making facilities. Walking distance to buses, shops, restaurants, take-aways, within 2 km to many antique shops.
Airport shuttle buses, hire car and tour buses call at house.
Both continental and cooked breakfasts are included in the price. Remuera *House has been featured in local newspapers and its history published in the Auckland Historical Magazine. A written history of the house is available. As a member of the Auckland Historical Society and a local history author, the Proprietor will be pleased to advise you on places of interest in and around Auckland and throughout New Zealand.*
Directions: *Travellers with own transport driving from airports or on Motorways North or South of Auckland, turn off at Greenlane Road, and follow the signs to Remuera. Catch Airport Shuttle Bus or phone from bus or rail station.*

B&B hosts do it because they enjoy meeting people.
It is a friendship business.

Remuera, Auckland City
Guest House
Address: 39 Market Road,
Remuera, Auckland 5
Name: Aachen House -
Jean and Don Goldschmidt
Telephone: (09) 520-2329
Beds: 5 Double rooms,
2 Single rooms (7 bedrooms,
3 guest bathrooms)
Tariff: B&B Double $67.50,
Single $54, Children $12,
under 3 free; Dinner $16
Nearest Town: 4 km from central city

Ours is a large Victorian house set in half an acre of garden. We overlook a large park and back on to Mt Hobson, one of Auckland's many extinct volcanos. We are close to the museum, showgrounds, hospitals and race tracks. The motorway off-ramp is nearby and there is an excellent bus service two minutes walk away. Our car will collect guests from the Railway Station while the shuttle buses have a door-to-door service from the airport. Off street parking is available.
We have created a friendly, homely atmosphere in our large, beautiful home and people feel relaxed and comfortable. Our seven bedrooms comprise singles, doubles, triples and quads. Each room has a handbasin and there are three shared bathrooms.
Our one rule is NO SMOKING and this seems to please the overseas guests as well as New Zealanders.
Directions: *Take Market Road turnoff from the motorway, phone from the railway or bus stations, or come by minibus from the airport.*

63

Epsom, Auckland City

Homestay
Address: 10 Ngaroma Road, Epsom, Auckland 3
Name: Janet and Jim Millar
Telephone: (09) 657-336
Beds: 1 Queensize, 2 Single (2 bedrooms, guest bathrooms)
Tariff: B&B Double $55, Single $35, Children $10; Dinner $15
Nearest Town: Auckland 5 km

*Our 72 year-old home is on the lower slopes of One Tree Hill
(Maungakiekie), and has walking access to its Domain, one of Auckland's
loveliest parks with glorious views. We are 200 metres off the direct airport-
downtown Auckland route in a quiet tree-lined street. Close by are several
good restaurants and the bus stop to the City, a bank and postal facilities.*

*Our two guest bedrooms both have their own private bathrooms and the one
downstairs has a sun lounge opening onto a patio. There are laundry facilities and off-street parking. It takes 10 minutes by car to downtown. We can
cater for family groups with extra bedding.*

*We have three grown-up children no longer living at home, and four lively
grandchildren. We enjoy meeting people and making them feel at home. We
have travelled extensively ourselves, both overseas and in N.Z. and we enjoy
exchanging experiences.*

We prefer people to refrain from smoking indoors.

*We have backpackers accommodation in Paeroa, 118 kms south-east of
Auckland – contact us or the Paeroa Information Office for details.*

Directions: *Leaving motorway at Greenlane, travel west past Greenlane
Hospital turning left into Manukau Road at the lights. Ours is the 4th street
on the left (south) just past the V-junction lights with Pah Road. which our
street runs off at Greenwoods Corner.*

Epsom, Auckland City

Homestay
Address: 82 St Andrews Road, Epsom, Auckland
Name: Kay and Bill Foley
Telephone: (09) 688-628
Beds: 1 Double (1 bedroom, guest bathroom)
Tariff: B&B Double $55, Single $35, Children half price
Nearest Town: Auckland city centre 5 km

Our 80-year-old villa is centrally located only 10 minutes from the city centre by car and is served by the Waikowhai bus route with stops to and from town outside our gate. We are a short walk from the Greenlane Rd. intersection stop for the Airporter bus, but would recommend using the shuttle service to our door. We are close to many of Auckland's attractions – One Tree Hill, trotting and racing tracks and the Domain with Auckland's Museum. A variety of shops and restaurants are close at hand and a supermarket visit is available if you don't have a car.

Our self-contained guest accommodation consists of a bedroom with double bed, private bathroom with laundry facilities and a lounge with a kitchen corner, TV and two single divans. Family groups can be catered for as we can supply extra beds.

Our three children in their twenties still live at home but have many plans for future travel. Our dog and two cats are very much part of our family and we have a house rule of no smoking indoors.

Our swimming pool, garden and big comfortable family home are here for you to enjoy.

Some hosts are away from home during the day. It will
help if you phone them the evening before you want to stay.

Epsom, Auckland City

Homestay
Address: "Pineapple Cottage"
27 Shipherds Avenue, Epsom, Auckland 3
Name: John D and Sheila Rose
Telephone: (09) 603-542 (collect). From 27 April 92, 630 3542
Fax (09) 5205 375 Pineapple.
Beds: 1 Double, 1 Single, Rollaway available (2 bedrooms, guest bathroom)
Tariff: B&B Double $62 Single $38, Children under 16 half price; Dinner (special) $22 (by prior arrangement)
Nearest Town: Inner city Auckland

Your hosts have travelled very extensively. They have married sons in London and Washington D.C. Their home is new, well heated and attractively furnished. Most conveniently situated to central Auckland, to four central bus routes, to airport and motorway transport and for sightseeing. 10 restaurants within 8-10 minutes walk.
The guest wing is self-contained, off the breakfast room, but full use of our sitting room, sun deck, laundry etc. No pets and non-smokers preferred.
The area is particularly quiet and restful.
Holiday home (2 hours south) available on the historic and beautiful Coromandel Peninsula.
Auckland is the gateway city into New Zealand and has much to offer. Your hosts can advise on travel throughout New Zealand from detailed knowledge. Extensive library of NZ travel books.
Directions: *Shipherds Avenue is off Brightside Road which is off Gillies Avenue in Epsom, near main motorway. Phone, write for detailed instructions and brochure.*
From airport use door to door shuttle buses.

"The pineapple - 18th Century symbol of hospitality and friendship"

Mangere East
Homestay
Address: 81 Raglan Street, Mangere East
Name: Enid and Terry Cripps
Telephone: (09) 275-5448
Beds: 1 Double (en-suite bathroom, private lounge)
Tariff: B&B Double $55, Single $35; Dinner $20 per person; Campervans $20 (laundry, kitchen, bathroom facilities)
Nearest Town: 12 km south from Auckland city on State Highway 1

Enid and Terry offer you a warm welcome to our home. We live in an area known for its ethnic diversity, considered by some to reflect the true multi-cultural nature of Auckland. Our comfortable home is within easy travelling distance to all our city has to offer, as well as to other points of interest in the surrounding areas. We offer a relaxing atmosphere and such comforts as a heated spa pool.
In addition to a cooked breakfast you are invited to join us for dinner, by arrangement and we would be happy to provide a picnic lunch on request.
A courtesy car to and from the airport and intercity bus depot which is 10 minutes away is provided.

Manukau City, Auckland
Homestay & Self-contained Accom
Address: Garden View Homestay, 7 Honey Place, Weymouth, Manukau City, Auckland
Name: Gordon & Yvonne Douglas
Telephone: (09) 266-5892
Beds: 2 Double, 1 Single (3 bedrooms, 2 guest bathrooms)
Tariff: B&B $80 Double, $45 Single, children 1/2 price, Dinner $20, (child under 5 dinner free), limited off-street parking for campervans
Nearest Town: Manukau City (7km), Auckland City, Manurewa, Papakura City

5 km West of State Highway 1. 10 km Auckland Airport. Our modern home in Manukau City is situated clsoe to the sea in Weymouth. Charming village on the shores of Manukau Harbour with pioneer cottages alongside the modern. Peaceful seaside haven yet central to 6 large shopping centres, restaurants, Botanic Garden, cycledrome, fun parks. Most within 15 km. Handy to Karaka Horse Sale Complex, fishing, farming and market garden areas. After experiencing Manukau City, take a 20 minute drive by motorway into Auckland City centre.
In our home each room has floor to ceiling ranchsliders opening onto a beautiful landscaped garden. Either barbeque, relax lazing by the goldfish pond or stroll anlong the harbour foreshore after shopping or sightseeing. An internal door leads into a two bedroom self-contained flat with its own external entrance. Choose 'do your own thing' or be our homestay guests. Either way, a friendly welcome is assured. Our interests are fishing, gardening, travel, music. Gordon plays in a concert band.
Directions: *Highways No 20 (Provincial) or 17 (Urban Route) will bring you to Weymouth from either the Airport - Great South Road Route 3 - or National Highway 1. Phone for further details.*

Manukau City
Homestay
Address: 48a Redoubt Road, Manukau City
Name: Chris and Dawn Kitzen
Telephone: (09) 263-8615
Beds: 1 Double, 2 bunk beds, also cot and high chair (2 bedrooms, guest bathroom)
Tariff: B&B Double $60, Single $40, Dinner $22; Children half price
Nearest Town: Manukau City 1 km

We are 400 metres from the southern motorway and within walking distance of Rainbows End Amusement Park, Manukau City shopping centre, cycling velodrome and greyhound racing with a bus to Manukau and Manurewa shops at the door. We are handy to the Botanical Gardens, bush walks and many restaurants. The airport is 15 minutes drive.
A fridge, tea, coffe etc making facilities are provided. We can offer you dinner with us or just bed and breakfast. We serve homemade muesli, and preserves. Kosher, vegetarian and barbecue meals, also cut lunches are available on request. Our freshly ground coffee is superb. Each bedroom opens onto a lovely private garden, patio and heated spa pool. We have an electronic organ for you to play and TV is available. Dawn has many handcraft hobbies and Chris likes to oil paint and do woodworking. We have 5 adult children. We have off-street parking and rental cars can be arranged. Smoking is allowed outside in the garden only. We regret no animals.
Directions: *please phone.*

Let the phone ring for a long time when telephoning.

Manurewa, South Auckland
Homestay
Address: "Birch Wood", 19 Beaumont Way, Manurewa
Name: Anna Meisel-Cowan
Telephone: (09) 266-5849
Beds: 2 Single (1 bedroom)
Tariff: B&B $55 Double, $35 Single, $15 Dinner
Nearest Town: Auckland

I am a retired Government Health Official, missing the close contact with the public, and I look forward to meeting and enjoying the company of guests from home and overseas.
My interest include gardening, classical music, antiques and horses.
I have a small pretty garden only 15 minutes from central Auckland, 20 minutes from Auckland International Airport. My home is only 3 minutes from Southern Motorway and Manukau City Centre with its 110 shops, the largest in New Zealand. The entire area is well services with licensed restaurants, plus family dining, Pizza Hut, Wendys, Georgi Pie, Kentucky Fried Chicken, all within 3 minutes of homestay area. I would love to have you for dinner if you so desired. No smoking or children.
Directions: *Please phone before arrival.*

Clevedon

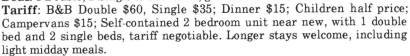

Farmstay + Self-Contained Accommodation
Address: North Road, PO Box 72, Clevedon
Name: John and Annette Hodge
Telephone: (09) 292-8707
Beds: 1 Double, 2 Single (3 bedrooms, guest bathroom)
Tariff: B&B Double $60, Single $35; Dinner $15; Children half price; Campervans $15; Self-contained 2 bedroom unit near new, with 1 double bed and 2 single beds, tariff negotiable. Longer stays welcome, including light midday meals.
Nearest Town: 40 km from Auckland, 23 km from Papakura

Our 270-acre property is only 35 minutes from the Auckland International Airport in a farming community. We offer a perfect environment in which to relax from the effects of prolonged travel before moving on, or a resting place to unwind.

We are available, by prior arrangement, at any time to meet your plane, train or coach at minimum rates.

Ours is a beef fattening farm, stretching from a native tree-clad hillside, across the flats to the coastal waters of the Waitemata Harbour. Views from our comfortable home include the lower reaches of the Wairoa River valley from Clevedon, parts of Waiheke Island and other smaller islands to the distant range of the Coromandel Peninsula.

Amenities available or nearby include: sheep shearing, native bush, farm or waterfront walks; horse riding; boat trips; fishing; visits to kiwifruit, dairy, rabbit or goat farms; Auckland Polo Club; Ardmore Airport, golf; Clevedon village and Maraetai Beach craft shops, service stations and other shopping facilities.

***Directions:** Clevedon is 14 km east of Papakura. Our home is on the left on North Road, 9 km from Clevedon.*

Many homes have facilities for campervans. The ideal camping spot with electricity, bathroom, laundry and friendly hospitality. Tell campervanners about this when you see them.

Clevedon
Farmstay
Address: "Willowgrove",
Kawakawa Bay Road,
Clevedon, RD5, Papakura
Name: Brian and Eileen Wallace
Telephone: (09) 292-8456
Beds: 1 Double, 2 single, (2 bedrooms guest bathroom)
Tariff: B&B Double $60, Single $30, Children half price; Dinner $15
Nearest Town: Auckland 40 km, Papakura 22km

Clevedon is a village in a rural area with craft shops, restaurants and all services. Eileen and I live and work on our property of about 11 acres.
We produce summer fruit, nectarines and peaches and have sheep, goats and calves. We produce our own vegetables.
The house is set in a delightful garden which has a very restful atmosphere.
We enjoy the special atmosphere and peaceful surroundings and are pleased to share it with others.
We are close enough for visitors to take in any of the Auckland attractions, and golf courses, fishing and swimming beaches are within 15 minutes drive.
The main guest room is a large upstairs room with its own sitting area, toilet and shower. You may share our family room and lounge or relax in your room as you please. We also have a games room including a pool table.
Directions: *Please phone. If required we can collect from airport or public transport for a small charge.*

Kawakawa Bay, Clevedon
Self-Contained Accommodation
Address: 19 Banks Road, Kawakawa Bay
Name: Ruth and Jack Johnston
Telephone (09) 292-2766
Beds: 1 Double 2 Single (2 bedrooms, guest bathroom)
Tariff: B&B Double $60, Single $35, Schoolchildren $12
Nearest Town: Papakura 28 kms

Our warm, comfortable home includes a self-contained flat with twin and double bedrooms, lounge with colour TV, kitchen and bathroom. We are situated at the end of a quiet cul-de-sac, two minutes walk from a very safe beach, tennis court, dairy and garage. Our home backs on to farmland and we can offer farm walks with glorious sea views.
Auckland International Airport is only 45 minutes drive and we are happy to meet you there if you make prior arrangements.
Longer stays are most welcome and the price is negotiable for longer than a two night stay. We look forward to meeting you and assure you of a peaceful and relaxing stay.

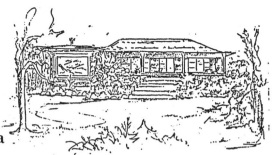

Papakura

Homestay
Address: 8 Mill End, Papakura, South Auckland
Name: Jack and Lilian Heathfield
Telephone: (09) 299-6243
Beds: 1 Double, 1 Single (2 bedrooms)
Tariff: B&B Double $50, Single $35, Dinner $15; Children half price

We enjoy meeting people and welcome to our home visitors from home and overseas. We are a retired couple living in a cul-de-sac in a quiet, attractive area. We have a small private garden with mature trees and shrubs and a restful view from our covered terrace. Our home is comfortable and in winter cosy with our log fire. We are situated conveniently twenty-five minutes drive to Auckland, the same to Auckland airport and two minutes from Wrightsons Bloodstock Sales and the Papakura turnoff on the motorway.
Local shopping and restaurants are a short distance away or you may prefer to have dinner with us. You are most welcome to help yourself to tea or coffee any time. We look forward to meeting you.
Directions: *Please phone.*

Pukekohe

Farmstay
Address: "Woodside", Ostrich Farm Road, RD1, Pukekohe
Name: Evelyn and Les Atkinson
Telephone: (09) 238-7864
Beds: 4 Single (2 bedrooms, guest bathroom)
Tariff: B&B Double $55, Single $30, Children half price; Dinner $15
Nearest Town: Pukekohe 6 kms, Auckland 48 kms

Pukekohe is a thriving farm and vegetable growing area situated 48 km south of Auckland. Our 10 acre farm is mostly beef fattening with a few sheep, geese, cats (2), a dog called Buddy, ducks and hens. We are 5 mins away from an excellent golf course and 10 mins to the famous Glenbrook vintage railway. The wild west coast of NZ is a pleasant 20 mins drive. Auckland, our wonderful "City of Sails" is only a 40 mins drive, making it close enough for our visitors to view all of its magnificent attractions. Over the years, Les and I have been fortunate to enjoy travelling throughout NZ and overseas to the UK, Continent and Australia. We love meeting people and can offer warm Kiwi hospitality - we, also, enjoyed 'farm stays' on our trips abroad. Our guests are very welcome to dine with us, or in their own dining/lounge area.
Directions: *southern motorway to Drury off-ramp - follow signs to Pukekohe-Waiuku. Right turn at Golf Course - first left to Ostrich Road, then left into Ostrich Farm Rd. "Woodside" 2 km down road on right.*

Pukekohe

Country Homestay
Address: Martyn Wright Road,
R.D. 3, Pukekohe
Name: Henk & Deborah Reimink
Telephone: (09) 236-3410
Beds: 1 Double with guest bathroom
Tariff: B&B $60 Double, $35 Single, Dinner $15, Campervans $22
Nearest Town: Pukekohe 12 km, Auckland 54 km

Our home is set on 30 acres, 20 of which is in native bush. This is one of the largest stands of bush in the area and is worth exploring. Enjoy the panoramic views of the surrounding district and sunrises from our verandah or dining room whilst breakfasting. The Mauku district is one of New Zealand's historic areas and we are happy to share our knowledge of the area with you. There is an 18 hole golf course within 10 minutes, and the Glenbrook Vintage Railway is 1 km away. the city of Auckland and its Airport are 45 minutes drive from our home. We can collect or drop off at the airport by arrangement. The township of Pukekohe is 12 km away and the West Coast Beaches and Waiuku forest within 20 mins.
Dutch, German and English are spoken. We look forward to welcoming you to our family home which is a non-smoking environment.
Directions: *Southern motorway take Drury offramp and follow signs to Pukekohe - Waiuku, turn right at the golf course and continue towards Waiuku, turn left into Gearon Road, left into Quinn Road, left into Martyn Wright Road. Please telephone and arrange your stay before setting out.*

Waiuku

Farmstay
Address: Waipipi Wharf Road,
RD3 Waiuku
Name: Wally and Heather Misa
Telephone: (09) 2358-306
Beds: 3 Single (2 bedrooms, guest bathroom)
Tariff: B&B Double $60, Single $30, Children under 13 half price, Dinner $15
Nearest Town: Auckland 50 miles, Hamilton 60 miles

We are a family of two. We have the lovely popular west coast beaches nearby (5 miles) also the interesting Manakau Harbour at our door step, being on the Awhitu Peninsula it is an easy drive to the beautiful regional park (15 miles).
Just 3 miles away is the international horse complex, Isola Equestrian Centre, and a short distance away is the Glenbrook Vintage Railway.
Our home is of modern design, very cosy and warm, situated on 5 acres of parkland grounds. We are in a district of dairy, deer, goat and sheep farming. Also near neghbours is kiwi fruit, nashi, plums, apples, citrus orchards.
Guest rooms - 1 bedroom, 2 single beds; 1 bedroom, 1 single bed. Use of private bathroom.
You are welcome to have a family dinner with us or, if you prefer, only bed and breakfast.

Pokeno
Farmstay
Address: Lyon's Road, Mangatawhiri, RD1, Pokeno
Name: Paul and Annette Bridgeman
Telephone: (09) 233-6076
Beds: 2 Single (1 bedroom, guest bathroom)
Tariff: B&B Double $55, Dinner $15, Lunches by arrangement
Nearest Town: Papakura 32 km, Auckland Airport 45 mins drive

Enjoy real country hospitality in a comfortable home in a quiet peaceful farming district, 75 kms south of Auckland Airport. Ideal for unwinding after a long flight. Minutes from all tourist routes south – Rotorua, Taupo, Coromandel, Waitomo Caves, etc. Share with us the garden (being extended now to 1 acre) plus 16 acres with several hundred trees and livestock. Farms surround us – dairying (visits can be arranged at milking time), sheep and beef, some cropping and horticulture, all in a tranquil valley ringed by bush clad hills.
With our family grown up we have the time and facilities to host guests in our home. We assure you of a warm welcome, a comfortable bed and definitely no calorie counting!
Our only requests of our guests - please phone in advance, and we would appreciate non smokers.
Directions: *From SH1 travel east on SH2 10 kms. Turn left into Lyon's Road. House 4 kms on right. Sign on roadside.*

Ask your hosts for local information. They are your own personal travel agent and guide.

Mercer
Farmstay + Self-Contained Accommodation
Address: Koheroa Road, Mercer, Pokeno
Name: Alan and Dorothy McIntyre
Telephone: (09) 232-6837
Beds: 2 Double (2 bedrooms, guest bathroom)
Tariff: B&B Double $55, Single $30, Children nego tiable; Dinner $15
Nearest Town: Papakura 25 km, Pukekohe 22 km, Auckland Airport 40 minutes –Ideal for last night's stay in N.Z.

We live on a 550 acre sheep and cattle farm with a modern brick home which has a self-contained unit attached. We have a large swimming pool and barbecue facilities. We are 3 km off the main Auckland–Hamilton highway. Our house site gives wide panoramic views of the countryside from Bombay to Thames.
We are very happy to provide dinner. There are also numerous eating facilities in the area.
The farm provides ample opportunity for taking walks and viewing farm animals plus turkeys, pheasants, ducks and quail.
Directions: *Travel State Highway 1 to Mercer, cross railway lines, travel 3 km up Koheroa Road, house is on left right near road just past Kellyville Road junction. Name clearly visible.*

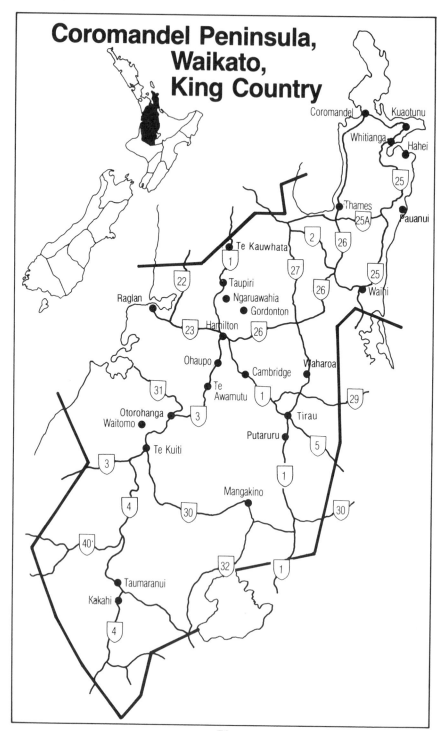

Coromandel Peninsula, Waikato, King Country

Coromandel
Kuaotunu
Whitianga
Hahei
25
Thames
25A
Pauanui
2
26
Te Kauwhata
27
1
25
22
Taupiri
26
Waihi
Raglan
Ngaruawahia
Gordonton
23
Hamilton
26
Ohaupo
Waharoa
Cambridge
31
Te Awamutu
1
29
Otorohanga
Waitomo
3
Tirau
Te Kuiti
Putaruru
5
3
1
4
30
Mangakino
40'
30
32
1
Taumaranui
Kakahi
4

Thames
Farmstay
+ Self-Contained Accommodation
Address: "Thorold", Kopu, RD1, Thames
Name: Helen and Tony Smith
Telephone: (0843) 88-480
Beds: 1 Double, 2 Single (2 bedrooms, guest bathroom)
Tariff: B&B Double $80, Single $40 Children $20 Dinner $20
Nearest Town: Thames 6 km to the north on State
Highway 25

Our spacious home is set in 30 acres of garden and farmland where we graze sheep and cattle. The guest wing is luxurious, separate, peaceful and private. There are two bedrooms – one double with queensize bed and a twin room. All with electric blankets. Bathroom adjoins bedrooms. There are coffee and tea making facilities with a fridge. The guest sitting room has comfortable chairs, television and billiard table. All rooms open out to a swimming pool.
We have three sons, one at university and the other two overseas. My husband is very involved in the farming industry and we both enjoy gardening, boating, fishing, tramping and many sports. The local golf course is five minutes away.
Dinner is available on request. Across the road is a hotel and a shop selling takeaways and in Thames which is 10 minutes from our home there is a wider choice of restaurants.
Thames and the Coromandel Peninsula have so much to offer and we would be pleased to be part of your stay.
Directions: *Please phone.*

Thames
Homestay
Address: 219 Reservoir Road, Thames
Name: Charles & Helen Burgess
Telephone: (0843) 89205
new number after Aug '92 - (07) 868-9205
Beds: 1 Double, 2 Single (2 bedrooms, guest bathroom)
Tariff: B&B $52 Double, $26 Single, Dinner from $15
Nearest Town: Thames

A clean comfortable twin or double bedded room with private facilities and breakfast (with hot home made bread) is offered for $26 per person. A New Zealand style evening meal is available from $15.
Our brick home with lovely gardens and sea views is 3 km from Thames. Our home is cool in summer and warm in winter. We are happy to meet or deliver you to the bus depot. You will be welcome at our place.
We are a NON SMOKING family.
Directions: *Please phone.*

Thames

Homestay
Address: Please phone
Name: Glenys and Russell Rutherford
Telephone: (0843) 87-788 or 75-185
Beds: 1 Double, 2 Single (2 bedrooms, guest bathroom)
Tariff: B&B Double $55, Single $35, Children half price; Dinner $15
Nearest Town: Thames 1 km

We have a spacious and comfortable home with sweeping views of the Firth of Thames.
Our interests include gardening, golf, music and entertaining family and friends.
The double room adjoins a private lounge with TV and reading material. A twin room upstairs opens onto a balcony. All beds have electric blankets. A swimming pool in summer and an open fire in winter help to make your stay enjoyable.
Being an historic goldmining settlement, museums and gold prospectors diggings are of particular interest. Due to its natural beauty the Coromandel has attracted many potters and painters. Their galleries can be visited on a scenic day trip up the coast to Coromandel village, and continuing back through the popular beach resorts of Whitianga, Pauanui and Tairua. The rugged hills and native bush appeal to hikers and nature lovers.
Our intention is for you to enjoy some of these features and we welcome your visit.
You may care to join us for dinner or simply enjoy a comfortable night`s rest and a satisfying breakfast to set you off on your day's journey.

Thames

Homestay
Address: "Grafton Cottage",
304 Grafton Road, Thames
Name: Ferne & David Tee
Telephone: (0843) 89971
Beds: 2 Double, 2 Single (3 bedrooms, each with guest bathroom)
Tariff: B&B $65 Double, $35 Single, Dinner $18
Nearest Town: Thames (1 km to town centre)

Grafton cottage is nestled in the foot hills of the Coromandel Peninsula, overlooking the historic town of Thames.
Thames, considered the Gateway to the Peninsula, boasts extensive bush reserves covering the rugged mountainous range. To the East lie the world renowned beaches, while to the West, the calmer waters of the Firth.
Also of interest are the many activities catering for the art and craft, goldmining and kauri history enthusiast.
The cottage itself consists of four bedrooms, dining area and two lounges. Of the four bedrooms, there are two double bedrooms with ensuite available for guests. Plus, adjoining the main house, are two chalets. Both of these are doubles with ensuites and tea and coffee making facilities.
As keen outdoor people, we have made available our own personalised outback tours, covering the Coromandel and central North Island (by prior arrangement).
Directions: *Turn right at Toyota factory (Bank St) follow to end, turn right into Parawai Road, 4th on left is Grafton Road.* ————

Kopu, Thames
Farmstay
+ Self-contained Accom
Address: "Wharfedale", R.D. 1,
Kopu Hikuai Highway, Thames
Name: Chris & Rosemary Burks
Telephone: (0843) 88929

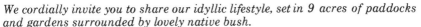

Beds: 1 Double, 2 Single (2 bedrooms, guest bathroom)
Tariff: B&B $60 Double, $35 Single, children (under 16) $20, Dinner $20,
Campervans $20
Nearest Town: Thames

*We cordially invite you to share our idyllic lifestyle, set in 9 acres of paddocks
and gardens surrounded by lovely native bush.*
*Meander across the lawn to the river - picking, perhaps, some peaches or
citrus fruits which abound and enjoy in total privacy natures swimming pools
whilst Kingfisher and Rosella swoop overhead.*
*Our gardens reflect our interest in herbs, old roses and no dig cultivation, we
enjoy wholefoods and organically grown produce. We have hardcourt tennis
and barbeque area.*
Our goat herd allow us to share their lives, milk and fibre for spinning.
*My husband practices medicine and our son is in final year at Wanganui
Collegiate.*
*The property is situated 1 hour from Auckland, 15 mins from Thames, close
proximity to beautiful Coromandel beaches and 5 mins golf course.*
*We offer a double room with double bed, electric blanket and private
bathroom. Or a self-contained flat with twin beds. Extra sleeping
arrangements as required.*
*Cosy farmhouse kitchen with range in winter and cool shade in summer. We
look forward to meeting you.*
Directions: *Please phone for directions.*

Hauraki Plains,
Thames through to the Coromandel
Home and Farmstays
Address: Hauraki Farm Holidays,
Freepost 25, Postshop, Thames
Name: Wendy McQueen
Telephone: (0843) 75244

Beds: Various
Tariff: B&B $45 per person per night, children $20, Dinner $15.
Nearest Town: Thames

Get in touch with nature, leave the city life behind and enjoy a getaway break.
*Our hosts are warm and friendly who want to share their homes and food
with you.*
*There is plenty to see from the Hauraki Plains through to the Peninsula. We
have hot pools, bush walks, gemstone factory and really great beaches, not
forgetting the farm animals. Everything within easy reach.*
We can give you a choice of stays which will be offered to you on booking.
Look forward to hearing from you.
Directions: *Please phone.*

Kuaotunu

Homestay
Address: Main Road, Kuaotunu,
Coromandel Peninsula
Name: John and Robin Twemlow
Telephone: (0843) 65-735
Beds: 2 Single (1 bedroom, guest bathroom)
Tariff: B&B Double $35, Single $20, Children half price; Dinner $12;
Nearest Town: Whitianga 16 km on State Highway 25

We are a Christian family of five with two adult sons (both left the nest) and one teenage daughter. Our house is across the road from the beach where we enjoy fishing, walking and spending time – in fact just plain relaxing. Rowboat, canoes and fishing gear for your use. This area offers bushwalks and exploring of old goldmines.

If you are looking for a stopover on your way round the Coromandel Peninsula, our home could well be the place you're looking for. We're a very relaxed household : no frills but food to fill. Vegetarian meals prepared on request.

We also have a very comfortable sofa that folds down to a double bed in the library for extra sleeping if needed.

Directions: *Please phone collect.*

Whitianga

Bed & Breakfast/Homestay
Address: "Cosy Cat Cottage",
41 South Highway, Whitianga
Name: Gordon and Janet Pearce
Telephone: (0843) 64-488.
(07) 866 4488 from 1 Aug. 92
Beds: 1 Double, 4 Single (3 bedrooms, guest bathroom)
Tariff: B&B Double $60, Single $40, (during peak season 24 December to 31 January and public holidays add $5 per person), Dinner $15
Nearest Town: 1 km south of Whitianga Post Office; Thames 93 km via SH25.

We look forward to welcoming you to "Cosy Cat Cottage". Come in and have a complimentary cup of tea or coffee. Relax in our guest lounge with TV, library and board games, or n the large shaded deck with pleasant garden and rural views.

Have a good night's rest in the comfortable beds, then enjoy your choice of breakfast treats from our a la carte menu, including home preserved fruits, honey from our own bees and home made muesli. Dinner is available on request, and we gladly cater for vegetarians and those with special diets - please ask.

If you like cats you'll love our decor - all on a cat theme. We also breed Tonkinese cats.

Our modern two-storey home has an interesting exposed post and beam design. It is carpeted throughout, and is set in a "cottage" garden. The guest bathroom is large and well appointed.

A courtesy car is available, and sightseeing and fishing trips can be arranged.

Whitianga, Mercury Bay, is famous for its safe, beautiful sandy beaches.

magnificent scenery, historic sites, boating, fishing, restaurants, shops and pleasant climate.
It is the perfect location from which to spend two or three days exploring the fascinating and lovely Coromandel Peninsula.
See you soon!

Whitianga

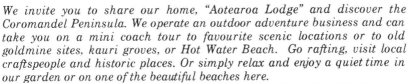

Homestay/Tourist Lodge
Address: Main Road, Coroglen, RD1, Whitianga
Name: Glenn and Rennie Leach
Telephone: (0843) 63-808
Beds: 8 Single (4 bedrooms, guest bathroom)
Tariff: B&B Twin $68, Single $37, Children half price; Dinner $25
Nearest town: 13 km south of Whitianga on SH 25

We invite you to share our home, "Aotearoa Lodge" and discover the Coromandel Peninsula. We operate an outdoor adventure business and can take you on a mini coach tour to favourite scenic locations or to old goldmine sites, kauri groves, or Hot Water Beach. Go rafting, visit local craftspeople and historic places. Or simply relax and enjoy a quiet time in our garden or on one of the beautiful beaches here.
Guests have their own toilet facilities, lounge and self-contained kitchen.
Enjoy a delicious 3 course dinner, our warm hospitality and many happy memories of your stay with us. Do telephone, you will be most welcome. Please mention The New Zealand Bed and Breakfast Book when telephoning.

Pauanui Beach

Farmstay
Address: R.D. Hikuai, Pauanui Beach, Thames
Name: Dave & Lois Robertson
Telephone: (0843) 47829
Beds: 1 Double (1 bedroom, guest bathroom)
Tariff: **B&B** $55 Double, $30 Single, children $15, Dinner $15, Campervans $20.
Nearest Town: Thames (35 km)

As drystock farmers in the picturesque Tairua River Valley we are in an excellent position to offer a warm welcome to travellers visiting the East Coast of the Coromandel Peninsula. We are a family of six - two daughters, 16 & 14, two sons, 12 & 10 - with numerous interests including travel, sport and fishing. Our home is a spacious Lockwood which overlooks much of our 150 acre property and affords spectacular views of the Pinnacles. Our guest accommodation consists of a comfortable double bedroom with private facilities. Additional accommodation is available in the house for children travelling with parents.
Only 10 minutes drive from a popular East Coast beach with excellent swimming, fishing and boating opportunities, we are very central to the many attractions of this part of the Peninsula. These include bush walks, river canoeing, pottery and craft shops and a variety of restaurants.
We are happy to offer a choice of breakfast and a family dinner if required.
Directions: *Please phone.*

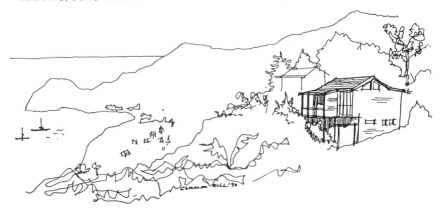

Hahei Beach, Whitianga
Homestay
Address: Grange Road, Hahei Beach, RD1, Whitianga
Name: Barbara and Alan Lucas
Telephone: (0843) 63-543
Beds: 2 Double, 1 Single, extra beds available (3bedrooms, guest bathrooms)
Tariff: B&B Double $60, Single $35, Children under 10 half price; Dinner $15, Packed lunches by prior arrangement
Nearest Town: Tairua 36 km, Whitianga 38 km

My wife and I are semi-retired and live in a Lockwood home overlooking the sea with panoramic views from the Alderman Islands to the Mercury Islands.

We are five minutes walk from Hahei Beach and are on the road to Cathedral Cove and its beaches, a must when visiting this area. Hot water beach is just a short distance away where you can enjoy a warm soak at any time of the year.

The area offers bush walks, surf beaches, fishing and spectacular views for photography.

Our interests are meeting people and gardening. We enjoy our own vegetables and can assure you of excellent meals, my wife is a first class cook, at least, I think so.

Please give us a telephone call when you wish to come and we can promise you a most enjoyable, relaxed stay. We look forward to hearing from you.

Directions: *Turn off at Whenuakite. Grange Road is on left by Hahei Store, We are on left near top of hill.*

Some homes share the bathroom, others have bathrooms
exclusively for guests - they are indicated in the listing.

Waihi
Homestay
Address: Chez Nous,
41 Seddon Avenue, Waihi
Name: Sara Parish
Telephone: (07) 863-7538
Beds: 2 Twin (2 bedrooms, guest bathroom)
Tariff: B&B $45 Double, $35 Single, children $10, Dinner $10, Campervans welcome
Nearest Town: Waihi, Tauranga 60 kms South

Waihi is the Southern gateway to the beautiful Coromandel Peninsula and a mere 15 minute drive from the spectacular expanse of Waihi Beach. The latter is a favourite with surfers and is also very safe for bathing.
The Bay of Plenty resort of Mt Maunganui is a comfortable sixty minute drive to the South. Waihi is steeped in history, particularly with respect to goldmining. Tourists can tour two goldmines which are currently under production. Waihi is also a mecca for small craft industries. With a superb golf course, salt and freshwater fishing and challenging bush walks, it is an outdoor sportsperson's paradise.
Chez Nous is a large modern house situated within easy walking distance of Waihi's shops, restaurants and hotels. I am interested in travel and enjoy meeting people from New Zealand and overseas. Guests have their own shower and toilet facilities.
Directions: *Seddon Avenue runs parallel to the main road leading out of Waihi to Paeroa.*

Waihi
Homestay
Address: 22 Roycroft Street, Waihi
Name: Josie & Bob French
Telephone: (07) 863-7208
Beds: 4 Single (2 bedrooms, share bathroom)
Tariff: **B&B** $40 Double, $20 Single, children (under 13) 1/2 price, Dinner $10
Nearest Town: Waihi

Waihi is on the East coast and is the gateway to both the Coromandel Peninsula with all its beautiful beaches and native bush and the Bay of Plenty, the kiwifruit centre of New Zealand. Local attractions include a vintage railway running between Waihi and Waikino. Also New Zealand's largest gold mine is operating on the out-skirts of the town and the workings can be observed from a look-out. The Martha lode was discovered in 1878 and was worked as an underground mine until 1952. It was reopened in 1989 as an opencast mine.
Our home has three bedrooms. The beds are new and have electric blankets. We have a large garden of 3/4 acre. Our interests are tramping and dancing. Non-smokers please.

81

Te Kauwhata
Farmstay + Self-Contained Accommodation
Address: Waerenga Road, D1, Te Kauwhata
Name: Rex and Trixie Browning
Telephone: (0817) 67718
Beds: 1 Double, 2 Single (2 bedrooms, guest bathroom)
Tariff: B&B Double $50, Single $35, Dinner $15, Children half price; Campervans $20
Nearest Town: Huntly 25 km, Thames 44 km, Auckland 80 km

We are on a typical Waikato dairy farm, close to SH1, also SH2. We have a comfortable family home plus self contained accommodation. You could have dinner with us or just bed and breakfast - children are always welcome. Electric blankets available. We are only 30 km from Miranda Hot Pools, 44 km to the beach at Thames, also very handy for all kinds of fishing. Just down the road is a lovely 18 hole golf course.
We are interested in travel and enjoy meeting people from New Zealand and overseas in our friendly home. We are handy to all areas.
Directions: *take Te Kauwhata turnoff from SH1, go 12 km, house on right. From SH2, take Te Kauwhata turnoff, go 12 km, 2nd place on the left past Waerenga Service Station.*

Raglan
Farmstay + Self-Contained Accommodation
Address: "Matawha", RD2, Raglan
Name: Peter and Jenny Thomson
Telephone: (07) 8256-709
Beds: 2 Singles; 1 Double or 4 Singles in self-contained unit
Tariff: B&B Double $30, Single $20, Children half price, Babies free; Dinner $15; lunch $10 per person; Campervans $20 (laundry and bathroom facilities available)
Nearest Town: Raglan 30 minutes, Hamilton 1 hour

We are a family of four with two boys aged 15 and 12 years. We are fortunate to farm right on the west coast with panoramic views of the Tasman Sea.
Our beach is very private with good fishing and hang gliding.
Our farm has been in the family for over 100 years and we take great pride in breeding top class Romney sheep, and stud and commercial Hereford cattle. We also do some riding and have a large flower garden. All vegetables and meat are supplied by a large vegetable garden and by the farm.
We have excellent scenic drives and bush walks plus of course our own beach. We enjoy having visitors from all over the world and they enjoy participating in all our farm activities.
Directions: *Take Hamilton—Raglan road (route 23) Travelling approx 30 minutes – through Te Uku, take the Kauroa and Te Mata Bridal Veil Falls (signposted) and turn left. Take the first turn to the right through Te Mata (Waimaori Road) and follow for 7 miles. Our place is named on letterbox at the 2nd "T" junction marked Ruapuke Road, Waimaori Rd, Swanns no exit Rd.*

Hamilton
Farmstay
Address: "Farndale", RD10, Hamilton
Name: Sylvia and Rod Smith
Telephone and Fax: (07) 829 8511
Beds: 1 Double, 3 Single (3 bedrooms, guest bathroom)
Tariff: B&B Double $60, Single $40, Children under 10 half price; Dinner with wine $25

Our home is roomy and comfortable with good views in every direction. We are situated in beautiful rolling countryside to the west of Hamilton.
We offer a generous three-course meal with New Zealand wines.
Local attractions include tramping, horse riding, golf, beach at Raglan (half hour drive), Waitomo caves (1 hour drive).
We farm deer and grow blueberries.Our interests include horticulture and animal farming, music, arts and crafts and travel.
Directions: *Please phone.*

Hamilton
Homestay
+Self-Contained Accommodation
Address: 2 Ruakiwi Road, Hamilton
Name: Richard & Pamela Harington
Telephone: (07) 8382-328
Beds: 4 Single (2 twin bedrooms, 2 guest bathrooms)
Tariff: B&B $65 Double, $45 Single, Dinner by arrangement
Nearest Town: Hamilton

Our well-appointed modern home is within 1 km of the inner city, the bus terminal and railway station and is opposite the Hamilton lake and its surrounding park.
We would particularly like to welcome you to our home as we have travelled widely and frequently ourselves, using B&B's wherever possible. We know its a wonderful way to get to know a country, its people and the lifestyle.
We moved back to Hamilton after 30 years of farming our nearby property. Pamela coupled this with a teaching career. Hamilton is a university city astride the Waikato River and is right in the middle of a magnificent farming area. We'll be happy to show you around and / or help plan an itinerary. Hamilton is a great place from which to make day trips to the East and West coasts, Waitomo Caves, Rotorua and various trout fishing spots e.g. Lake Taupo.
One guest room converts to a self-contained suite.

Claudelands, Hamilton
Homestay
Address: 24 Pearson Ave, Claudelands, Hamilton
Name: Maureen & Graeme Matthews
Telephone: (07) 855-4269
Beds: 3 Single (2 bedrooms, share bathroom)
Tariff: B&B $50 Double, $35 Single, children 1/2 price, Dinner $15, Campervans $20 (up to 4 persons)
Nearest Town: Hamilton

We would like to welcome you to our home situated 2 seconds off the city by-pass on number 1 highway in the Five Crossroads area. Adjacent to the showgrounds and only 1.6 km from the inner city, it is a comfortable walk if you wish to shop. Ruakura, the world famous agricultural research station is just two blocks from our home, if farming is your interest.

Our home is a 'lived-in' comfortable home, warm in winter and cool in summer with an in-ground swimming pool for your use.

Our four children have left home and we enjoy spending time with guests from both NZ and overseas. We have hosted people from many parts of the world and for seven years Maureen taught conversational English to Japanese students. We have travelled extensively and therefore are able to help you plan your holiday.

We look forward to having you in our home as part of our family.

The standard of accommodation in The New Zealand Bed and
Breakfast Book ranges from homely to luxurious but you can
always be sure of superior hospitality.

84

Hamilton
Homestay
Address: 7 Delamare Road,
Bryant Park, Hamilton
Name: Mrs Esther Kelly
Telephone: (07) 849-2070
Beds: 2 Single (1 bedroom, guest bathroom)
Tariff: B&B Double $55, Single $35; Dinner $15
Nearest Town: Hamilton

I have travelled in many countries and would welcome tourists and would be happy to advise you on travel in New Zealand.
I live in the suburb of Bryant Park, close to the Waikato River with its tranquil river walks and I am within walking distance of St Andrews Golf Course. Hamilton is a picturesque city with rose gardens, a new museum, Ruakura Animal Research Farm and an agricultural museum called "Farmworld". Hamilton is in the centre of the dairy industry.
My interests are cooking, gardening, tramping, boating, trout fishing, playing golf, art and also Mah Jong. I am a member of Business and Professional Women's Club.
I look forward to offering you friendly hospitality.
Directions: *If approaching from Auckland – leave main highway just after passing Te Rapa Air Force Station on right. Turn left at Pukete Road, turn right at Sandwich Road and Delamare Road is 1 km on left.*
If approaching from Hamilton – travel north 1.5 km on Ulster Street until you reach four cross-roads with lights. Just after lights, turn right to Beerescourt Road. Travel 2 km to Braid Road shops on right and after shops turn left to Sandwich Road and Delamare Road is on right. (4.5 km from Hamilton city)

Hamilton
Homestay
Address: 17 Alanbrooke Place, Beerescourt, Hamilton
Name: Lin & Laureen Walcott
Telephone: (07) 849 3457
Beds: 1 Double, 1 Single (2 bedrooms)
Tariff: B&B $50 Double, $30 Single, children 1/2 price, Dinner $15
Nearest Town: Hamilton

Your hosts are a retired couple with a comfortable family home and we invite you to share this informal atmosphere with us. We are located in the North-West area of Hamilton, handy to St. Andrews Golf Course, Te Rapa Aquatic Centre and Te Rapa Race Course, but in a nice quiet cul-de-sac. The house is centrally heated and overlooks a park.
Our interest range from handcrafts to vintage cars to music to travel. We are members of the V.V.C.C. of NZ and Vintage Chevrolet Club of America. We enjoy walking, gardening and meeting people from different cultures.

Hamilton

Homestay
Address: 530 Grey Street, Hamilton
Name: Norman and Frances Wills
Telephone: (07) 838-2120
Beds: 1 Twin Room, 1 Single Room (guest bathroom)
Tariff: B&B Double $55, Single $30, Children half price; Dinner $15
Nearest Town: Hamilton

Spacious nicely renovated family home away from traffic noise but only 3 minutes from CPO and central shopping. Easily accessible from all main highways. Grey Street runs off Cobham Drive (Highway 1 from Cambridge) through Hamilton East to Claudelands Showgrounds.
We have travelled overseas and are accustomed to entertaining visitors – American, Asian and European. We can assist with local and district sight-seeing information or with planning your tour further afield. Comfort guaranteed.

Gordonton, Hamilton

Homestay
Address: Gordonton Road, RD1, Hamilton
Name: Tim and Nan Thorrold
Telephone: (07) 8556-742
Beds: 4 Single (2 bedrooms, guest bathroom)
Tariff: B&B Double $60, Single $35, Children $20; Dinner $20
Nearest Town: 11 km N.E. of Hamilton P.O.

We have a lovely garden home with extensive rural views that we would love to share with you. Situated in the centre of the Waikato dairying district we are involved with farming and will be happy to arrange farm visits.
We are handy to golf courses.
Catch up on your washing if you wish – auto washing machine and drier available.
Directions: *Hamilton East–Taupiri bypass via Gordonton, 6 km from city boundary.*

Hamilton

Self-Contained Accommodation
Address: 45 St Andrews Terrace, Hamilton
Name: Niel and Betty Andersen
Telephone: (07) 8493-258
Beds: 1 Double Settee, 2 Single (1 bedroom, guest bathroom)
Tariff: B&B Double $50, Single $40, $10 each extra, reasonable weekly rates on request

My husband and I are of retirement age and live in a quiet location of Hamilton about 4 km from the Central Post Bank. Our home overlooks the St. Andrews Golf Course and Hamilton Golf Club and we are within close proximity of twelve other courses.
We have a self-contained flat at the back of our home, which consists of one twin bedroom, bathroom, large lounge with billiard table, plus kitchenette and lounge area. The six foot settee opens up to sleep two, if required. We let

this on a motel basis of clean towels each day, etc.
*Our aim is to give travellers time to relax and do as they wish and it is with
this in mind that we supply a Continental Breakfast in the flat to have at
leisure.*
*Through business and pleasure we have travelled extensively throughout
New Zealand and overseas, so have been able to assist our guests in making
further travel plans.*
*Hamilton is only one and a half hours driving time from Auckland Airport
and is centrally located for making day trips to Rotorua, Waitomo Caves
and many other interesting places.*

Hamilton
Homestay
Address: "Rose Ash", 22 Donny Avenue, Hamilton
Name: Pam Southcombe
Telephone: (07) 855 7755
Beds: 2 Single (1 bedroom)
Tariff: B&B $55 Double, $35 Single, children 1/2 price
Nearest Town: Hamilton

*You are welcome to my home which is situated just off River Road, close to
the Waikato River and Day's Park, a great area for walking, feeding the
ducks or fishing for trout or coarse fish. In summer rowers and waterskiers
make use of the river and the paddle steamer "Waipa Delta" can be observed
from the small beach.*
*I am just 3 minutes walk away from the bus-stop where you can catch a bus
only 5 minutes ride to Chartwell Square Shopping Centre or the central city.
There are several good cafe's and restaurants close by. Non-smokers
preferred.*
My interests include angling, gardening, bridge and travel.
Directions: *Please phone.*

Waharoa
Farmstay
Address: Wardville Road, R.D., Waharoa
Name: Joe & Anne Minkhorst
Telephone: (07) 888-0874
Beds: 1 Double, 2 Single (2 Bedrooms, guest bathroom)
Tariff: B&B $50 Double, $30 Single, children $15, Dinner $25
Nearest Town: Matamata

*We live on a deer / drystock farm close to Highway 27 en route between
Auckland and Rotorua.*
*This is an opportunity for tourists to relax, on arrival or before departure by
air from Auckland, on a farm amongst friendly deer and cattle and enjoy our
hospitality.*
*Our comfortable home in a rural setting with an outlook on the Kaimai Range
will provide you with rest and for the active person, swimming, tennis,
feeding deer and cattle, tramping, golf, sky-diving, hunting, fishing etc.*
*We speak Dutch, German and English and can provide tasty home-cooked
meals prepared from farmed venison, beef and mutton with fresh vegetables
from the garden.*

Cambridge

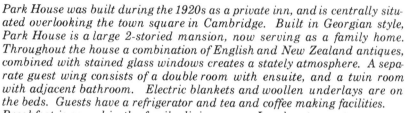

Bed & Breakfast
Address: Park House, Cambridge
Name: Bill and Pat Hargreaves
Telephone: (07) 8276-368
Beds: 2 Double, 2 Single (3 bedrooms each with own bathroom)
Tariff: B&B Double $100, single $80
Nearest Town: One block to town centre

Park House was built during the 1920s as a private inn, and is centrally situated overlooking the town square in Cambridge. Built in Georgian style, Park House is a large 2-storied mansion, now serving as a family home. Throughout the house a combination of English and New Zealand antiques, combined with stained glass windows creates a stately atmosphere. A separate guest wing consists of a double room with ensuite, and a twin room with adjacent bathroom. Electric blankets and woollen underlays are on the beds. Guests have a refrigerator and tea and coffee making facilities.
Breakfast is served in the family dining room. Local restaurant menus are available, most of the restaurants being within walking distance of Park House.
Cambridge offers an excellent selection of antiques and quality handcrafts. It is an hour's drive to Waitomo Glow Worm Grotto, a similar distance to Rotorua, the Coast, and a leisurely 2 hour drive to Auckland.

Tirau

Farmstay
Address: Rotorua Road, R D2, Tirau
Name: Lin and Joy Cathcart
Telephone: (07) 8831-471
Beds: 1 Double, 2 Single (2 bedrooms)
Tariff: B&B Double $57, Single $28.50, Dinner $15
Nearest Town: Tirau

Our 75 hectare dairy farm is on State Highway 5, an easy 2 1/2 hour drive from Auckland International Airport. We have two adult children who have 'flown the nest' and a lovable cat called Ben. Visitors are welcome to wander our farm, visit the cowshed at milking time or fish for rainbow trout in the two streams that border our property.
By car we are: 35 minutes from Rotorua, one and a quarter hours from Waitomo Caves, one and a quarter hours from Lake Taupo, two and a half hours from Ruapehu Ski Fields.
Our interests include gardening, cooking, golf, patchwork, bridge, travel and meeting people from other countries. Non-smokers preferred and sorry no children under 12 years.
Directions: *follow SH1 south from Tirau 2 km. Then take SH5 left to Rotorua for 3 km, cross Waihou River Bridge, and 200 metres on left is our gate - name on mailbox.*

Putaruru
Self-Contained Accommodation
Address: R.D.3, Putaruru
Name: Lola and Tony McCormack
Telephone: (07) 883 8221
Beds: 4 Single (2 bedrooms, guest bathroom)
Tariff: B&B Double $40, Single $20, Dinner $15, Children under 15 $10
Nearest Town: Putaruru 9 km west of us

We are offering accommodation for up to 4 people in bunkrooms opening into a family room, bathroom, toilet and kitchenette.
Our quiet 2 hectare rural property is just off SH1 and SH5 near Putaruru. Three hours from Auckland and 45 minutes from Rotorua makes it ideal for an overnight stop.
We comprise two parents, four children (usually only one or two at home), one dog, one cat, a pigeon, assorted animals and a swimming pool. The assorted animals don't live in.
Lola and Tony both travelled overseas in their youth. They see this invitation to you as a way of returning the warm hospitality they experienced.
Come stay with us. You're welcome for an evening meal but ring in advance so we can do justice to your visit.
Directions when you phone.

Te Awamutu
Farmstay
Address: "Tregemere",
2025 Ohaupo Road, Te Awamutu
Name: Ray and Betty Johnson
Telephone: (07) 871 8861
Beds: 1 Double, 2 Single (3 bedrooms, guest bathroom)
Tariff: B&B Double $50, Single $25, Dinner $15, Campervans $20
Nearest Town: Te Awamutu

A two hour drive south of Auckland makes Te Awamutu a pleasant stop-over before visiting the famed Waitomo caves. Our home is modern, warm and comfortable set in approx two acres of garden, with a beautiful view west to Mt. Pirongia and easy walks to ponds and bush area.
We are middle-aged plus – retired – then decided to go farming again on a 64 acre dry stock farm on the verge of suburbia, and one minute from the Te Awamutu Post Office.
Te Awamutu is the Rose Town of New Zealand with a superb rose garden and beautiful park – a pleasure to visit!
Directions: *Very easy to find with a white stone entrance and black railing fence. Situated on State Highway 3, the main road. On the right hand side coming from Hamilton, or first farm on left after leaving Te Awamutu.*

Te Awamutu
Farmstay
+ Self-Contained Accommodation
Address: McGee Road,
RD 2, Te Awamutu
Name: David and Colleen Cullen
Telephone: (07) 872-7857
Beds: 2 Double, 2 Single (2 bedrooms, guest bathroom)
Tariff: B&B Double $50, Single $25, Children $5, Dinner $15;
Campervans welcome
Nearest Town: Te Awamutu 10 km

Our modern homestead is set in a tranquil garden setting where you can enjoy peace and quiet or you are welcome to a game of tennis or table tennis then relaxation in our hot spa pool.
You may have dinner with us or just bed and breakfast. Restaurants are 10 minutes away.
The guest room and flat have electric blankets, TV and their own bathrooms.
Our farm is 50 hectares on which we grow maize and graze stock.
Access to Dairy Farm, deer and draught horses close by.
We have a variety of interests and have travelled through the United Kingdom, Holland, Paris, Hong Kong, Asia and the United States. Colleen enjoys gardening, handcrafts, yoga, tramping and tennis and is an owl collector, member of the B&PW club, WD. Both of us are members of the Methodist Church and David is a member of the Masonic Lodge.
Directions: *Take main road south of Te Awamutu to Kihi Kihi, turn left, Arapuni Road, 4 km to Orakau Monument, first turn left McGee Road, first house.*

Te Awamutu
Farmstay

Address: Storey Road, Te Awamutu
Name: Mrs Regula Bleskie
Telephone: (07) 871-3301
Beds: 1 Double, 6 Single (4 bedrooms, guest bathroom)
Tariff: **B&B** $60 Double, $40 Single, children $20, Dinner $15
Nearest Town: Te Awamutu

The 85 acre farm is situated in beautiful rolling countryside with cattle, horses and pets (your pets are welcome). A spacious home with large living area, swimming pool and tennis court in a well planned garden. It welcomes you in winter with underfloor heating, spa-pool and huge open firplace. Large guestrooms and some with lofts, the ball-room being available for your exclusive use.
You are welcome to have dinner with us or if preferred only bed and breakfast.
Our farm lies near Te Awamut and is an excellent base for visiting the Waitomo Caves, Otorohanga Kiwi House and the Waikato area.
If transport is not available, guests can be met and returned to public transport.
Directions: *Please phone.*

Otorohanga
Farmstay
Address: "Chindie", No 5RD, Otorohanga
Name: D and A McRae
Telephone: (081332) 733
Beds: 4 Single (2 bedrooms, guest bathroom)
Tariff: B&B Double $50, Single$35, Dinner $20, Children half price, Campervans $20
Nearest Town: Otorohanga 23 km

We live on a large farm approximately 23 km from Otorohanga and we have a modern spacious home. A private bathroom is available for guests The farm is steep to rolling countryside suitable for walks with lovely blocks of native bush on our property. We farm sheep and cattle.
Our garden is around 2 acres with ponds walks and tranquility.
We like cooking also, and guests are welcome to share our evening meal.

When you stay at B&Bs you are meeting "dinkum Kiwis".

Otorohanga
Homestay
+ Self-contained Accom
Address: "Brake's B&B",
147 Main North Road, (SH3), Otorohanga
Name: Ernest & Ann Brake
Telephone: (081) 33-7734

Beds: 2 Single (1 bedroom); Self-contained unit 1 Queensize, 1 single, plus rollaway bed, cot and high-chair (1 bedroom, guest bathroom)
Tariff: B&B $39 per person; In self-contained unit $50 Double, $35 Single, $15 each extra, $10 children, $5 cot. Breakfast optional $4 each.
Nearest Town: Otorohanga

We are a retired farming couple with an adult family and have travelled overseas. Our home is on the northern outskirts of Otorohanga and we enjoy extensive views of the countryside from our elevated position.
The self-contained unit is a quaint little garden cottage tastefully furnished with walls of natural timber panelling. It has tea/coffee making facilities, toaster, fridge, TV; laundry facilities available.
Evening meals are available at several restaurants in Otorohanga, while we invite you to enjoy breakfast with us.
Otorohanga is an interesting rural town with its native bird park featuring a Kiwi house and aviary. It is the nearest town to Waitomo Glow-worm Caves and numerous bush walks, Waitomo Golf Course and the Waipa River, a good trout fishing stream. Visits to sheep and dairy farms, local gardens and orchards can be arranged.
Directions: *from Otorohanga town centre take the main road (SH3 north and find us on the left approx 2 km from town.*

Waitomo, Te Kuiti
Farmstay
Address: Aria Road, Piopio
Name: Maurice and Jennifer Kearns
Telephone: (0813) 77801
Beds: 4 Single (2 bedrooms, guest bathroom)
Tariff: B&B Double $50, Single $25,
Dinner $15, Children half price; Campervans $20
Nearest Town: Te Kuiti 30 km, Piopio 8 km

We welcome visitors to our modern home on a 163 acre sheep and cattle farm in the clean green King Country. 8 km from SH3 on a sealed road, it is an ideal stopover after visiting the Waitomo Caves area en route to Taranaki or the Central North Island region.

Our home is nestled amongst limestone outcrops, with attractive garden, a swimming pool, and a duck pond - a quiet, secure environment for rest, relaxation and friendly company. Should you prefer, there are farm or scenic walks. Public tennis courts, a bowling green and an 18 hole golf course are nearby.

Guest rooms consist of 2 twin rooms, each with feather duvets, electric blankets and heaters. There is a guest toilet, shower, and bathroom with spa bath. Use of laundry facilities included. For campervans we provide power connection close to our house and the use of all bathroom and laundry facilities. Breakfasts willingly supplied - fruit, cereal, toast - $5, fully-cooked - $7.50.

Directions: *travelling south on SH3, turn left at crossroads in centre of Piopio. Proceed for 8 km. We are first home on right after passing the Paekaka Road (which turns off to right). Name on mailbox.*

Waitomo, Te Kuiti
Farmstay
Address: Glenview Station, R.D. 8, Te Kuiti
Name: Cindy & Warren Clayton-Greene
Telephone: (0813) 87705
Beds: 2 Double, 1 Single (3 bedrooms, guest bathroom)
Tariff: **B&B** $50 Double, $30 Single, Dinner $10, Campervans welcome (though no power supply)
Nearest Town: Waitomo (6 km), Te Kuiti (23 km), Otorohanga (20Km)

You're invited to stay on a New Zealand sheep and cattle station. Enjoy the quietness and hospitality rural life has to offer. Relax amongst the beautiful countryside while enjoying the farm's bush, trout streams and unique limestone formations. Many of our guests enjoy hiking around the farm, or taking a drive out the back of the station. The farm is ran in the traditional way with horse and dog, we carry approximately 6000 sheep and 600 cattle on 2,200 acres.

We are a young couple with 2 small children. We will share with you our attractive home set in beautiful gardens. You'll find us nestled in the hills above the Waitomo Caves with a panaromic view.

Directions: *Follow the road West from Waitomo Caves towards Marakopa for approximately 6 km. We're on the right, look for our name on the mailbox and "Glenview" sign. Please call.*

Waitomo, Te Kuiti
Farmstay (sheep & cattle station)
Address: Te Toko Station, Putaki-Hauturu Road,
Name: Bob and Judy Osborne
Telephone: (0813) 88-372
Beds: 4 Single (2 bedrooms)
Tariff: B&B Double $52, Single $32; Dinner $10
Nearest Town: Waitomo Caves Village 14 km, Otorohanga 29 km, Te Kuiti
approximately 40 minutes

We are a family of four, with our son working on the station and our daughter at university.
Our sheep and cattle station consists of 2,500 acres carrying 3,500 sheep and 300 head of cattle plus 150 goats.
We have a generous proportion of native bush (birdlife galore) and lime stone formations seldom seen elsewhere. This is a pocket of New Zealand scenery that you will have little trouble falling in love with.
Our homestead is a 4-bedroom Lockwood, six years old and the grounds are shaping up nicely with rhododendrons in the foreground covering an embankment which enhances the entrance to our home.
We are very happy for our guests to take part in or be shown the activities on the station.
Stay a night or two with us - others say it is a great way to get to know New Zealand.
Directions: *Second turn on right, 10 km from Waitomo Caves. First house on left, 5 km up the road.*

Waitomo,
Country Homestay
Address: Main South Road,
R.D. 7, Otorohanga
Name: Michael & Riki Loughnan
Telephone: (08133) 8620
Beds: 1 Double room, 1 Twin room, guest bathroom
Tariff: B&B $60 Double, $35 Single, Dinner with wine $15 per person
Nearest Town: Otorohanga 5 kms

Our near new ranch style home is situated on State Highway 3, 5 kms from Otorohanga and only 10 minutes by car from the famous Waitomo Caves. Other attractions in the area include: The Otorohanga Kiwi House, the Angora Rabbit farm, The Ruakuri Bush Walk, Marakopa Falls, the Natural Bridge walk and Black Water Rafting. For the golfing enthusiast we are only an eight iron from the third green of the Waitomo Golf Club (Championship Course) where visitors are always welcome.
We are an active semi-retired farming couple, enjoying life and sharing our activities with guests from either overseas or New Zealand. We are well travelled and are sure you will enjoy your stay with us in this most interesting part of New Zealand.

Taumarunui
Homestay
Address: "Hide-away", P O Box 294, Taumarunui, King Country.
Name: Hugh & Anna Halliday
Telephone: (0813) 55-075
Beds: 1 Double, 4 Single (3 bedrooms, guest bathroom)
Tariff: B&B $60 Double, $35 Single, $15 Dinner
Nearest Town: Taumarunui

We have bought our 4 bedroom home in a quiet suburb with the purpose of having people to stay. It is on a double section with off-street parking. There is a separate bathroom (shower and bath) and toilet for guests.
Our 3 sons are all grown up and working in New Zealand. We have lived overseas, travelling in Europe, Africa and Asia and enjoy meeting overseas visitors.
All meals are vegetarian, healthy and nutritious. Taumarunui is the gateway to the Tongariro and Whanganui National Parks, giving visitors a wide choice of outdoor pursuits such as tramping, canoeing, rafting, jet boating and skiing (winter). Taumarunui has a top-rated golf course and a heated swimming pool.
Directions: *Brochures with map or directions available from the Taumarunui Information Centre (Railway Station). Phone or write direct for booking.*

Kakahi, Taumarunui
Farmstay
Address: "Rawhide", Kakahi via Taumarunui
Name: Rex and Barbara Taylor
Telephone: (0812) 26-550
Beds: 4 Single (2 bedrooms)
Tariff: B&B Double $60, Single $35; B&B, Lunch and Dinner – Double $110, Single $60; Dinner $15; Campervans $12
Nearest Town: Taumarunui 20 km

Be our guest in a modern home on 20 acres at Kakahi which is 20 km south of Taumarunui, one of the country's best, yet least-used vacation spots in New Zealand.
Our property is next to bush reserve and the Wanganui river. Good country-style cooking with 90% of the food being home produced on the property. We have a quarter horse stud, western saddlery and leather craft workshop.
Attractions include trout fishing, tramping, swimming, glow worms, handy to jet boat tours, canoeing, top golf course. Three-quarter hour drive to ski fields. Large gun collection short drive away. Guided horseback treks available, half-day, full day or four-day-wilderness camping and trout fishing trips by horseback.
Packed lunch available for day trips away. Special diets can be catered for. Extra charge for liquor or bring your own.

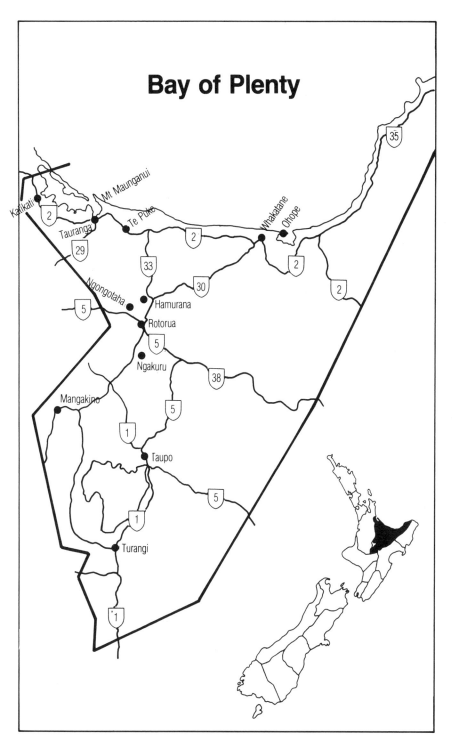

Bay of Plenty

Kafikati

Mt Maunganui

Tauranga

Te Puke

Whakatane

Ohope

Ngongotaha

Hamurana

Rotorua

Ngakuru

Mangakino

Taupo

Turangi

95

Katikati
Homestay
Address: 53 Levley Lane, Katikati
Name: Robert and Judy Noble
Telephone: (07) 549-0984
Beds: 1 Double, 1 Single (2 bedrooms)
Tariff: $B&B $50, Single $28, Dinner $15, Children half price
Nearest Town: 2.5 km from post office

Our new home is warm and comfortable. It is off a quiet cul-de-sac and overlooks a river estuary and wet-lands with extensive views of farmland and bush covered hills.
The guest room is a pleasant double bedroom adjacent to the bathroom.
You are welcome to join us for dinner and spend the evening relaxing in our cosy lounge or on the deck overlooking the river, or you may wish to visit one of the attractive restaurants in the area.
We are retired orchardists / farmers. We are happy to escort visitors on bush tramps - by arrangement.
Katikati is a small town in the Bay of Plenty only 2 1/2 hours drive from Auckland. There are many interesting activities in the area, eg visits to the Waihi gold mining area, to the beach, either harbour or ocean, to the Bird Gardens or to the bush.
Take advantage of our hospitality to rest and relax or as an overnight stop en-route to the Coromandel Peninsula or Rotorua.
We do request visitors not to smoke in our home.
Please ring or write for directions.

Katikati
Farmstay
& Self-Contained Accommodation
Address: Jacaranda Cottage, Thompson's Track, RD2, Katikati
Name: Lynlie and Rick Watson
Telephone: (07) 5490 616 after 4 pm

Beds: 2 Single in twin room
Tariff: B&B Double $50, Single $30; Dinner $14; Campervans $20; Budget accommodation $10; Children discounted; Cyclists and backpackers welcome; Self contained cottage sleeps 2-4, tariff negotiable
Nearest Town: 40 km north of Tauranga, 8 km south of Katikati

Jacaranda Cottage, on a 5-acre farmlet, enjoys magnificent views in every direction - from sea to mountains, from rolling farmlands to native forests.
Our aim is to provide you with a taste of simple country life at an affordable cost. We offer friendly hospitality; clean, warm accommodation; and plenty of wholesome farmhouse food - with fresh farm eggs and milk, organically reared meat, etc. We do ask guests not to smoke inside the house.
Enjoy the variety of animals on our farmlet. Try things you might not have done before – hand-milk a cow or goat, collect warm, freshly laid eggs, scratch a pig's back, ride a pony, cuddle a cow.
Jacaranda Cottage is situated amidst farms of deer, goats, sheep and dairy cattle, as well as kiwifruit, avocado, persimmon and other orchards. The area

offers unspoilt beaches, hot pools, bird gardens, winery, good restaurants, doll collections, arts and crafts, a private museum, and more. Our teenage children enjoy tramping the many bush walks in this area and we can organise informative guided tramps if you wish. Transport can be arranged to any nearby places of interest, or you can simply relax in the tranquil surroundings of Jacaranda Cottage.
Directions: *Thompson's Track is 6 km south of Katikati, on the Tauranga side of the Forta Leza Restaurant. Jacaranda Cottage is 2.4 km up Thompson's Track on the right.*

Tauranga
Homestay
Address: 2A Tenth Avenue (at end of drive), Tauranga
Name: Gordon and Christine Ross
Telephone: (07) 5784-826
Beds: 2 Single (1 bedroom, guest bathroom)
Tariff: B&B Double $55, Single $30 per person

"Welcome to Our World"
Our home is an attractive townhouse, easily located and handy to town. Overlooks Memorial Park – great for an early morning jog, or a leisurely stroll to the water.
We are retired although I still do some caring work. A family of three all married. Our interests include golf porcelain doll making and miniatures. Travel too.
The guest room is large with every comfort. Own bathroom. TV available. Breakfast of your choice. Any other meals by arrangement.   Off-street parking.

Tauranga
Homestay
Address: 48 Sutherland Road, Tauranga
Name: Bill & Edna Fitzgerald
Telephone: (07) 576-2860
Beds: 6 - 10 people, children welcome
Tariff: **B&B** $55 Double, $35 Single, $15 Backpackers - nominal charge for tours, fishing etc. Campervans welcome
Nearest Town: Tauranga

We live in the city but with a rural outlook, 10 minutes drive to popular Mount Maunganui beach and scenic walks. Our house is a large family home with large sunny decks. The Bay of Plenty is renowned for fresh local fruits of the season. We like to serve local fruits with croissants, bread rolls and freshly baked muffins for breakfast but cooked breakfast and dinner is also available. Both semi-retired, we enjoy meeting interesting people and are happy to join you in a game of golf, billiards, walking or listening to Country or Rock-n-roll music. We can also arrange for you to do bush walks, cycling, fishing, diving, jogging, bowls and a dip in the local hot thermal pools is a delightfully relaxing experience.
Directions: *Turn off at McDonalds to Waihi Road, then turn right at Summit Service Station into Bellvue Road, then first right into Sutherland Road, number 48 with "Fitzgerald's" on gate.*

Tauranga
Homestay
Address: 75 Manuwai Drive, Matua, Tauranga
Name: Trevor and Gloria Shepherd
Telephone: (07) 576 2791
Beds: 1 Double, 2 Single (2 bedrooms, guest bathroom)
Tariff: B&B $25 per person, Children half price; Dinner $15; Campervans $20 for 4 persons

We are a retired couple in our late 60's with a family of three who are now married and we have nine grandchildren. We have travelled extensively overseas and within New Zealand and enjoy meeting people from places around the world, also fellow New Zealanders.

We offer hospitality in a modern home, close to the sea (harbour) in a very quiet location 6 km from the centre of Tauranga town. There are pleasant walks and scenic drives within close proximity and it is only 12 km to Mt Maunganui beach and hot salt-water baths.

Our special interests include Church, travel and nursing.

We can offer two bedrooms, one with a double bed and one with two single beds, and a guest bathroom. You may have family dinner with us, or if you prefer, only bed and breakfast. We can provide the breakfast of your choice. We will meet the plane or bus.

Directions: *Travel out to the Matua Peninsula. Proceed along Levers Road to Matua Road. This runs into Manuwai Drive.*

Ask your hosts for local information. They are
your own personal travel agent and guide.

Tauranga
Homestay
Address: Minden Road, RD 6, Tauranga
Name: Mostyn & Marilyn Bowler
Telephone: (07) 552 5340
Beds: 1 Double, 2 Single (2 bedrooms)
Tariff: B&B Double $60, Single $38, Dinner $20, Morning and afternoon teas free
Nearest Town: Tauranga

The Lions built the Minden Lookout right next to our home and advertise it as "The finest view in New Zealand". The unequalled view from our large landscape windows takes in all the Bay of Plenty coast.
Our six level home is situated sixteen kilometres ffom Tauranga, three kilometres up Minden Road from Te Puna Tavern. It has wheelchair access and is set in 8 acres which includes a mixed orchard and friendly farm animals.
We are handy to many tourist attractions and beautiful beaches. A day's trip to Rotorua is always enjoyed.
Our main interest is filming and editing videos as we own "Video-Plus" a film production unit. Mostyn is a handyman and builder and Marilyn's interests are cooking, calligraphy and pottery. We enjoy entertaining and often organize musical evenings. Hospitality is very important to us. We are very happy to provide dinner as an extra and look forward to visitors' company.

Mount Maunganui
Homestay
Address: 1228 Papamoa Beach Road, Papamoa, Bay of Plenty
Name: Max & Shirl Braun
Telephone: (07) 542-2076
Beds: 1 Double, 2 Single (2 bedrooms, guest bathroom)
Tariff: B&B $50 Double, $30 Single, children 1/2 price, Dinner $15
Nearest Town: Mount Maunganui or Te Puke

We have a large two storeyed home with a special guest wing consisting of 2 bedrooms, your own bathroom and toilet, and a large billiard room. (Max will delight in giving you a game if you wish).
We are a two minute walk across the road to a beautiful beach, 10 minute drive to the Mount or Te Puke, and a 40 minute drive to the thermal area of Rotorua.
We can pick you up from the bus station at Te Puke, Mount Maunganui or Tauranga if you don't have your own transport.
We assure you of a very warm welcome and we look forward to you visiting us.

Mount Maunganui
Homestay
Address: 169c Oceanbeach Road,
Mt Maunganui
Name: Dave & Jenny Demler
Telephone: (07) 575 2838
Beds: 1 Double (1 bedroom with guest bathroom)
Tariff: B&B $50 Double, $25 Single, Dinner $15
Nearest Town: Mount Maunganui

We live in a cosy contemporary home at Mount Maunganui. The beautiful ocean beach which you can view from our balcony is a three minute walk away.
We're a young at heart middle-aged couple with a seventeen year old son.
Tauranga, with its many scenic attractions is a ten minute drive away.
We enjoy healthy food and you are welcome to share an evening meal with us if you wish.
We look forward to sharing our home with you. We would appreciate it if you didn't smoke in our home.

Mount Maunganui
Address: 36 Rita Street, Mount Maunganui
Name: Margaret and Lloyd Seed
Telephone: (07) 575 5250
Beds: 2 Single (1 bedroom)
Tariff: B&B Double $60, Single $40, Children $15; 3 Course Dinner $20, we also offer Campervan site with power, shared bathroom and laundry $12; 2-berth caravan with power and gas on site $28; Breakfast for campervan and caravanners $8
Nearest Town: 1/2 km downtown The Mount, 6 km Tauranga city

We are a retired couple who have travelled, so we have an interest in people, especially from overseas. We have chosen Mount Maunganui for our place of retirement and live just five minutes' walk from the ocean, harbour and downtown. There are delightful walks in close proximity e.g. therapeutic hot salt pools 1 km away at the foot of the Mount; Mount Drury Leisure Island and Blowhole all 500m away, the walk around or part way up and around the Mount, or even to the top, all commanding glorious views. We are blessed with magnificent views, both harbour and ocean, from our home.
We are 6 km from Tauranga now that the new harbour bridge is opened thus bringing us very close to the historical village rose gardens and all sports. For the fisherman the wharf where boats leave for Mayor Island and fishing trips is in easy walking distance.
Please phone first for booking and directions. We look forward to meeting you.

Mount Maunganui
Homestay
+ Self-Contained Accommodation
Address: 7 Percy Road, Papamoa
Name: Joan and Jim Francis
Telephone: (07) 542-0815
Beds: 1 Double, 4 Single (3 bedrooms)

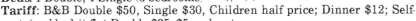

Tariff: B&B Double $50, Single $30, Children half price; Dinner $12; Self-contained bedsit flat Double $35, $5 each extra
Nearest Town: Mount Maunganui or Te Puke 11 km each on SH 2

We are an informal, middle aged couple with four children out in the world, three grandchildren (two are in England) and friends in many countries. Our interests are gardening, travel, meeting people – our home is full of souvenirs, antiques, sunshine, books and we hope – welcome!
All beds have electric blankets, there are two toilets bathroom, and a separate shower. You can soak in our spa; sit and admire the sea and rural views – walk / swim at the beach 250 m away or eat at the top class restaurant.
The self-contained flat at the rear of our house has a double bed, two fold-up singles, TV, automatic washing machine etc. and linen is available at additional cost.
We are only 10–15 minutes from local tourist attractions and we will meet public transport or take you sightseeing.
Directions: *We are about 2 km from State Highway 2 (Rotorua–Te Puke–Tauranga) turning at the Garden Centre signpost 'Papamoa Domain', Percy Road is the first left after the Papamoa Tavern. Joan and I look forward to welcoming you to our house.*

Mount Maunganui
Homestay
Address: 85c Oceanbeach Road, Mt Maunganui
Name: Larraine and Bernie Cotter   **Telephone:** (07) 575 4879
Beds: 1 Double, 2 Single (2 bedrooms, guest bathroom)
Tariff: B&B $60 Double, $40 Single, Children $10, Dinner $10, Campervans $20
Nearest Town: Mount Maunganui & Tauranga

Bernie is in Real Estate and I work part time in a Fragrance Manufacturing Showroom. Our children have left home, so we enjoy company. Our home is situated right on the beach. Three levels, modern with seaviews from every room. We have both travelled extensively, and enjoy entertaining. For our guests, we have separate lounge with TV. Beverage making facilities. Both bedrooms have own ensuites.
We are close to golf course, bowling greens, bridge clubs, tennis courts and surf club at our front door, making it a safe place for swimming.
Therapeutic hot salt pools, 4 kms away at the foot of the Mount.
We are only 45 mins drive to Rotorua.
Off street parking and small shopping centre at our front gate.
We look forward to having you stay and exchanging stories.
We also have a Chalet in National Park, 3 hours drive South which sleeps 8.
Fully self contained for either skiing, trout fishing or tramping.
Directions: *Please phone on arrival.* ————

Mount Maunganui
Homestay
Address: 311 Oceanbeach Road, Mount Maunganui
Name: Roger & Kay Farrell
Telephone: (07) 575-2136
Beds: 2 Single (1 bedroom, guest bathroom)
Tariff: B&B $60 Double, $40 Single, $25 Dinner
Nearest Town: Tauranga

Our large modern home overlooks the Oceanbeach which offers swimming, surfing and beach walks. For guests there is a separate lounge with TV, tea-making facilities and a single trundle bed. Both lounge and bedroom (with 2 single beds) open onto large sundeck and have ocean views. There is a guest bathroom and separate shower room.
Mount Maunganui is a popular seaside resort 2 1/2 hours from Auckland. It has a large port, good shopping and is linked to Tauranga by a harbour bridge. Hot salt-water pools are five minutes away.
We are really keen golfers. There are two first class courses in Mount Maunganui only minutes away and there is also one at Tauranga.
The tourist city of Rotorua is one hour away.
We have been selling wines for the last twenty years and have travelled extensively to vineyards of the world.

Te Puke
Farmstay
Address: Shearers Road, No.3 RD, Te Puke
Name: Warwick and Elizabeth Elliston
Telephone: (075) 573 7718
Beds: 4 Single (2 bedrooms)
Tariff: B&B Double $60, Single $35, Dinner $15
Nearest Town: Te Puke

We welcome you to the beautiful Bay of Plenty and our home. We live on a kiwifruit orchard with our own packing shed which will be of interest. Our home is comfortable, surrounded by gardens and shade trees with views of the ocean. There is also a swimming pool. Altogether a peaceful place.
Being in our sixties, having travelled, we are interested in other travellers and delight in sharing our home.
For the tourist there are many attractions within a short distance. Beautiful safe beaches, kiwifruit country, river rafting, golf, deep sea fishing as well as many attractive walks. Rotorua is one hour away where there is excellent trout fishing as well as the thermal area. Tauranga, an attractive city by the sea, offers many places of interest as well as good shopping only 20 minutes from here.
Our family of four are all away from home. We offer 2 rooms with two single beds in each. Please phone.
Directions: *From Auckland on Highway 2 from Tauranga, the Rangiuru Club is on the corner of No.3 Road before reaching the town. Travel up to junction of Shearers Road and No.3 Road. Take Shearers Road which is straight ahead. Cherryhill Orchard is signposted first on left, just 8 kilometres from main road turnoff.*

Papamoa Beach

Homestay
Address: 8 Taylor Road, Papamoa
Name: Genyth & Neil Harwood
Telephone: (07) 5420-279
Beds: 1 Double, 2 Single (2 bedrooms, guest bathroom)

Tariff: **B&B** $55 Double, $35 Single, children 1/2 price, Dinner $15, Campervans $20 (4 persons)
Nearest Town: Tauranga 20 km, Mt Maunganui 15 km, Te Puke 13Km

Our beachfront home is situated about 50 metres from the waves of the Pacific Ocean, with beautiful views of Mayor & Motiti Islands.
Things to do include swimming, fishing, sunbathing, or beach walks plus, endless interesting excursions round the district.
We have a two storeyed home with guest accommodation on the lower level serviced by a shower, toilet and laundry facilities.
Continental or cooked breakfast is offered and a home cooked dinner if desired - we also enjoy a barbeque in warmer weather.
Resorts such as Mt Maunganui and Rotorua with its thermal attractions are within easy reach.
Directions: *Turn off State Highway 2 (Tauranga to Rotorua) at GARDEN CENTRE, proceed about 2 kms to roundabout at Papamoa Domain, take right turn then about 4 kms to Motiti Road on left and left again into Taylor Road.*

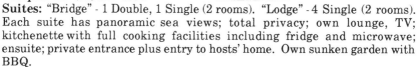

Ohope Beach

Homestay, self-contained suites
Address: "The Rafters",
261A Pohutukawa Avenue, Ohope
Name: Mavis & Patrick Rafter
Telephone: (07) 312-4856
Suites: "Bridge" - 1 Double, 1 Single (2 rooms). "Lodge" - 4 Single (2 rooms). Each suite has panoramic sea views; total privacy; own lounge, TV; kitchenette with full cooking facilities including fridge and microwave; ensuite; private entrance plus entry to hosts' home. Own sunken garden with BBQ.
Tariff: B&B $70 Double, $60 Single, infants free; each extra person $10 (limit 2). Dinner $35 each includes pre-dinner drinks and premium wines throughout four course top rate cuisine meal. A two-course dinner may be served in your suite with wine $15 per person.

Safe swimming and surfing on our beachfront plus use of host solar heated pool. Many interesting walks. Golfing, fishing, tennis, bowling, chartered club within minutes. Trips to White Island, fishing, jet boat etc arranged.
Mavis, an experienced cook, interests include nursing and art. Pat, Head of History, Whakatane High School, keen on golf, bowls , music and literature. We look forward to welcoming you into our home. Courtesy car would collect you at airport if desired. House trained dogs welcome.
Directions: *On reaching Ohope turn right, proceed 2 km to 261A (beachside).*

Whakatane
Farmstay
Address: State Highway 2,
RD2, Whakatane
Name: Jim and Kathleen Law
Telephone: (07) 308-7955
Beds: 1 Double (1 bedroom)

Tariff: B&B Double $50, Single $30 ; Dinner $15; Campervans $15
Nearest Town: 7 km west of Whakatane on SH2

Whakatane is the centre of the Sunshine Coast. It is off the beaten tourist track, and it has many attractions. We have both lived here all our lives and although our four sons have all left home — one still at University — we have chosen to remain.
Two 50/50 sharemilkers manage our farms. We operate a craft shop called The Red Barn, promoting local craftspeople. This is an outlet for fruit grown in our commercial orchard of citrus, apples and feijoas. As a hobby we breed black and coloured and spotted sheep.
We have travelled extensively overseas and enjoy meeting people of all ages.
Bowls, genealogy and organic gardening are some of our other interests outside of farming.
We can cater for vegetarians or special diets. There is one double bed in our guest room which shares some bathroom facilities. Large recreation room with pool table and extensive library. You are invited to join in any of our activities. We can arrange sightseeing trips or you may just relax in peaceful surroundings. The local golf course is nearby.
Directions: *7 km west of Whakatane. Please phone first for booking.*

Rotorua
Homestay
Address: 7B Mountain Road, Rotorua
Name: Rita and Harry Figgest
Telephone: (07) 347-0675
Beds: 2 Single (1 bedroom, toilet facilities)
Tariff: B&B Double $55, Single $30
Nearest Town: Rotorua Town Centre 3 km

We live in a lovely Spanish townhouse which has one guest bedroom downstairs with two single beds and own toilet facilities and,and living area and bathroom upstairs. Also very attractive lounge area upstairs with magnificent swimming pool outside in very pleasant, quiet surroundings with country views.
Harry and I have travelled extensively and are in our fifties, originally from England, and enjoy immensely meeting people from all over the world, and give our own warm hospitality and friendliness to our visitors to make them very welcome in our home.
We are both interested in outdoor and indoor bowls, and watching any sort of sport, and Harry likes fishing particularly sea fishing.
We are pretty central to town, only 5 minutes drive away, and easy reach to tourist attractions. Aorangi Peak is just up the mountain from where we live.

Ngakuru, Rotorua

Farmstay
Address: "Te Ana" Poutakataka Road, Ngakuru, RD1, Rotorua
Name: Heather and Brian Oberer
Telephone: (07) 333 2720
Beds: 2 Double, 4 Single (3 bedrooms, guest bathroom)
Tariff: B&B Double $85, Single $60, Children 12 and under $35; Dinner $20, 12.5 % GST included
Nearest Town: Rotorua 20 miles

"Te Ana"is a 500 acre dairy, beef, sheep, goat and deer farm situated 20 miles south of Rotorua and bounded for nearly 2 miles by Lake Ohakuri, with its rainbow and brown trout. "Te Ana" has a beautiful country setting. It has been a family farm since 1936.

Our homestead is a clinker brick ranch-style with full length verandah at front and views of farm or garden from each of its large windows. Triple bedroom has private bathroom and two double rooms share. Electric blankets on all beds with featherdown duvets and heater in each room.Our home is decorated in a mix of cream and peaches, with a mixture of modern and antique furniture.

We have a daughter aged 19 and two sons aged 22 and 23 and have been hosting for the past ten years.

A canoe and fishing rod are available for use, a pony to ride, four-wheel-drive tour of farm and viewing of cows being milked. Families are most welcome. Transfers to and from Rotorua can be provided at additional cost.

We serve wine with 3 course dinner of lamb, venison, beef, chicken or trout and plenty of iced spring water. Breakfasts include fruit juice, fruit, cereals, toast, bacon and eggs, etc, percolated coffee.

Family interests include waterskiing, hunting, snow skiing, music, art, gardening, farming, reading, tennis, swimming, rugby, knitting, cross stitch and Zonta Club. Family pets include 2 cats, dogs, sheep and horses.

We are only a short distance from thermal mineral swimming pool and Waiotapu Thermal reserve. 30 minute drive to Rotorua attractions.

Directions: *Please phone*

Lake Tarawera, Rotorua
Lakestay
Address: 287-291 Spencer Road,
Lake Tarawera, Rotorua
Name: Jean Tregidga
Telephone: (07) 345 6745 (day) -
evening refer directory service
Beds: 1 Double, 2 Single (2 bedrooms, guest bathroom)
Tariff: **B&B** $55 Double, $28 Single, $12 Children (cot available n/c),
Campervans $25.
Nearest Town: Rotorua 21 km

*I am the mother of a 24 year old son who lives and works in Auckland. I now
live on my own.*
*During the day I manage a New Zealand Post Shop and enjoy meeting and
helping people. I am a "people" person but enjoy the peace and tranquility
that Lake Tarawera offers. I would like to share my experience with you.*
*My home is large, 3 storey, open plan set on full sunny section of 2 acres with
lawn, trees and shrubs. Full views overlooking beautiful Lake Tarawera and
the mountain.*
*Lake access to reserve, small rowboat, lifejackets, trout fishing line available
for use - (fishing licence extra charge).*
*Enjoy the many sights this wonderful city of Rotorua has to offer and return
to this lovely quiet setting for the night.*
Directions: *Travel on Te Ngae Road, turn into Tarawera Road, travel well
past Buried Village. Pass Waitangi Road on right, 287 is the first driveway
past First Aid Post.* ————————————

Lake Tarawera, Rotorua
Homestay
Address: "Glenfiddich Heights', Lake Tarawera, R.D.5, Rotorua
Name: Warwick & Lorraine Ramsey
Telephone: (07) 3628-296
Beds: 2 Single (1 bedroom, guest bathroom)
Tariff: **B&B** $75 Double, $50 Single, Dinner $20
Nearest Town: Rotorua (15 mins by car)

*Unique homestay accommodation at one of the world's most beautiful lakes.
Situated in the heart of New Zealand's tourist mecca, just 15 minutes drive
from Rotorua City, through magnificent forest and native bush.*
*"GLENFIDDICH HEIGHTS" (valley of the deer) is a 6 1/2 acre deer and
wallaby park, with private guest suite with tea/coffee facilities and ensuite
with fabulous views of the famous Rainbow lake - Tarawera, and the historic
Mount Tarawera. Spa also available.*
*A stay at Glenfiddich Heights Retreat offers guests the opportunity to
experience true New Zealand wilderness, seventeen square miles of safe,
uncrowded waters, beautiful bays with unspoiled natural bush and seclusion.*
*Trout fishing, lake cruises, water skiing, swimming, bushwalks and
recreational hunting all adjacent to property. Floatplane and helicopter scenic
flights available.*
Picnic lunch hampers and evening meal with wine and liqueurs upon request.
Directions: *Bookings are necessary and we invite you to write or phone for
our brochure.* ————————————

Rotorua

Homestay
Address: 3 Raukura Place, Rotorua
Name: Ursula and Lindsay Prince
Telephone: (07) 347-0140 Please phone to confirm vacancy
Bedrooms: 1 Double with 1 single, 2 Single (2 bedrooms, each with guest bathroom)
Tariff: B&B Double $60 ($65 for one night only), Single $40, Children half price; Dinner by arrangement $20 with complimentary NZ wine

You can be sure of a warm welcome when you decide to stay with us at our beautiful new home right at the lakefront in Rotorua. Quiet and secluded, yet only five minutes by car from the centre of our busy city with its many attractions, our house is an ideal situation.

Two spacious guest rooms, each with private bathroom, well-cooked meals in a relaxed and informal atmosphere – the feeling to be amongst friends is what we offer you. We will be happy to help you plan your Rotorua visit. Make use of our extensive range of maps and guide books.
Relax on the deck, enjoy the tranquil lake and mountain scene, watch the waterbirds or explore the lake by Canadian canoe.
We are an active, middle-aged couple, enjoying life with all its challenges. We take an interest in world affairs, have travelled and lived overseas, love the outdoors and enjoy meeting people from all walks of life.
Being non-smokers ourselves, we thank you for not smoking in the house.
How to find us; Turn on to Bennetts Rd from Lake Rd, then first left on to Koutu Rd, then first right on to Karenga St. Now first right on to Haumoana St. and a left turn at the end brings you down Raukura Place to our door.

Ngongotaha, Rotorua

Farmstay + Self-Contained Accommodation
Address: Jackson Road, Kaharoa (PO Box 22), Ngongotaha, Rotorua
Name: 'Deer Pine Lodge', Hosts: John and Betty Insch
Telephone: (07) 332 3458
Beds: Double 1, Single 4 (3 bedrooms, guest bathrooms)
Tariff: B&B Double $60, Single $35, Infants Free, Dinner $20; Campervans $20
Nearest Town: Rotorua

We welcome you to Deer Pine Lodge. Enjoy the panor-amic views of Lake Rotorua. We have a deer farm approximately 16 km from Rotorua. The property is surrounded with trees having been planted by the New Zealand Forest Research Institute as experimental shelter belts. Photographs of the shelter belts from this property being used by NZ Forest in their overseas magazine.

Guests are free to go on the morning tour of the farm and observe the different species of deer and get first hand knowledge of all aspects of deer farming. We are running approximately 250 deer, with sheep.

The nearby city of Rotorua offers trout fishing, lake trips, geysers, hot mineral pools, Maori village, buried village.

Our home is a large modern Lockwood home. Our guests have the best of both worlds; their own private units complete with bathroom, shower, etc. All beds have electric blankets and woollen underlays, electric heaters in rooms with coffee and tea making facilities, microwave, fridge, TV, radio. Meals can be served in their unit or main dining room with the family. The venison dinners are very popular with our guests. Pre-dinner drinks, NZ wine with meals. For breakfast try our venison sausages with your bacon and eggs.
Directions: *Please phone.*

Rotorua
Homestay
Address: "Woodbery",
Hawthornden Drive, R.D. 4, Rotorua
Name: Neville & Shirley Mann
Telephone: (07) 3455-853
Beds: 4 Single (2 bedrooms, guest bathroom)
Tariff: B&B $55 Double, $35 Single, $15 children (under 12), $20 Dinner
(with NZ Wine), Campervans $15
Nearest Town: Rotorua (10 km)

We would like you to share with us our country living in a comfortable centrally heated Lockwood home. Set on 6 acres with an assortment of animals and birds we have sweeping views of Lake Rotorua. Our home is quiet and restful yet only 1.5km from State Highway 30 and 2 km from Rotorua Airport.

Woodbery is a small wholesale nursery and our semi retirement is spent tending this and the on-going development of a new 2 acre home garden.

Our home has two twin bedrooms with guests own bathroom and toilet. We can offer a convenient central base from which you can explore our district. If wanted, our local knowledge enables us to plan enjoyable outings. A picnic lunch is available on request.

For many years we were involved in the hospitality industry and enjoy meeting people. We have facilities for campervans, caravans and boat parking.

Directions: *We would welcome your phone call before arrival.*

Hamurana, Rotorua
Farmstay
Address: Te Waerenga Road, R.D. 2, Rotorua
Name: Rod & Dianne Daniel
Telephone: (07) 332-3560 (after 5pm)
Beds: 1 Double, 4 Single (3 bedrooms - 2 twin, 1 Dble, guest bathroom)
Tariff: B&B $55 Double, $35 Single, Dinner $18
Nearest Town: Rotorua (20 km), Ngongotaha (12 km)

Welcome to Rotorua and the many tourist attractions in our locality.

We have a new home with panaromic views of the lake and city. The upstairs area, whihc is for guests' exclusive use, has a twin room with balcony overlooking Rotorua Lake and City, a double bedroom, games room and private bathroom facilities. Downstairs there is a twin room with private toilet and vanity also available for guests.

Although only a short distance from Rotorua's major tourist attractions we maintain a rural lifestyle on our 70 acre deer farm. Hamurana Park with its 9-hole golf course is 2 km away.

We have travelled widely during the last 10 years, enjoy meeting people and wish to extend our hospitality to visitors to the Rotorua and Bay of Plenty area.

Directions: *Please phone after 5pm for bookings and directions.*

Waikite, Rotorua
Farmstay
Address: Te Kopia Road, RD1, Waikite Valley, Rotorua
Name: Brian and Barbara Hunt
Telephone: (073) 31-578
Beds: 2 Single (1 bedroom)
Tariff: B&B Double $50, Single $25;
Dinner $15; Campervans $15; Children half price
Nearest Town: Rotorua

We are farmers who have 193 hectares on which we farm sheep, bulls and deer. We have a three young children and an assorted backyard menagerie. We have a large home and garden with panoramic farm and thermal views - the house is adjacent to thermal activity.
We live in a very peaceful location, central to many attractions - within a thirty minute drive you can reach Orakikorako, Taupo, Rotorua, Waiotapu, Waimangu Valley and many others. Just 10 km up the road are the lovely Waikite thermal bathing pools - not to be missed.
We enjoy visitors and take pleasure in providing wholesome meals from our farm-grown produce. We look forward to sharing our home and any farm experiences.
Directions: *Mid-way between Rotorua and Taupo on Highway 5 is Waiotapu. Turn onto Waikite Valley Road adjacent to the Waiotapu Tavern and travel for approximately 10 km. Look for Te Kopia Road on your left - a gravel road on which you travel exactly 10 km to reach our front gate. We are on the right - our name is on the letterbox.*

Rotorua
Farmstay
Address: "Pukeha Farms", Kaharoa Rd, R.D. 2, Rotorua
Name: Ian & Janet Woolsey
Telephone: (07) 332-3471
Beds: 6 Single (3 bedrooms, guest bathroom)
Tariff: **B&B** $55 Double, $35 Single, children 1/2 price, $18 Dinner, campervans welcome
Nearest Town: Ngongotaha 19 km, Rotorua 27 km

"Pukeha Farms" is situated in a quiet peaceful valley with an abundance of wildlife. Our farm is 2500 acres, running mostly deer, both red and fallow herds, cattle, sheep and goats.
We have a comfortable Lockwood home set in landscaped gardens with swimming pool. Main guest room attached to the carport with 2 single beds, tea making facilities and own shower and toilet. Other two bedrooms with two single beds each, share own bathroom.
Rotorua, with many attractions, is only 35 minutes away. Trout fishing, thermal activities, lovely lakes and forests, golf courses. We love the outdoors, hunting, fishing, gardening and crafts. Have travelled extensively throughout New Zealand and overseas and enjoy meeting people.
You are welcome to have dinner with us, but we must have notice.
Being non-smokers ourselves, we thank you for not smoking in our home. A longer stay with us is welcomed.
Directions: *Please telephone.*

Westbrook, Rotorua

Homestay
Address: Please phone
Name: David and Vene Jones
Telephone: (07) 3479-194
Beds: 1 Double, 2 Single (2 bedrooms, guest bathroom)
Tariff: B&B Double $55, Single $30, Children under 12 half price; Dinner $15 (with prior notice)
Nearest Town: Rotorua 4 km, 10 minutes by car

We live in a quiet cul-de-sac, down a right of way in a split-level home over-looking several parks and golf courses and sports venues. We are close to all tourist sights.
We are both retired with family all married. Our hobbies are the great outdoors, walking club, travel, arts and crafts. We love meeting people and have travelled overseas.
I guess you would class our home as a comfortable quality abode with comfortable beds – electric pads.
You have your own toilet, bathroom and shower.
We prefer non-smokers.

Rotorua

Farmstay
Address: Please phone
Name: Maureen and John Hunt
Telephone: (073) 481-352
Beds: 1 Double, 2 Single (3 bedrooms, guest bathroom)
Tariff: B&B Double $60, Single $35, Children half price; Dinner by arrangement $20
Nearest Town: Rotorua 4 km (10 minutes by car)

Guests will be warmly welcomed at our large, modern home on the city out-skirts. Superb views of the lake, city, forest and surrounding countryside. Enjoy our garden and solar heated swimming pool.
We farm 150 acres running deer, beef and sheep.
Scenic farm tours available.
Our adult family of five have now sought pastures new allowing us to offer an attractive suite of rooms consisting of one double bedroom, two single bedrooms and a small sunroom.
Underfloor heating, innersprung mattresses, plenty of room for cars, campervans and luggage storage. Non-smokers preferred.
Be sure and allow a few days stay so you have time to rest as well as enjoy the many nearby world renownedattractions.
We enjoy gardening, water-skiing, tramping and travelling and look forward to sharing our home and farm with you.

111

Rotorua

Homestay
Address: 88 Otonga Road, Rotorua
Name: Brian and Kate Gore
Telephone: (07) 347-9385
Beds: 1 Double 2 Single (2 bedrooms)

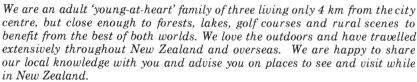

Tariff: B&B $25 per person, Children half price; Dinner $15; Campervans $15 for 2, $20 for 4
Nearest Town: Rotorua

We are an adult 'young-at-heart' family of three living only 4 km from the city centre, but close enough to forests, lakes, golf courses and rural scenes to benefit from the best of both worlds. We love the outdoors and have travelled extensively throughout New Zealand and overseas. We are happy to share our local knowledge with you and advise you on places to see and visit while in New Zealand.
Our large comfortable home is set amongst trees and bush and you are free to join us in our usual activities, explore for yourselves or just simply relax. Rotorua, being the heart of the tourist industry, has so much to offer but we like to think we can share that little bit more to make your New Zealand experience more memorable.
Directions: *Please phone.*

Mourea, Rotorua

Homestay
Address: 30 Okawa Bay Road, Okawa Bay, Mourea, Rotorua
Name: Marijke and Rein Klazes
Telephone: (073) 24-703
Beds: 1 Double, 1 Single (1 bedroom)
Tariff: Double $55, Single $35,Dinner $15; Campervans
Nearest Town: Rotorua, 17 km

We are a couple in our early 40's with a wide variety of interests in social activities, outdoors and arts and crafts.
We speak Dutch, English, German and a few words of French and Japanese.
Our home is on a 1-acre lake edge section with extensive views over Lake Rotoiti with a jetty and a marina, 5 minutes from the airport. The sitting room / guest room is spacious and comfortable with floor heating in winter.
The wide variety of activities you can undertake in our immediate environment includes trout fishing, waterskiing, canoeing, rowing, swimming, hot pools, launch trips, scenic flights, bush walks, golfing, horse riding, dining out. In 15 minutes you are in Rotorua with its Maori cultural activities and an abundance of tourist attractions like thermal areas with geysers, lake scenery, trout pools, Agrodome, restaurants, etc. We are 30 minutes from Maketu beach.
Directions: *From Rotorua take SH30, direction Tauranga. Keep heading for Tauranga from the Whakatane turn-off another 4 km on SH33. Turn right over the crest of a hill into Okawa Bay Road. Neur the Yacht Club Reserve end of the road turn into our driveway in front of the "steep grade, change down" sign.*

Rotorua

Homestay
Address: 7 Walford Drive, Lynmore, Rotorua
Name: Selwyn and Dulcie Collins
Telephone: 455-778
Beds: 1 Double, 2 Single (2 bedrooms, guest bathroom)
Tariff: B&B Double $70, Single $40, Children under 12 $20, Dinner $18; Campervans
Nearest Town: Rotorua

Your hosts are a middle-aged couple who built their sunny, very comfortable home three years ago. Around the corner we have tennis courts and in the Redwood Forest many walks. Further up Tarawera Road there are the many beautiful lakes.

Our guest accommodation is upstairs and fully self-contained but we hope you will enjoy the downstairs living areas indoor and outdoor. Our gardens are now looking established and great with the Camellias and in the summer the roses. An outdoor gas barbecue gets lots of use. We have six grandchildren and would welcome your children.

Selwyn and I have enjoyed travelling abroad and for many years have enjoyed having visitors from overseas to stay with us.

We both work at times so would appreciate a call the evening before or a message on the answerphone. I do enjoy cooking but would like notice if you wish to have dinner with us. We do look forward to your visit. If you smoke we ask that you do so outdoors.

Directions: *Off the Tauranga/Whakatane Highway from Rotorua. Turn right up Tarawera Road, left into Hilton Road ext and Walford Drive is on the right. Approx. 4 km from PO.*

Rotorua - Rainbow & Fairy Springs

Homestay
Address: "Cambrook", 9 Barnard Road, Rotorua
Name: Betty C Price
Telephone: (07) 348 2485
Beds: 1 Double, 2 Single (2 bedrooms, share host's bathroom)
Tariff: B&B $50 Double, $25 Single, children welcome, Dinner $12
Nearest Town: Rotorua

My 1/2 acre property is enhanced by a trout stream on the boundary, grass tennis court, para pool, barbeque area, gardens, large trees and many shrubs. Very efficient bus route leaves from corner 100 metre away. Many interesting places to visit, good restaurants at hand, but I am very happy to provide a meal. Children are welcome and I have a cot and high-chair.

My interests are meeting people, bowls indoor & out, tennis, swimming, gardening and I have a group of ladies to 'Scrabble' every fortnight. I have a gentleman friend I call upon to help me in the evenings as I have been a widow for 8 years. I love people and learning about other countries and experiences and can assure you of a comfortable and happy stay.

Directions: *Coming from North, Barnard Rd is opposite Rainbow and Fairy Springs.*

Ngongotaha, Rotorua
Homestay
Address: 42 Parawai Road,
Ngongotaha, Rotorua
Name: Heather Radford
Telephone: (07) 357-5104
Beds: 1 Double, 2 Single (2 bedrooms, guest bathroom)
Tariff: B&B Double $55, Single $33, Dinner $20 by arrangement.
Nearest Town: Rotorua City (Ngongotaha township)

Haeremai. Welcome. My home is situated on the shores of Lake Rotorua, set amongst lovely old trees and gardens, in a quiet, private locality.
The guest bedrooms open on to a balcony overlooking the lake and the upper floor is for guests' exclusive use so privacy is assured. For the keen angler, a guided fishing trips' operation is situated next door and major tourist attractions - the Agrodome (2 km), Fairy Springs and Rainbow Farm (3 km) and Rotorua's many other attractions are nearby.
Ngongotaha, a friendly little township which serves the rural communities of Kaharoa, Hamurana and Ngongotaha is 2 km distant, has a Post Office and a regular bus serve to and from Rotorua City 7 km away.
Directions: *Only 2 km from Highway 5-Ngongotaha Road Junction.*

Ngongotaha, Rotorua
Homestay
Address: 20 Waikuta Road, Ngongotaha, Rotorua
Name: Sally & Peter Griffiths
Telephone: (07) 357 4119 or Auckland (09) 520 4031
Beds: 2 Double, 4 Single (3 bedrooms)
Tariff: B&B Double $65, Single $38, children under 12 half price, Dinner $20
Nearest Town: Rotorua
Auckland Address: 57 Koraha Street, Remuera, Auckland 5

If you cannot contact us please phone our Auckland home as we may be there. We can be in Rotorua to meet you in a couple of hours.
We live at Ngongotaha. Our house is on the waterfront and has its own jetty. We are close to the major tourist attractions such as Rainbow Springs, the Gondolas, Luge and the Agrodome. Rotorua central is an easy 10 minute drive as are thermal and tramping parks. Trawling and harling for both the experienced and inexperienced fisherman is an additional option which can be taken advantage of at competitive rates from the ease of our well equipped boat. Fly fishing trips are also available. You can then have your day's catch barbecued, smoked or frozen to take home.
We tend to serve traditional New Zealand food, either outside in the summer or next to the log fire in the winter.
We are a relaxed easy going household with one loveable spaniel dog.
We invite you to share with us in some of the above activities.

Ngongotaha, Rotorua
Homestay
Address: "Waiteti Lakeside Lodge",
2 Arnold Street, (off Waiteti Rd),
Ngongotaha, Rotorua
Name: Brian and Val Blewett
Telephone (07) 357 2311
Beds: 1 Double, 2 Single (2 bedrooms, guest bathroom)
Tariff: B&B Double $65, Single $40, Dinner $20

Guests will be warmly welcomed to our new home situated on the shores of Lake Rotorua and the mouth of the Waiteti Stream. We have panoramic views of lake, city, forest and surrounding countryside. Our natural timber and stone home is in a private locality with no traffic noise or sulphur fumes, with private trout fishing from 1st December to 30th June, a jetty and boat ramp.

Originally from England, we have been in New Zealand for 35 years, and as a fishing guide I skipper my own boat.

Join us for a fishing, hunting, tramping, water or snow skiing holiday. We will arrange white-water rafting, golfing, horse riding and 4 wheel drive tours. Or you can relax on the deck in the heated spa pool or explore the lake and stream by Canadian canoe or dinghy. Fishing rods free to guests.

The upper floor of the lodge is designed exclusively for your privacy with a double bedroom with private bathroom and spacious lounge.

Tasty New Zealand or English dinner by arrangement.

Ngongotaha, Rotorua
Homestay
Address: Please phone
Name: Brian and Joy
Telephone: (07) 357-2088

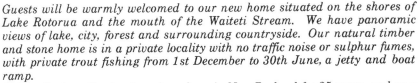

Beds: 4 Single (2 bedrooms, guest bathroom)
Tariff: B&B Double $60, Single $40, 10% discount for 2 nights or more; Dinner $15 by arrangement
Nearest Town: Rotorua 10km

Our comfortable Lockwood type home is situated in a quiet tree lined street close to Lake Rotorua and the Waiteti trout stream. There is no traffic noise or sulphur fumes. Golf, horseriding, natural springs, walks and trout fishing are in easy reach. We are 2 km from HW5 Auckland-Hamilton.

We are retired, and share our home with Winston, our friendly grey cat. Our married daughter lives nearby. Our son is in London. We are involved in church and community, and are members of Probus. We enjoy stamp collecting, homemaking and entertaining. We should be pleased to include you among our friends. We have provided hospitality for visitors from several countries, and hope you too will sign our visitors' book.

Bedrooms are comfortable with electric blankets on all beds, and guests have use of their own bathroom facilities.

Come and stay awhile, a warm friendly welcome awaits you.

We request visitors not to smoke in our home.

Off-street parking available.

Ngongotaha
Farmstay
Address: Please phone for directions
Name: Rex and Ann Wells
Telephone: (07) 3572-014
Beds: 1 Double, 2 Single (2 bedrooms, guest bathroom)
Tariff: B&B Double $60, Single $35; Dinner $20
Nearest Town: Ngongotaha 3 km, Rotorua city 8 km

Being the closest farm home to Rotorua (8 km) and the world famous Agrodome (1 km) we are very easy to find. We farm 50 acres now, having over 200 red deer, purebred Simmental cattle and sheep.

Our interests in life, other than our grown up family are our farm, our dogs, tennis, table tennis, photography, travel, rugby, birds, and our large roomy garden. Having stables we operate as a horse motel. Our home is warm and comfortable. Electric blankets on all beds. We have an inside spa and billiard table and Rex is always ready to learn new shots!

We are close to an 18-hole golf course, trout hatchery, fishing, (fishing guides available) horse riding, and 12 km to Whaka thermal area.

Rex has been farming all his life, Ann born in England, and both have travelled overseas hence we enjoy meeting new friends the Bed and Breakfast way.

We ask guests not to smoke inside our home

Taupo
Farmstay
Address: Oruanui Road, RD1, Taupo
Name: Donna and Mike Smith
Telephone: (07) 377 6451
Beds: 1 Double, 3 Single (3 bedrooms, 2 guest bathrooms)
Tariff: B&B Double $70, Single $40, Dinner $18
Nearest Town: Taupo – 18 kms to the south

We are situated at the north end of Oruanui Road, some 18 km north of Taupo but very handy to SH1. The farm is 48 ha (120 acres) and we run bull beef, deer and a small flock of coloured sheep. Our other main interest is growing timber type trees and several trial blocks are established. Visitors are welcome to tour the farm. The home is a near new 2 storey Lockwood offering pleasant rural views.

Taupo has much to offer. Trout fishing, thermal activity, hydro lakes and dams, golf courses that are never closed by weather and numerous walks.

Directions: *turn off SH1 approx 9 km north of Wairakei (Oruanui Road), Challenge manure bin on corner. Approx half kilometre along on right. Please phone first.*

Taupo
Homestay
Address: 23 Rokino Road, Taupo
Name: Colleen and Bob Yeoman
Telephone: (07) 377 0283
Beds: 1 Double, 3 Single (3 bedrooms, guest bathroom)
Tariff: B&B Double $80, Single $45, Children half price, Dinner $25
Nearest Town: Taupo 20 minutes walk

Your hosts Colleen and Bob extend a warm welcome. We offer comfortable beds and pillows, electric blankets and luxurious duvets. Guest bathroom for twin room and single room upstairs. Own shower and toilet for double bedroom downstairs. Please feel free to use laundry and ironing facilities.

Spa pool, billiard room, spacious lounge and sun deck with panoramic views of Lake and mountains. We are familiar with boating and fishing, keen golfers, have interesting books on New Zealand. We have recently sold our sheep and cattle farm in the Hawkes Bay and will continue our involvement with home hosting after four years of farm stay hosting.

Taupo is a lovely place to catch your breath, to relax, to enjoy some pleasant walks. Taupo has many splendid restaurants, or you may prefer to share a three course dinner with your hosts and enjoy complimentary wine.

We are situated en route to Wellington, Auckland and Hawkes Bay. Guests can be met at Taupo Airport and off public transport.

Directions: *Turn into Huia Street from lake front, take fourth turn on right into Rokino Road.*

Taupo
Farmstay
Address: Reeves Road, Acacia Bay, Taupo
Name: Jay and Bruce McLeod
Telephone: (074) 87-901
Beds: 1 Double, 2 Single (2 bedrooms, guest bathroom)
Tariff: B&B Double $75, Single $50, Dinner $25, Children half price; Campervans $20
Nearest Town: Taupo

We have a large modern farm house situated on a hill with a panoramic view of Taupo and the Lake. It is only 5 km from the centre of the town. The main guest rooms upstairs have one king and two single beds, private bathroom, facilities, a small lounge TV and kitchenette. We farm deer and goats on 100 acres and enjoy showing people round our property. We have a 30 ft launch. Fishing trips can be arranged. As we are widely travelled we enjoy meeting people from other countries.

Directions: *please phone.*

Taupo (North-West)
Homestay
Address: Mapara Road, R.D. 1, Taupo
Name: Guido & Dianne Jakschik
Telephone: (0737) 81305
Beds: 1 Double, 2 Single (2 bedrooms, share host's bathroom)
Tariff: B&B $25 B&B per person, children 1/2 price, Dinner $15
Nearest Town: Taupo

*Guido (originally from Germany), Dianne, Benjamin (7) and Natasha (6)
welcome you.*
We like chatting over good food and New Zealand wine.
*Our farmlet, 8 1/2 hectares, is surrounded by sheep, beef and deer farmers -
we rear calves.*
*We are a career minded couple, B.Sc in Agriculture and working nurse, we
have travelled and worked around the world.*
*Lake Taupo offered daily cruises with entertainment and fishing. Have your
rainbow or brown trout smoked or served hot and fresh!*
Taupo offers many recreational activities:
*AC Baths - swim, soak in natural thermal water, slide, private pools, sauna,
Barbeque.*
Dancing Club - Modern, rock-round ballroom dancing on Saturday nights.
*Wairakei Tourist Park - thermal area, Huka Falls, Geysers, silica terraces, jet
boating, horse trekking, craft shops, scenic walks and tramping.*
Hunt for sika, red deer or wild pigs.
Ski at Mt Ruapehu, Ngauruhoe or Tongairiro or tramp them during summer.
*Canoeing, kayaking, water ski-ing, windsurkers, white wate rafting, tennis
and golf.*
We wish you a nice time here in Taupo.
Directions: *1.5 km from Town Clock North on State Highway 1, turn left 8
km West Piohipi Rd left 2.7 km Mapara Road left "A" framed house.*

Taupo
Farmstay + Self-Contained Accommodation
Address: 'Apple Tree Bridge Farm', Highway 32, RD Mangakino (nr Taupo)
Name: James and Virginia Dysart
Telephone: (07) 372 8232
Beds: 4–6 in cottage, 1 twin in homestead (guest bath room)
Tariff: B&B Double $70, Single $50, D.B.B. $110 per person;
Self-Contained Cottage (linen provided) sleeps 4–6 $130 per night, 1 week
$400, meals arranged as extra if required, Dinner $15; Campers, Caravans
and Campervans welcomed

*We welcome visitors to our farm in the Taupo region. The self-contained
cottage sleeps 4–6 comfortably. A family's needs met including a microwave
oven and coal and wood burning range for winter that burns continuously.
Electric blankets on beds.*
*The homestead offers a twin bedded room with private facilities with meals
and living shared with the family. Dinner B&B, B&B, campervans are welcomed.*

The farm is 218 hectares, sheep and cattle and pine trees. Situated at the north west end of Lake Taupo. It is an ideal base being central; trout fishing, photography pursuits, golf, hot pools, skiing in winter.The Pureora Forest Park is close by for walking, bird watching and taking a picnic. The Waitomo Caves and Rotorua are an easy day's trip away. Mt Ruapehu is just over one hour's drive.

Horse riding on the farm is available. Farm activities change with the seasons and such things as lambing, mustering with sheep dogs, haymaking, and various other farm activities can be observed or participated in by the visitor.

Simply phone us to book, or write, and you will receive a detailed map. We are very easily located, directions are not difficult.

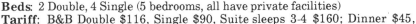

Taupo

Lodge
Address: "Koha Lodge",
50 Koha Road
(cnr Gillies Ave, Koha Rd), Taupo
Name: Lindsay and Pat Turner
Telephone: (07) 378-7647
Beds: 2 Double, 4 Single (5 bedrooms, all have private facilities)
Tariff: B&B Double $116, Single $90, Suite sleeps 3-4 $160; Dinner $45, children's meals to suit age and taste; Campervans $25+

Built 12 years ago as a large comfortable home Koha Lodge has glorious views overlooking the lake, mountains, town and country. We now enjoy pampering guests from New Zealand and around the world, in a warm, friendly and relaxed atmosphere.

A separate guest area has private bathrooms adjacent to bedrooms, each with tables and comfortable chairs, electric blankets and woollen underlays on the beds, and electric heaters and bathrobes provided. Guests have refrigerator and tea and coffee making facilities. A lower level has a dining room and two lounges _ with thermal heating and fire. There is a thermal pool, a games room with full-sized billiard table, as well as outdoor balconies, decks and sheltered garden areas including B.B.Q.

We offer an extensive breakfast selection, and our menu features N.Z. gourmet foods with N.Z. wine for dinner following complimentary pre-dinner drinks. Local restaurant menus are available.

As Taupo is superb for deer hunting nearby, famous trout fishing, water sports as well as many other activities, wilderness areas and sightseeing, we recommend longer than an overnight stay. We are happy to arrange guides, and have a courtesy car.

Directions: *From State Highway 1 along lakefront at fire station, turn onto Rifle Range Road, about 1 km to Koha Road on right. Two blocks to Gillies Avenue corner.*

Taupo
Homestay
Address: 51 Wakeman Road, Acacia Bay, Taupo
Name: Jim and Wilma Cousins
Telephone: (07) 378-8901
Beds: 4 Single (2 bedrooms, guest bathroom)
Tariff: B&B Double $70, Single $45, Dinner $20
Nearest Town: North west Taupo 6 km

We are a retired farming couple with one cat. Our house in quiet Acacia Bay has a magnificent view of Lake Taupo. Taupo and district have innumerable attractions from four golf courses to hot baths, walks, fishing, etc. Launch hire for fishing or cruising can be arranged.
Directions: *Follow Acacia Bay Road signs for 6 km to Garden Centre and store. Go straight up hill 1/2 km to Mapara Road. Wakeman Road first on left.*

Turangi
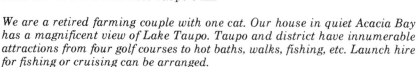
Homestay
Address: 4 Huriana Grove, Turangi
Name: Eleanor MacRae
Telephone: (07) 386 8977
Beds: 4 Single (2 bedrooms)
Tariff: B&B Double $55, Single $35; Dinner $15; Children half price;
Nearest Town: Taupo 53 km north

I live in a three bedroom house. I am close to the shopping area and local park with swimming pools and tennis courts.
I enjoy other people's company and don't mind having children to stay. Turangi is an all seasons region and has a lot to offer such as tramping, hunting, canoeing, skiing, white water rafting, fishing and golf.
I am very close to the central mountains, Lake Taupo and Tongariro River. Close by at Waihi is a lovely Maori Pa and Catholic Church which has Maori artefacts. Hot mineral pools are close by at Tokaanu.
Directions: *Turn at Turangi Hotel, turn left, first right, first right again past the shopping area. Huriana Grove is the third street on the right.*

Turangi
Homestay
Address: Omori Road, R.D. 1, Turangi
Name: Joy Wardell
Telephone: (07) 386-7386
Beds: 2 Single (1 bedroom, guest bathroom)
Tariff: B&B $30 Single, children welcome
Nearest Town: Turangi

My home is 16 km West of Turangi (off State Highway 41) with magnificent views across Lake Taupo and over the surrounding farmland and bush clad mountains. I share a property with my family whose home is next door to mine and we all enjoy meeting and entertaining people. It gives me much pleasure to cook and serve tasty meals for my numerous guests.
We have a few sheep and there are deer and goats on an adjoining property. There is a private study with television for the use of guests if required.
You need travel only short distances to the many attractions of this area, e.g.

Mountains - Ngaruahoe, Ruapehu and Tongariro, the Tongariro River and of course Lake Taupo itself. Activities such as trout fishing, bush walking, skiing, rafting, jet boating and many more can be enjoyed or if you prefer just relax and enjoy the fresh air and country atmosphere.

Turangi

Homestay
Address: 26 Ohuanga Road, Turangi
Name: Colin & Juan Mourie
Telephone: (07) 386 8452
Beds: 1 Double, 2 Single (2 bedrooms, guest bathroom)
Tariff: **B&B** $60 Double, $35 Single, children 1/2 price, dinner $15, Campervan $10
Nearest Town: Turangi - Taupo 53km

We are a retired couple, husband keen fisherman, living in a three bedroomed house an easy five minute walk from the Turangi Shopping Centre.
Turangi caters for every sporting activity you would care to name, trout fishing, boating, rafting, tramping, golf, squash, hot & cold swimming pools or just lying on one of our beautiful lake beaches.
We are approximately half an hour from Mt Ruapehu's ski-ing fields, just ideal for skiers or sightseers.
Directions: *To find us after driving from the main road towards the shopping area, take the first turn left into Ohuanga Road. We are number 26, four houses up from the fire station, two down from the Catholic Church. Please phone in advance.*

Turangi, Bay of Plenty

Self-contained Accom
Address: 72 Taupehi Road, Turangi
Name: Jean & Leslie Bird
Telephone: (07) 386-7518
Beds: 1 Double (Queen), 2 Single (2 bedrooms, guest bathroom)
Tariff: **B&B** $70 Double, $55 Single, Dinner by arrangement $20
Nearest Town: Turangi

We have a modern home, with a self-contained apartment attached which has 1 Queensize bed and two singles, all innerspring mattresses with Woolrest Sleepers and feather duvets. Own kitchen facilities, dining area, sitting room with own TV, electric fan heating, ensuite bathroom and carport. Laundry available.
We have a solar-heated swimming pool, private spa pool and barbeque area. Our home is close to the Tongariro River, Tongariro National Park and Lake Taupo. These areas cater for trout fishing - lake and rivers, tramping, ski-ing and other outdoor activities. We have spent 10 years in the tourist industry and have travelled extensively in New Zealand and overseas, and are now retired and can offer our hospitality to New Zealand and overseas visitors.
We and our Cocker Spaniel Katie will be pleased to greet you.
Directions: *Please phone.*

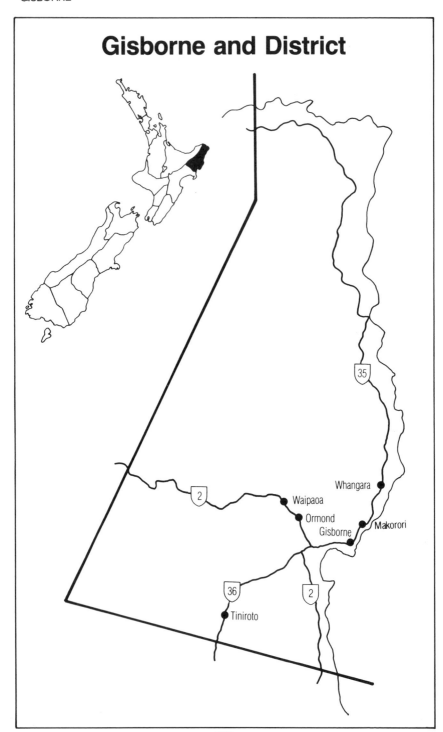

Gisborne and District

35

2

Whangara

Waipaoa

Ormond

Gisborne

Makorori

36

2

Tiniroto

Waipaoa, Gisborne
Farmstay
Address: "The Willows",
Waipaoa, RD1, Gisborne
Name: Rosemary and Graham Johnson
Telephone: (06) 862-5605
Beds: 1 Double, 2 Single (2 bedrooms, guest bathroom)
Tariff: B&B Double $55, Single $40; Dinner $20 (including wine); Campervan facilities $15
Nearest Town: Gisborne 20 km

We live near the world's 'first city to see the sun' and enjoy some of the longest sunshine hours in New Zealand. We enjoy the amenities available in the city and also the country life on our 550-acre farm involving sheep, cattle, deer, grapes and cropping.
Our home is probably best described in the American Colonial style with a panelled entry and dining room of our own oak timber milled from our own trees of which we have some lovely specimens planted by our forefathers. The guest rooms have two single beds in each and there are separate bathroom and toilet facilities available for guests. We welcome you to have dinner with us, or if you prefer only bed and breakfast.
We have a swimming pool and a grass tennis court which, as our three sons pursue their own interests, can only be described as available for a 'fun game'. We would appreciate it if you could ring prior to your arrival.
We enjoy meeting people and look forward to your visit.
Directions: *We are situated 20 km north of Gisborne on State Highway 2 through to Opotiki and the Bay of Plenty approximately 6 km from the Ormond Store or 9 km from Te Karaka. We have a sign "The Willows" at the end of our driveway. Our house is white with a black tiled roof situated on a hill overlooking the Waipaoa river.*

Gisborne
Homestay
Address: 805 Childers Road, Gisborne
Name: Alec and Barbara Thomson
Telephone: (06) 8689-675
Beds: 1 Double, 2 Single (2 bedrooms,)
Tariff: B&B Double $55, Single $35; Dinner $15; 10% discount for any bowlers staying with us when participating in local tournaments

Our home is situated in the suburb of Elgin, which is approximately 5 minutes by car from the City Centre. The City Bus Route runs a regular service to and from the city and we have a bus stop at our front gate. We can also offer off-street parking if you have your own car.
Both Alec and I enjoy meeting people and we look forward to welcoming all who wish to spend time with us.
We are both active members of the lawn and indoor bowls clubs. We also enjoy a game of bridge.

Whangara, Gisborne
Farmstay
Address: "Hikatu"
Whangara, RD3, Gisborne
Name: Ian and Sue Fraser
Telephone: (06) 862-2850
Beds: 1 Double, 2 Single (2 bedrooms, guest bathroom)
Tariff: B&B Double $50, Single $30, Children half price; Dinner $15; Campervans $15
Nearest Town: 30 km from Gisborne via East Coast Road

We live in the old family homestead which was built in the early 1900s. It is a comfortably sunny old place that we have renovated over the years and happily still retains the old world atmosphere we enjoy so much and would like to share.

Our garden would be of particular interest to gardeners and garden lovers alike as we have spent many years creating a varied and interesting place.

There is a swimming pool and a tennis court too, the latter used for social tennis.

The farm runs a Hereford stud, sheep, and various other animals. You are welcome to watch seasonal work in progress or ramble over the farm. There are also beautiful sandy beaches in easy driving distance.

You may dine with us or just have bed and breakfast, as you wish. Light lunch is available.

To those who wish to enjoy the country way of life, a peaceful garden, or to just get away from it all, Hikatu is a tranquil spot.

Ormond, Gisborne
Farmstay
Address: "Meadowbank",
Ormond, Gisborne
Name: Tim and Elizabeth Burke
Telephone: (06) 8625-610
Beds: 1 Double, 2 Single (2 bedroom, guest bathroom)
Tariff: B&B Double $50, Single $30, Children half price; Dinner $15
Nearest Town: Gisborne 19 km

Our family of four children is grown up now so we have a large old homestead waiting to be filled. There is a tennis court and swimming pool for use during the summer and a spa pool for those that like the water warmer in winter.

Our farm is 490 hectares running sheep, cattle, horses and goats with a small amount of cropping, mostly for stock feed. We have the usual domestic animals associated with farming – ducks, chooks, pigs, dogs, cats, peacocks and lambs in season. We have a house cow too. It is a family affair we would love to share.

Fly fishing is available about one hour's drive from here and day trips to suitable rivers can be arranged. We are 20 minutes away from Gisborne's good swimming and surfing beaches. Horses are a large part of our lives and riding can be arranged for anyone interested – basic instruction too. Time needs to be allowed for riding.

Taranaki, Wanganui

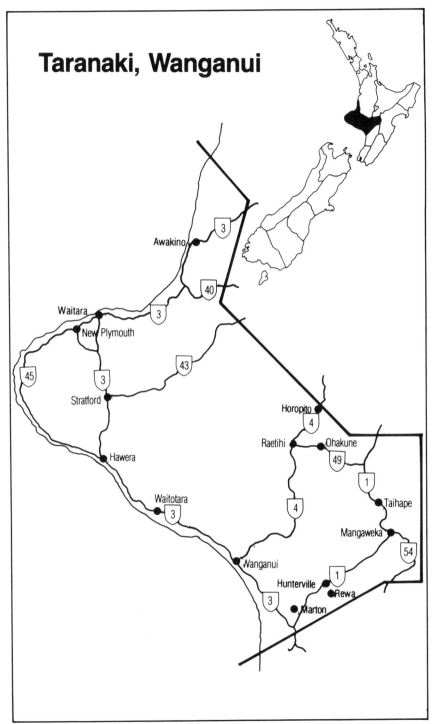

Awakino
Farmstay
Address: Maunganui Road, Awakino. Postal: Private Bag, Mokau
Name: Nawton and Sherryl Telfer
Telephone: (067) 29-835. (06) 752-9835 from Dec 91
Beds: 1 Double, 4 Single (3 bedrooms)
Tariff: B&B Double $50, Single $25, Dinner $15, Children half price;
Campervans $20

*We have a coastal property carrying 6000 sheep, 600 cattle and 300 deer.
The farm surrounds the 1500 acre Stewart Russell native reserve.
We have a large five bedroom home, with an indoor heated swimming pool,
spa pool and sauna which is available at all times.
All meals available. Lunch, morning and afternoon teas free.*
Directions: *10 km from Awakino, 8 km off the main highway. Awakino is
halfway between Te Kuiti and New Plymouth, 1 hour's drive either way.*

Waitara
Farmstay
Address: 2 Armstrong Ave, Waitara
Name: Bev & George Moratti
Telephone: (06) 754-6164
Beds: 1 Double, 2 Single (2 bedrooms, guest bathroom)
Tariff: **B&B** $55 Double, $30 Single, $15 Dinner
Nearest Town: Waitara

*Our 13 acre farmlet is situated on the outskirts of Waitara - 2 minutes from the
shopping centre and 10 minutes from New Plymouth. We have a new home
in pleasant and tranquil surroundings - we have beef cattle - two dogs, a cat
and a small aviary. We also have tunnelhouses in which we grow vegetables
and flowers for market. The Petrochemical Industrial sites are only minutes
away as are several beaches, walkways and picnic spots. We are interested in
travel and enjoy meeting people from both within New Zealand and from
overseas. Non-smokers preferred. All meals are prepared with home-grown
produce.*

Waitara
Farmstay
Address: Tikorangi Road, RD 43, Waitara
Name: John and Anne Megaw
Telephone: (067) 46-768, (06) 754-6768 from Dec 91
Beds: 1 Double, 2 Single (2 bedrooms)
Tariff: B&B Double $55, Single $30, Children half price, Dinner $15

*Our three bedroomed cosy brick house is situated on a hill with panoramic
views of Mt Egmont, the Waitara River Valley farmlands and even a
glimpse of the sea.
We live on a dairy farm where we milk 170 cows, have tunnel houses for
courgettes and melons and shade houses for begonias and ferns. Visitors
are welcome to participate in any farm activities, or wander to the river if
they wish.*

Taranaki has much to offer scenically with numerous parks and gardens, the mountain and coastline plus walkways long or short. The McKee energy field, Waitara petrolgas and Motonui synfuel plants are all close to Waitara.

Directions: *Travel on Highway 3 to Waitara. Turn inland to Tikorangi on Princess Street to Ngatimaru Road. Pass Tikorangi school and continue to very end of Ngatimaru Road. Turn right on no exit road and our house is second on the left, 3 km from school. Entrance by "Watch for Children" sign.*

New Plymouth
Homestay
Self-contained Beach Cottage
Address: "River Glen",
313 Mangorei Road, New Plymouth
Name: Val & Martin Massey
Telephone: (06) 758-3995
Beds: 1 Double, 2 Single, cot available (2 bedrooms)
Tariff: **B&B** $50 Double, $25 Single, children over 5 1/2 price, Dinner $12, Cottage price on application.
Nearest Town: New Plymouth

We invite you to come and enjoy our hospitality, beneath the shadow of Mount Egmont, relax amid our beautiful lakes and gardens, or laze on our popular beaches.
Retired, with a grown-up family, we can spend time with our hobbies, growing flowers, craftwork and fishing.
Our home is modest and comfortable, set on 4 acres within the city boundary, overlooking the Waiwhakaiho River.
The double room has toilet and handbasin, share bathroom with us (guests have priority).
Guests are invited to use our swimming and spa pools, games room and barbeque.
We offer a courtesy car to and from public transport, and scenic tours can be arranged.
Our Beach Cotttage is 20 minutes drive North of New Plymouth, with good fishing, river and sea swimming and adjacent golf course.
Breakfast is either continental or cooked and guests are invited to dine with us.
Directions: *Travelling North on State Highway 3, turn right in Mangorei Road. We are 2.2 km on right. Travelling South along Northgate, turn left at Mangorei lights, we are 2.8 km on left.* ————

New Plymouth
Homestay
Address: 39 Plympton Street,
Brooklands, New Plymouth
Name: Felicity and Neal Spragg
Telephone: (067) 32265. (06) 753-2265 from Dec 91
Beds: 1 Double, 2 Single (2 bedrooms, guest bathroom)
Tariff: B&B Double $55, Single $35

*Our home is large, modern and comfortable with a private wing for guests'
use. It consists of two bedrooms, one queen size and one twin room with
own bathroom and toilet facilities.*

*From our sundeck we overlook a peaceful bush walkway. We are only min-
utes from the central city, the beautiful Pukekura and Brooklands Park
areas and the sea.*

*From the slopes of the mountain to the shores of the Tasman Sea, Taranaki
offers a unique diversity of attractions and landscapes. Our central location
is advantageous to travellers, being within easy reach for either half or
whole day trips in the province.*

*Our family of three are grown up and living away from home so we enjoy
the company of other people. We look forward to meeting you in a warm
friendly and relaxed atmosphere.*

New Plymouth
Homestay
Address: 4 Hobson St, New Plymouth
Name: Myrtle Thomas
Telephone: (067) 83124
Beds: 2 Single
Tariff: B&B $45 Double, $25 Single, supper included
Nearest Town: New Plymouth

*A lovely sunny home, with off the street parking only 200 metres from the sea.
Share bathroom, beds have electric blankets.*

*Enjoy beautiful views of the sea and also along the coastline. In less than five
minutes you can walk to the bathing beaches, two reserves, Te Henui Scenic
Walkway, 2 bowling clubs and a croquet club.*

*There is a New Plymouth Bus stop a short distance away but if you prefer
walking it takes 10-15 minutes or a very little time by car to reach the city
centre.*

*Mount Egmont (Taranaki) is a short distance by car. It is said you can be
skiing or tramping up the mountain then take a leisurely drive to the sea for
swimming or sunbathing within 30 minutes.*

*My interests are floral art, gardening, New Zealand and overseas travel, and
particularly in people who like to share their interests with others.*

New Plymouth
Farmstay
Address: 606 Carrington Road,
R.D. 1, New Plymouth
Name: Marion & Geoff Rivers
Telephone: (06) 753-5123
Beds: 1 Double, 2 Single (2 bedrooms, guest bathroom)
Tariff: B&B Double $70, Single $35
Nearest Town: 12 km from New Plymouth

Our home is situated 12 km (8 miles) out of and overlooking the New Plymouth city. We have extensive views over the surrounding countryside with Mt Egmont to the South and the Tasman Sea to the North On a clear day a panoramic view of the central mountains can be enjoyed.
Accommodation is upstairs and includes large lounge with balcony, tea and coffee making facilities.
We live on a 160 acre Dairy farm on which Pony trekking or walking is enjoyed. Easy 1 hour walk or 10 min drive to world renowned Pukeiti Gardens, 15 minutes to Historical Maori Pa site, 5 minutes to private zoo, 10 minutes to golf course. Go tramping in Mount Egmont National Park or go to the Mountain top. Great surf beach 10 minutes away, fishing or diving arranged.
Active outdoor hosts prepared to show guests around for small fee. Adults only. Operate form 1st Nov to 1st May.
Directions: *Please phone for reservation and directions. Courtesy car to plane, bus or city.*

New Plymouth
Homestay
Address: 38 Hua Street,
Bell Block, New Plymouth
Name: Neal & Vera Fowler
Telephone: (067) 72399.
From Nov 91 (06) 755 2399
Beds: 1 Double, 3 Single (3 bedrooms)
Tariff: B&B $50 Double, $30 Single, $15 Dinner
Nearest Town: New Plymouth 7 mins, Stratford 25mins, Hawera 40 mins

Our home is in a very sheltered sunny locality next to a Reserve featuring a lovely walkway alongside a stream leading to the beach - about 10 minutes away. We are about 7 mins by car to New Plymouth city centre and approximately 10 / 20 mins away from most of our local points of interest e.g. Synfuel Energy Centre, beautiful gardens, Historic Places, Pioneer Village, Glass Blowing, Museum, Mountain, beaches and craft shops etc. Just one minute off State Highway 3.
As our children have now left home we felt that we would enjoy sharing our large modern home with others and also benefit from meeting new people.
Our bathroom, shower and toilets (2) are all separate and are shared by us. A separate loung available if required plus off-road parking. Lovely barbeque area.

New Plymouth
Homestay
Address: 'Puketotara',
31 Durham Avenue, New Plymouth
Name: Gerry & Beryl Paulin
Telephone: (06) 758-2900
Beds: 2 Double (2 bedrooms, guest bathroom)
Tariff: B&B $55 Double, $35 Single, $15 Dinner per person
Nearest Town: New Plymouth

Welcome to "Puketotara". We are a semi-retired couple living in a two storeyed home, within the New Plymouth boundary, situated on a hillside overlooking the beautiful Te Henui River and walkway to the sea. The river forms the boundary of our 10 acre property where Gerry grows cut flowers, mainly protea, for export and local markets. As flower growers, we will be happy to arrange garden visits and day trips to places of interest. We have explored New Zealand from Cape Reinga to Stewart Island and since our sons married and moved away, we have travelled extensively overseas. Gerry's interests are all things horticultural and he relaxes on the golf course. Beryl enjoys needlework, floral art and cooking. We look forward to meeting you.
Directions: *Please phone.*

New Plymouth
Homestay
Address: 481 Mangorei Road, New Plymouth, RD1
Name: Evelyn and Laurie Cockerill
Telephone: (067) 86-090. (06) 758-6090 from Dec 91
Beds: 4 Single (2 bedrooms)
Tariff: B&B Double $50, Single $30, Dinner $15

We live close to the city but with a rural background. Our home is situated next to New Plymouth's well known Tupare gardens which are always worth a visit, especially in spring when they are at their best. Taranaki is world renowned for its beautiful parks and gardens — the Pukeiti Rhododendron Trust gardens being only a twenty-five minute drive away. Mt Egmont can be viewed from our garden and can be reached within 20 minutes by car. We are only minutes from local beaches and the centre of the city by car.
Laurie is a blacksmith-farrier and has a keen interest in horses. We have followed all equestrian sports as our children rode at all levels. Now we have a few sheep and also a bird aviary. Bathroom and toilet facilities are shared with us.
We moved from the South Island 20 years ago so we have a good knowledge of most of the country and have recently travelled overseas.
Mangorei Road can be approached from either north or south on entering New Plymouth boundaries. Our name is on the letterbox. Off street parking is available.

One of the differences between staying at a hotel and a B&B is that
you don't hug the hotel staff when you leave.

Merrilands, New Plymouth
Homestay
Address: 11 Tamati Place,
Merrilands, New Plymouth
Name: Ashley & Evelyn Howan
Telephone: (06) 758-8932
Beds: 4 Single (3 bedrooms, guest bathroom)
Tariff: B&B $55 Double, $30 Single
Nearest Town: New Plymouth

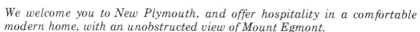

We welcome you to New Plymouth, and offer hospitality in a comfortable modern home, with an unobstructed view of Mount Egmont.
We are a middle aged working couple who enjoy meeting and entertaining people from all countries.
Guests have their own shower, toilet and bathroom (spa bath). The beds have electric blankets and innerspring mattresses.
Taranaki has a host of things to do and see, being a popular tourist destination. All Taranaki's main attractions are within easy reach of New Plymouth.
We will provide either a continental or cooked breakfast. Evening meals can be enjoyed at your choice of a variety of good restaurants.
No animals please, and we request no smoking in the house.
We will do our best to make your stay enjoyable.

Stratford
Homestay
Address: "Woodhill",
Mountain Road South, RD23, Stratford
Name: John and Elaine Nicholls
Telephone: (0663) 5497, (06) 765-5497 from Nov 91
Beds: 1 Double, 4 Single (3 bedrooms, guest bathroom)
Tariff: B&B Double $60, Single $35, Children $15; Dinner $20; Campervans $25 (up to 4 people)
Nearest Town: 46 km south of New Plymouth on State Highway 3

Come and enjoy the tranquility and beauty of the countryside in the heart of Taranaki. Our home is nestled in two acres of old English gardens and is over a hundred years old.
Each bedroom opens out onto the gardens and there is a separate guest bathroom.
We offer you warmth, hospitality and a haven from the stresses of everyday life. After a generous, leisurely breakfast enjoy a walk in the gardens or a swim in our large, outdoor pool. In the evenings you are welcome to join us for dinner, or if you prefer there are several restaurants in Stratford.
Our home is only 3 km from Stratford and 15 km from the Stratford Mountain House.
Stratford offers a wide range of activities including a pleasant golf course, lawn bowls and all types of mountain sports. For garden enthusiasts there is the Taranaki trail of gardens of which our home is a participant.
Directions: *We are situated 3 km south of Stratford on State Highway 3, adjacent to the Ngaere railway overbridge.* _____

Waitotara

Farmstay
+ Self-Contained Accommodation
Address: Ashley Park, PO Box 36,
Waitotara, Wanganui
Name: Barry Pearce and Wendy Bowman
Telephone: (06) 346-5917
Beds: 1 Double, 4 Single (3 bedrooms, guest bathroom)
Tariff: B&B Double $60, Single $30; Dinner $20; Power points for caravans and campervans with full facilities; Cabins available; Self-contained unit for 7 people

We are 2 km from Waitotara village and 8 km to the beach. We have a mixed farm, sheep cattle, deer and cropping. We have a large, comfortable home set in an attractive garden with a swimming pool and avaries with exotic birds and pheasants. Also in the garden is an antique and craft shop which also serves Devonshire teas and sandwiches from 9 am–5 pm daily.
Situated 100 metres from the house and garden is a 4-acre park of native and English trees, surrounding a picturesque lake with waterfowl.
We like to serve New Zealand fare and hope you enjoy the tranquility of the countryside. Guests are welcome to observe farm activities where possible and there are scenic drives locally.
Directions: *We are situated 32 km north of Wanganui and 12 km south of Waverley on State Highway 3.*

Waitotara

Farmstay
Address: "Hanui", Pakakara Rd, Waitotara, Wanganui
Name: Gillian and Michael Tallott
Telephone: (06) 346-5289
Beds: 2 Single (1 bedroom, guest bathroom)
Tariff: **B&B** $60 Double, $30 Single, children 1/2 price, Dinner $15, Campervans $20 (up to 4 people)
Nearest Town: Wanganui - 30 km North from Wanganui on SH3

Michael, myself and two boys live in a 5000 sq ft homestead built at the turn of the century. We own a 700 acre sheep and cattle property situated between Wanganui and Mt Taranaki, New Plymouth.
In the summer we make the most of a large concrete pool, Barbeque area and enjoy looking after extensive gardens.
We are only a 10 minute drive to beaches and 20 minutes from Wanganui.
Our interests include 4x4 driving, gardening, wines, reading, antiques, crafts and shooting.
Our home is for you to relax and have a quiet time in or join Michael in some farming activities if you wish to do so. ———————

Wanganui
Farmstay
Address: "Rusthall",
No. 2 Line, RD2, Wanganui
Name: Tom and Derryn Johnson
Telephone: (06) 342-4865
Beds: 2 Single (1 bedroom, guest bathroom)
Tariff: B&B Double $65, Single $45; Dinner by arrangement $20;
Campervans $20
Nearest Town: Wanganui 5 km

*Our eight-year-old home, which is situated on a 240-hectare sheep, cattle
and cropping farm was designed to blend with the background of beautiful
English trees. We enjoy the country life as well as having the advantage of
living in close proximity to the city of Wanganui.*
*Guests may enjoy our farm walks where there is natural beauty in the
native trees, birds and patches of native bush – added beauty with the
excellent views of Mt Ruapehu and surrounding countryside.*
*Our guest room has two single beds –guests have their own bathroom and
toilet facilities.*
We enjoy meeting people and offer warm, friendly hospitality.
As we are non-smokers we request that guests do not smoke indoors.
We do request guests phone in advance.
Directions: *Please phone.*

Wanganui
Homestay
Address: 10 Photinia Place, Wanganui
Name: Betty & Vic Falkner
Telephone: 343-7441
Beds: 1 Double, 2 Single (2 bedrooms)
Tariff: B&B $45 Double, $25 Single, $12 Dinner
Nearest Town: Wanganui

*We have recently retired from our farm at Waitotara to live in Wanganui.
Photinia Place is situated in a cul-de-sac, so there is no passing traffic and
our section looks out onto rural views. Wanganui has much to offer its
visitors. We can arrange jet boat trips on the Wanganui River, visits to a
winery, or if you care a day trip to our farm in the country.*
Directions: *Drive along Somme Parade as far as Camelia Avenue,
Photenia Place is the 2nd street turning left - off Camelia Ave. We have
ample off-street parking. We do ask guests to phone ahead if possible. You
can be sure of a warm welcome, comfortable bed, and home cooked meals.* ——

133

Horopito - Tongariro National Park
Homestay + Self-Contained Accommodation

Address: Ruapehu Cottage and Homestay
Matapuna Road, Horopito, RD 6, Raetihi
Name: Conon and Jackie Fraser
Telephone: (0658) 54-495, (06) 385-4495 from Dec 91
Beds: 2 Double, 4+ single (2 bedrooms, guest bathrooms)
Tariff: B&B Double $75, Single $50, Children half price, Dinner by arrangement, Campervans $20
Self-Contained Cottage: 1 Double, 6 Single (3 bedrooms), full facilities, self-catering
Tariff: B&B $22.50 per adult, min. hire whole cottage $90 per night. 10% discount midweek & off peak seasons
Nearest Town: Raetihi and Ohakune, both 16 km

Now that our sons have left home we have left the city to lead a life in the country, right on the boundary of Tongariro National Park. We have just finished building our warm and comfortable home with spacious guest rooms each with a glorious view of Mount Ruapehu, and one with its own balcony. Extensive decking overlooks the Park. There are 3.2 hectares of beautiful bush, pond, streams, and paddocks with a few sheep and ducks. Both Mount Ruapehu and Mount Taranaki can be seen from our newly renovated self-contained cottage. The nearest shop is in either Ohakune or Raetihi but we are only 2.2 km from S.H.4 on the way north to National Park and the Chateau. There is a daily free delivery of bread, milk and groceries. Table tennis and a small pool table are in the barn. There is a sandpit for children and indoor family games and books.

We live in one of New Zealand's finest areas for summer and winter activities. Tramping, skiing, white river rafting, golf, fishing etc are all near at hand. We enjoy developing our new garden, tramping, deer hunting, birdwatching, writing and photography. We know New Zealand well and enjoy having people to stay.

Write for information leaflet, or phone. We are easy to find.

Raetihi
Farmstay

Address: Pipiriki Road, R.D. 4, Raetihi
Name: Ken & Sonia Robb
Telephone: (0658) 54581
Beds: 1 Double, 2 Single (2 bedrooms, guest bathroom)
Tariff: B&B $60 Double, $30 Single, children 1/2 price, $10 Dinner, campervans welcome
Nearest Town: Raetihi

With the youngest of our nine children now attending boarding school we enjoy being able to welcome visitors from New Zealand and overseas to a farmstay experience.

We live on a 400 hectares (1000 acres) hill country farm running Romney sheep and a Simmental Cattle stud. Between July and October we feed hay to the cattle - an activity in which many of our guests have enjoyed taking part.
Sonia is a Nurse and works part time at the local hospital.
The double guest room has a very comfortable queen-sized bed and for those travelling with small children there is room to put up a cot which we have available. Ensuite facilities and a lovely view of Mount Ruapehu from the bedroom window.
Shearers quarters are also available.
Directions: *From Raetihi take the road to Pipiriki and we are 6 km along on the right.*

Raetihi
Farmstay
Address: State Highway 4, P O Box 91, Raetihi
Name: Brian & Pixie Chambers
Telephone: (0658) 54310. After 29 Nov 91 (06) 385 4310
Beds: 2 Single (1 Bedroom, guest bathroom)
Tariff: B&B $60 Double, $30 Single, $15 Dinner per person
Nearest Town: Raetihi 1 km

Our four children have left home to pursue their own careers and we now enjoy making new friends and sharing our lives with them.
We have a 1600 acre farm on which we run sheep, cattle and deer.
There is an outdoor swimming pool, set in idyllic garden surroundings and an indoor spa pool for the cooler season. As we both enjoy gardening, our home is set in gracious, peaceful surroundings, with a panoramic view of mountains and farmland. This is often described by visitors as a "million dollar view". One of the first pleasures you will notice is the crisp, clear, mountain air.
We are 30 minutes from the Turoa Ski Resort and scenic mountain drive. There is also a lovely golf course to enjoy nearby.
Brian runs his own stock and station business and enjoys taking visitors with him on his trips to buy stock from farmers in the district.
Accommodation is twin bedroom, with private shower and toilet.
Directions: *1 km North of Raetihi.*

Ohakune
Self-Contained Accommodation
Address: 3209 Raetihi Road, Ohakune
Name: Noeline and Trevor Reynolds
Telephone: (0658) 58-412
Beds: 1 Double, 2 Single (2 bedrooms, guest bathroom)
Tariff: B&B Double $70, Single $35, Children $20, Dinner $15
Nearest Town: Ohakune

Our modern home is situated on an 11 acre park-like grounds and our home includes a warm centrally heated and sunny visitors' flat, a fully equipped kitchn, bathroom, washer/dryer. The living room includes colour TV and has views of the lovely Waimarino Golf Course.
Ohakune offers good restaurants and the Tongariro National Park has

continued over

135

many splendid walks, and the Turoa Ski Fields. The nearby Wangaui River offers jet boating and canoe safaris. Horse riding and white water rafting, trout fishing and other activities.
Directions: *From the Ohakune town centre take the Raetihi Road and travel 4 km to 3209 and ND & TR Reynolds' letterbox on the left hand side. The road is tree lined to our home.*

Ohakune - Tongariro
Homestay+ Self-Contained Accommodation
Address: Queen Street, Raetihi
Name: Bavarian Lodge
Telephone: (0658) 54-389. (06) 385-4389 from Dec 91
Beds: 5 Double, 5 Single, Self-contained 3-bedroom apartment sleeps 9
Tariff: B&B Double from $66, Single from $40, Children half price; Dinner from $10
Nearest Town: Wanganui 1 hour, Ohakune 5 min

The Bavarian Lodge, one of Raetihi's historical buildings, and home of operating, interesting farmers, can offer outdoor adventures and activities for all seasons, ages and abilities.
Farm Life, Tongariro National Park, fantastic skiing at Turoa Ski Resort only 5 minutes from Bavarian. Trout fishing (experienced taxidermist available for home delivery), tramping, picnics, ornithology, painting, photography, magnificent native flora and fauna, a wealth of educational studies and historical pursuits, small game shooting, mountains, clean fresh air, rivers, lakes, peace, and nature 'in the raw', all offer a memorable holiday.
Evenings are always interesting — usually hilarious with local characters, lively banter, dancing and fun — making new friends for all.
Having hosted successfully for many years, we guarantee an unforgettable stay.
Transport to and from airports can be arranged if required — additional charge.

Ohakune
Homestay/Farmstay
Address: "Mitredale", Smiths Road, Ohakune
Name: Audrey and Diane Pritt
Telephone: (0658) 58-016, (06) 385-8016 from Dec 91
Beds: 1 Double, 2 Single (2 bedrooms)
Tariff: B&B Double $60, Single $30, Children -25%; Dinner $10; Campervans $20
Nearest Town: Ohakune 6 km, Raetihi 9 km

We are farmers who farm sheep and cows in a beautiful peaceful valley with magnificent views of Mt Ruapehu. The Waimarino is an excellent area for holidaying summer or winter. The Tongariro National Park offers excellent walks, opportunities for photography and great skiing at Turoa and Whakapapa. The rivers offer good sport for the fisherman or canoeists and an excellent 18-hole golf course only 3 km from our door. We are keen members of the Conservation body Ducks Unlimited. Diane also manages the wine shop in Ohakune.
We have two guest rooms – one with two single beds, the other has a double

*bed. All equipped with electric blankets. The home is heated with a log fire
and open fire – excellent for drying gear after a day`s skiing, a comfortable,
cosy atmosphere to relax in.*
*We offer dinner with the traditional farmhouse fare or just breakfast – gives
you the opportunity to sample our excellent home-made jams.*
*We enjoy sharing our lifestyle with others so come and spend some time on
the farm.*
Directions: *Take the Raetihi Road (State Highway 49) at Ohakune Hotel
corner, travel 4 km to Smiths Road, second side road on the left. An unsealed
road. We are the last house 2 km at the end of the road. If you prefer you
may call at the wine shop in Ohakune for directions.*

Taihape
Homestay
Address: "Korirata', 25 Pukeko Street, Taihape
Name: Noel and Pat Gilbert
Telephone: (0658) 80-315.   (06) 388-0315 from Dec 91
Beds: 4 Single, electric blankets (2 bedrooms, guest bathroom)
Tariff: B&B Double $55, Single $35, Dinner $15

*We have recently renovated and added to a residence built in the early
twenties in an extremely quiet area of Taihape.*
Warmth and comfort is a feature.
*The entire section —three quarters of an acre — has been landscaped with
shrubs, a hydroponic house (supplying us with vegetables), an orchid house
and a very large area planted in chrysanthemums.*
*We are situated on top of the hill and have panoramic views of Mt Ruapehu,
Ruahine Ranges and extensive farming country.*
*We are one hour to skiing on Ruapehu, 1 hour to Lake Taupo, 2 1/2 hours to
Rotorua or Wellington.*
*Farm visits, tramping, all types of rafting, river fishing and jet-boating are
within 30 minutes plus Titoki Point Gardens.*
*Dinner and lunch are available on request. Almost all types of meals are
available. Meals with hosts. Cooking using our home-grown produce is one
of our hobbies.*
Separate toilet, bathroom and shower is available for sole use of guests.
Directions: *Please phone.*

Taihape
Homestay
Address: 12 Lark Street, Taihape
Name: Jack and Joyce Gilbert
Telephone: (0658) 80-915, (06) 388-0915 from Dec 91
Beds: 2 Single (1 bedroom)
Tariff: B&B Double $55, Single $35, Dinner $15

New Zealand
Association
FARM & HOME
HOSTS

*We are a retired farming couple with a grown up family. We offer you a
warm and friendly welcome to our home which is surrounded by a large
garden of flowering shrubs and roses.*
*Our home, situated on the hill, has panoramic views of extensive farmlands
with the Ruahine Ranges in the background. Our guest room has twin beds*

continued over

137

with electric blankets. Dinner would be by arrangement.
Taihape, situated on SH1, is only 2 hours 30 mins drive from either Wellington or Rotorua. A one hour drive would take you to the Ruapehu Ski Fields or Lake Taupo (renowned for its trout fishing). We can arrange a farm visit, tramping, all types of rafting and jet boating. Titoki Point Gardens or Cross Hills Rhododendron Gardens are well worth a visit.
Our son runs the home farm (700 hectares) of sheep, cattle and grain.
Our hobbies are spinning (Coopworth fleece), knitting and gardening.

Mangaweka
Farmstay
Address: "Mairenui Holidays", Ruahine Road, Mangaweka 5162
Name: Sue and David Sweet
Telephone: (065825) 564. (06) 382-5564 from Dec 91
Beds: 1 Double, 3 Single (3 bedrooms, guest bathrooms)
Tariff: B&B Double $75, Single $45, Dinner $20; Campervans: $5 per person (All prices exclusive of GST)

We have a sheep and cattle farm situated on a picturesque through route from Mangaweka to Feilding (SH54).
Our double bedroom has an ensuite bathroom with sunken bath and its own verandah. The twin bedroom has an ensuite shower and toilet and also its own verandah. Each room has tea and coffee making facilities, and a jar of home-baked biscuits is provided.
We have a concrete tennis court (racquets available), horse riding, farm walks, river swimming. We can arrange trout fishing, white water rafting, jet boating, bungy jumping and heli-skiing in season, or alternatively we can offer you a peaceful rest in the tranquil countryside.
There is an excellent cuisine, using fresh garden produce, and we have a fine selection of New Zealand wines available. Special diets can be catered for, and cooked or continental breakfasts are provided. The evening meal comprises three or four courses, with a glass of house wine. Complimentary pre-dinner drinks are served in the comfortable living room or on the large sunny verandah. Percolated coffee, espresso or capuccino are specialities of the house. We enjoy meeting people and sharing our unique lifestyle. Both French and German are spoken.
Directions: *The farm is situated 12 km from Mangaweka and 84 km from Palmerston North on SH 54. There is a B&B "Mairenui Holidays" sign at the gate.*

Mangaweka
Farmstay
Address: 'Cairnmuir Farmstays', State Highway 1, Mangaweka
Name: David and Elizabeth Buchanan
Telephone: (0658) 25-878. (06) 382-5878 from Dec 91
Beds: 4 Single (2 bedrooms, guest bathroom)
Tariff: B&B Double $80, Single $45, Dinner $20
Nearest Town: 18 km south of Taihape

Our farmstay can offer you a comfortable, relaxed and fun-filled time with us. We have a grownup family of three so we are free to spend time with our guests.
Both of us enjoy outdoor life, have a keen love of gardening, enjoy tennis on our concrete court, golf, and all the recreational activities this unique area offers.
We live on a 735 hectare sheep and cattle hill-country property which offers panoramic views of the Rangitikei district. Our spacious home has a welcoming atmosphere. The open fire and pleasant living room give people an opportunity to relax and enjoy the country lifestyle.
We like our guests to share a three course dinner with us which is served with quality NZ wines. We use home-grown produce which is presented with flair and imagination. A breakfast of your choice is provided.
Mangaweka abounds in opportunities for all to have a welcome break from city life.
Our home is situated within easy access to several gardens of world renown in the Taihape and Rangitikei districts.

and Campervan Park

Hunterville
Farmstay
Address: Vennell's Farmstay, Rewa, R.D.
Name: Phil & Oriel Vennell
Telephone: (06) 328-6780 or if no reply try 328-6769
Beds: 4 Single (2 bedrooms, guest bathroom)
Tariff: B&B $80 Double, $40 Single, $25 Dinner includes complimentary pre-dinner drinks.
Nearest Town: Hunterville

We are third generation farmers on a sheep cattle and cropping hill country farm. Our spacious, modern and comfortable home is in a tranquil setting of mature trees and garden with swimming pool. We have a large family room with pool table and living room with exposed beams and large open fire. Beautiful rural views can be seen from our home and surrounding farm hills. We are situated just off State Highway One near Hunterville on the scenic route to Feilding and in the centre of Rangitikei Private Gardens. We are 3 hours drive south from Rotorua, 1 1/2 hours from Mt Ruapehu skifields and 2 1/2 hours from Wellington. Trout fishing, rafting, jet boating, bungy jumping can all be enjoyed on the nearby Rangitikei river.
Our interest include current affairs, fishing, boating, gardening, sport, general. Transport to and from bus and airport can be arranged. Approved Farmstay hosts since 1980. Longer stays welcome.
Directions: *Please phone for directions.*

Hunterville
Farmstay
Address: "Homecroft", R.D. 5, Hunterville
Name: Kathryn & Philson Marsh
Telephone: (0652) 29890
Beds: 3 Single (2 bedrooms)

Tariff: **B&B** $60 Double, $35 Single, children (under 13) 1/2 price, $15 Dinner - morning & afternoon teas free
Nearest Town: 12 km North of Hunterville, 1 min from SH1

We are a family of four with two pre-school boys. We farm a 1300 acre sheep and cattle farm, a mixture of flat and hill country, only minutes from the scenic Rangitikei River with its easy access, excellent swimming and picnic spots, and trout fishing. Heli-jet, Bungy-jumping and rafting facilities are 15 minutes North, with the Rangitira Golf Course only 2 minutes away. The Turoa Ski-fields are one hours drive North and Wellington is three hours drive South.
Our home is an 80 year old traditional farmhouse, well-heated and spacious, set amongst established trees and garden. Guests are welcome to participate in farm activities or just relax and enjoy our beautiful surroundings. Bathroom and toilet facilities are shared.

140

Hunterville
Farmstay
Address: Turakina Vally Road, R.D.1, Hunterville
Name: Fraser & Annemarie Horrocks
Telephone: (0652) 28311
Beds: 1 Double, 2 Single (2 bedrooms, 1 guest bathroom)
Tariff: B&B $55 Double, $35 Single, children (under 13) 1/2 price, Dinner $20
Nearest Town: Hunterville

Having travelled extensively overseas we are delighted to be able to invite you to our home and farm. On reflection, highlights of our trips were the people we met and experiences through farmstays.
Situated in a sunny sheltered valley, our 840 acre farm is mixed sheep and cattle with a river running through ideal for fishing and swimming in summer. If you are looking for a real taste of New Zealand farm life there is always something happening and another pair of hands is always welcome.
Nestled amongst beautiful mature trees our spacious home is comfortable and warm, we have a room with shared facilities and a detached room with its own facilities.
We are very centrally located with hand bush walks, white water rafting and jetboating (45 minutes) and handy (1 1/2 hours) to Mount Ruapehu if you enjoy skiing.
In our early 30's with a daughter we would ensure you enjoyed our home, food and hospitality.
Directions: *Please phone.*

Hunterville
Self-Contained Accommodation
Address: "Otairi", RD 2, Hunterville
Name: David and Vicky Duncan
Telephone: (0652) 28-027
Beds: 1 Double, 8 Single
(6 bedrooms, 3 bathrooms)
Tariff: Price on application
Nearest Town: Hunterville

We invite you to say in "Otamaire", a lovely architect designed 50 year old home set in landscaped gardens, 15 minutes off State Highway One. "Otamaire" was until recently our home and is part of an historic sheep and

141

continued over

*beef cattle station of 12,000 acres which has been farmed by four genera-
tions of the Duncan family. We have moved to the 100 year old homestead
1 km away and "Otamaire" is available to guests who wish to have the privacy of the self-catering option with all comforts and still be part of a farming operation. The house is large and well appointed. Spa bath, dishmaster,
automatic laundry, television, oil fired AGA cooker, wall panel electric
heaters, open fires (wood supplied), fully carpeted, linen, towels and all
other requirements. Daily delivery from Hunterville. Housekeeping
services available on request.*

*The garden has roses, mature trees, sweeping lawns and a grass tennis
court. All well maintained. There is a stable complex and reliable mounts
and good rides can be arranged. The Turakina River runs behind the house
with good swimming holes. Other activities could include garden tours of
well known Rangitikei Gardens, "Rathmoy", "The Ridges", Cross Hills,
Westoe and Titoki especially in the spring.*

*We are 2 1/2 hours from Wellington, 2 1/2 hours from Taupo, 1 hour from
Palmerston North, 1 hour from Wanganui, 1 1/2 hours from Ruapehu
Skifield, 1/2 hour from Rangitikei River for rafting, trout fishing and jet
boating and bunji jumping.*

Please phone for precise directions.

Marton
Farmstay
Address: "Tataramoa",
R.D. 2, Howie Road, Marton
Name: Mrs Janice Gower
Telephone: (0652) 8778
Beds: 1 Double, 6 Single (4 bedrooms, guest bathroom)
Tariff: B&B $60 Double, $30 Single, children under 12 1/2 price, $15
Dinner per person
Nearest Town: Marton

*Tataramoa is a 135 year old large wooden homestead set in peaceful
landscaped gardens, surrounded by spacious beautiful mature New Zealand
bush filled by many native birds. We have 1000 acres on which we run
sheep, cattle and deer and we also have cropping paddocks. There are great
opportunities for interesting walks around the flats, hills and valleys.*

*Within reasonable distance from Palmerston North and Wanganui cities and
beaches. We have a friendly and homely atmosphere with a very welcome
cosy log fire.*

*Traditional New Zealand farm roast dinner with private lounge or billiard
room if preferred. We enjoy opening our home to visitors from all over the
world, with ample space for you to relax and unwind. Tataramoa welcomes
you.*

Directions: *10 km from Marton township*

Hawkes Bay

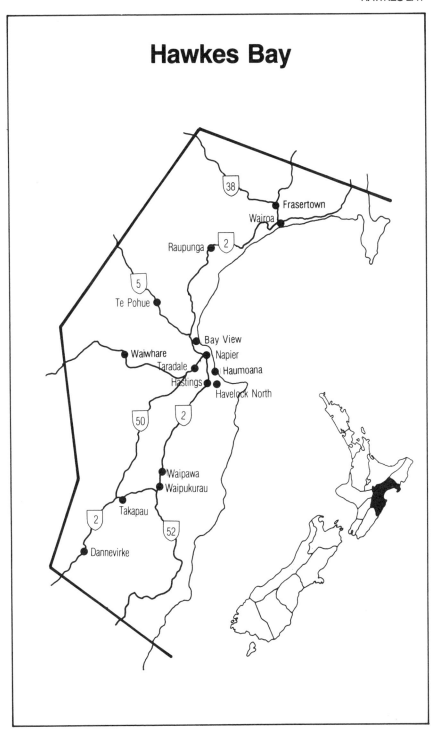

Raupunga

Fishermen's Farmstay
Address: "Waikohe" RD4,
Raupunga, Northern Hawkes Bay
Name: Brian and Janice Batson
Telephone: (06) 838-6969
Beds: 1 Double, 2 Single (2 bedrooms)
Tariff: On application
Nearest Town: Wairoa

We are situated in a very remote farming area adjacent to the Urewera National Park and a one-hour drive north-west of Wairoa. We farm an 815 acre sheep and cattle property. Recently we diversified into a Sportsmen's Lodge catering for game hunters and trout fishermen worldwide which has proved very popular and successful.

Our isolated lakes and rivers are well-stocked with quality rainbow and brown trout and guests like the fact that they can fish all day without seeing another angler. Top quality red deer, goat, wild ram and wild boar trophies are readily available.

Our ranch style home, at an elevation of 1500 ft has panoramic views of the countryside. This is complemented by well-manicured gardens, fish pond with waterfall, swimming pool, concrete tennis court and spa pool on our spacious patio which is lovely for outdoor meals.

Whether you require our hunting or fishing services, or just require a few days on the farm relaxing or enjoying bush walks, mustering, shearing, visiting the Urewera National Park, we can assure you a warm and friendly hospitable stay.

Due to our isolation, we recommend a minimum stay of two days and it would be easier to phone for directions when booking.

Frasertown, Wairoa

Homestay
Address: State Highway 38, Ardkeen, Wairoa
Postal: P O Box 66, Frasertown, Wairoa
Name: Peter & Dawn Bedingfield
Telephone: (06) 838 6524
Beds: 3 Single (2 bedrooms)
Tariff: B&B $50 Double, $30 Single, $15 Dinner
Nearest Town: Wairoa

We have a new open living style home situated at Ardkeen - 25 kms from Wairoa on State Highway 38. Guest rooms open onto a sunny deck. Wholesome farm-cooked meals are available.

We farm sheep and cattle, plus harvest asparagus in the season (Sept to Dec). Guests may join in farm activities or go sight seeing - at their discretion.

We are situated 1/2 hour from Waikaremoana and the Urewera National Park, with fishing for trout, hunting and many bush walks. 3/4 hour from the Mahia Peninsula, with its beaches and sea fishing. 1 1/2 hours from sunny Gisborne and 2 hours from sunny Napier.

Campervan facilities are available and the Wairoa / Rotorua bus passes our gate. Runs both ways, three days a week.

We also have available a fully self contained holiday home at Lake

Waikaremoana. Assistance with fishing or sightseeing on the lake or tramping trips around the lake or in the bush is available.

Te Pohue

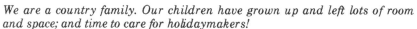

Farmhouse
Address: Rock Station,
Te Pohue, RD2, Napier
Name: Beryl and Peter King
Telephone: (06) 839-1851
Beds: 1 Double, 2 Single (2 bedrooms)
Tariff: B&B $40 per room, Dinner $14 p.p.
Nearest Town: Napier 45 mins, Taupo 1 hr on Napier/Taupo Highway

We are a country family. Our children have grown up and left lots of room and space; and time to care for holidaymakers!
Our home is 35 years old built from timber cut from our farm. We are 1500 feet above sea level so winter woollies are required in winter.
Great scenery, fresh air and water. There are country walks and animals to see if you like them, also native birds.
Our home is friendly, cosy, quiet and comfortable. We are interested in woollen crafts. Our hobbies include gardening, trees, animals, painting and floral art.
Non-smokers preferred.

Waiwhare

Country Farm Homestead
Address: "Mangawhare",
Waiwhare, Taihape Road,
PO Box 159, Hastings
Name: Pat and Brian Tolley
Telephone: (06) 8742-875
Beds: 1 Double, 6 Single (4 bedrooms, guest bathroom)
Tariff: B&B Double $55, Single $30, Dinner $15, Children half price; Campervans $20 up to 4
Nearest Town: Hastings 50 kms

A warm welcome awaits guests at Mangawhare (sheep and cattle farm) at our large historical Elizabethan homestead which is situated just off the Napier/Taihape (Gentle Annie) Road, 60 km from Napier, 50 km from Hastings.
Nearby there are deer farms, one with bow hunting a speciality. Water rafting and hunting also available in close proximity with native bush walks, fishing and golf and squash facilities within easy access. In season there are local country gardens open to public viewing.
We are also classic car enthusiasts (Daimler).
Directions: *Taihape Road turn off at Fernhill (State Highway 50) follow Taihape Road to Glenross, River Roads cross roads. Mangawhare is situated 1 km on the Glencross Road, first on the right with our name on the mailbox. Likewise 100 km from Taihape on the Taihape/Napier Road.*

Bayview
Luxury Farm Guest House
Address: "Mont Cebu Lodge", Bayview, Hawkes Bay
Name: Clive and Kelly
Telephone and Fax: (06) 836-6960
Beds: Selection Queens/Singles (6 bedrooms including honeymoon suite) & sailboat
Tariff: B&B Double $75-$190 - Stay and sail.
Nearest Town: Napier 10 minutes driving, Napier Airport pick-up (5 minutes drive)

The "Mont Cebu Lodge" is situated high on top of the hill overlooking the 100 acre coastal property. In the town of Bayview, surrounded by excellent vineyards and wineries, also noted for its early fruit orchards. The Bay views are truly spectacular, with the entire Hawkes Bay and inland country clearly visible.

"Mont Cebu Lodge" was created by a wealthy race car driver who has spent most of his life in America, and needed a lavish retreat to enjoy the New Zealand summers (race car movies if interested). The Lodge is a large modern contemporary design, just completed. Stunning! and very decadent.

Built using mostly matai timber a really beautiful interior of high pitched ceilings with open beams spanning 5 levels. There are 6 large bedrooms, separate lounges with views from most rooms.

Guests are welcome to take advantage of the large swimming pool and glassed in spa pool with ample outside seating decks etc. Barbeques are used most all summer. Fresh fruit and vegetables are used in all the food preparations together with our excellent selection of local wines.

Clive and Kelly together with their 3 year old son Clive Junior will help to make your stay in Hawkes Bay a truly memorable experience. Guided trout fishing excursions or visiting the local wineries, there's always something to do or go see around Napier.

The surrounding property is currently being developed into a recreation park incorporating a downhill cart run, miniature golf, cable run, grass skiing, etc. Planned opening is 1992. This is somewhat removed from the Lodge surroundings and privacy will be assured at all times. Meanwhile there are angora goats - black and white sheep, horses, peacocks, keeping the grass down. A stroll over the hill after dinner is most satisfying.

Napier

Homestay
Address: 17 Cobden Road, Napier
Name: Kay & Stewart Spence
Telephone: (06) 835-9454
Beds: 1 Double, 4 Single (3 bedrooms, guest bathroom)
Tariff: B&B $60 Double, $35 Single, $20 Dinner
Nearest Town: Napier

Our early colonial, two-storeyed home with comfortable and modern facilities is pleasantly situated in a sunny position on Napier Hill. The home is set in attractive grounds spread over almost an acre, in a quiet area - just a 10 minute walk from the Napier City Centre.

Guest rooms include a bedroom suite with double bed, ensuite bathroom and sitting room with tea-making facilities; a twin room with ensuite bathroom and a twin room with share bathroom facilities. Tea making facilities for these rooms are on hand in the sun porch.

We have been welcomed into private homes in New Zealand and overseas and wish to extend a warm welcome to you to share our home in sunny Hawkes Bay.

We will be happy to meet you at the Hawkes Bay Airport, Napier Railway Station or city bus depot.

Directions: *if you are travelling privately - please phone.*

Always telephone ahead to enquire about a B&B.
It is a nuisance for you if you simply arrive
to find someone is already staying there.
And besides, hosts need a little time to prepare.

Napier
Farmstay
Address: "Hilltop Farm", Puketitiri Road, R.D.2, Napier
Name: Jean & Bob Wilson
Telephone: (06) 844-3205
Beds: 3 Single (2 bedrooms, guest bathroom)
Tariff: B&B $50 Double, $30 Single, $15 Dinner
Nearest Town: Napier

We live close to the two Hawkes Bay cities of Napier and Hastings. It is approximately a 20 minute drive to the Napier Post Office and 25 minutes to Hasting Post Office. The Hastings area is known as the "fruit bowl" of New Zealand.
Our home is only a few years old, is spacious and comfortable and guests have separate bathroom and toilet facilities. It is situated on 60 acres of farm land, on which sheep and a few cattle are run and has panoramic views of Napier and Hawkes Bay. We also have a swimming pool and outdoor spa pool. The following attractions are within easy distance, the gannet colony, local beaches, Marineland, aquarium, native bush reserves and scenic walkways and visits to local winemaking breweries.

Our B&Bs are mostly private homes.
Most do not accept credit cards.

Napier
Homestay
Address: 19 Alamein Crescent, Napier
Name: Pam and Bill McCulloch
Telephone: (06) 8436-744
Beds: 1 King Size Double, 4 Single, 1 Cot (3 bedrooms)
Tariff: B&B Double $70, Single $35, Dinner $15 each
Nearest Town: Napier 3 km

We are retired and enjoy sharing our home with overseas guests. We have hosted many guests through our involvement with Rotary, Servas and the Friendship Force.
Three of our four children are married and our youngest daughter is currently overseas.
We have a swimming pool, spa pool, rumpus room and a well kept garden and 2 cats.
Our guest's rooms have single beds or a king-size bed and share bathroom facilities. There is a cot and highchair available.
Family dinner available each evening by arrangement.
Napier has many tourist attractions, suitable for a good family holiday destination for young and old. Napier has an excellent climate, plenty of sunshine, attractive shops and restaurants and is only 25 km from the twin city of Hastings.
Being non-smokers ourselves we thank you for not smoking in the house.

Taradale
Homestay
Address: "Twinpeak", 100 Puketapu Road, Rawhiti Heights, Taradale
Name: Soe Schofield
Telephone: (06) 844-9319
Beds: 1 Double, 3 Single (3 bedrooms, guest bathroom)
Tariff: B&B Double $80, Single $60, 3 course dinner $25
Nearest Town: Taradale 5 min, Napier 9 km north, Hastings 10 km south

Twinpeak is a spacious home on 5 acres in an elevated location, with unsurpassed views overlooking Taradale, Napier and the rural surrounds. A tranquil garden setting away from the hustle and bustle yet only minutes away from all that Hawkes Bay has to offer – Marineland, art deco walks, wine trails, beaches, shopping, walkways, lovely weather.
For the executive, space and quiet to plan relax and recover. Use of IBM compatible computer if required.
Looking forward to meeting new friends.

Taradale
Homestay
Address: 50 Puketapu Road, Taradale
Name: Don and Sheila Copas
Telephone: (06) 844-2182 (h), 835-7933 (w)
Beds: 1 Double, 3 Single (3 bedrooms)
Tariff: B&B Double $45, Single $22.50, Children half price; Dinner $15
Nearest Town: Napier 10 km

Our home is situated in an attractive and interesting one acre garden with sheep in the orchard, a putting green and a swimming pool contributing to its unique rural atmosphere although it is only five minutes walk from the town of Taradale and ten minutes drive from Napier.
The climate of Hawkes Bay justifies the title of "Sunny Napier" and the area in and around the city has much to offer of interest and activity, i.e. sailing, fishing, windsurfing, bush walks, etc.
Napier is also well endowed with tourist attractions _ museums, aquarium, Marineland and can lay a claim to being the 'Art Deco' centre of the world.
We love to entertain and you will be assured of a warm welcome at our comfortable family home.
Directions: *10 km west from Napier. Area maps are available from the Information Centre on Marine Parade or the A.A. Centre in Dickens Street, Napier or phone us for directions.*

Haumoana

Homestay
Address: 88 Beach Road, Haumoana, Hawkes Bay
Name: Ingrid and Paddy Griffin
Telephone: (06) 875 0572
Beds: 3 Single (bed-sitting room)
Tariff: B&B Double $55, Single $40, Dinner $15, Children half price
Nearest Town: Equidistant from Napier and Hastings

Haumoana is on the coast equidistant from the cities of Napier and Hastings.
We are a recently retired couple who enjoy meeting tourists, especially from overseas as we have travelled extensively overseas ourselves.
Our home is less than 5 minutes walk from the beach and has a magnificent view from Cape Kidnappers around to the coast beyond Napier.
When the beautiful gannets from the colony at Cape Kidnappers dive off our beaches, the surf casting is exciting and would thrill the heart of any fisherman. You can visit the gannet colony at the Cape overland by range rover, or around the coast at the base of the cliffs by tractor drawn trailers (we prefer this method). Set aside a day for this never to be forgotten adventure.
There are several organised 'wine trail trips' when you can visit some of the many wineries and sample the products. You can also make your own way by car.
We have available a Bed/Sitting room with own access. Two single beds and ample room for a third bed.
Directions: *from Hastings, turn off opposite Mangateretere School 5 km from centre of Hastings and follow AA signs to Haumoana and Beach Road. From Napier, turn off 500 m past Clive and follow AA signs.*
We look forward to your visit. Have a happy day.

As distances in New Zealand are not great check out the
maps of the neighbouring provinces for other B&Bs nearby.

Hastings
Homestay
Address: Please phone
Name: Maralyn and Ray   **Telephone:** (06) 878-5959
Beds: 1 Double, 2 Single (2 bedrooms, guest bathroom)
Tariff: B&B $30 per person

We are a professional couple with a large, old, very comfortable family home.
Our three adult children no longer live at home. Our main leisure activities
are scouting and tennis.
Guests can enjoy their own sitting room and bathroom.
Off-street parking is available.
We are situated four blocks from the heart of Hastings city.

Hastings
Farmhouse
Address: Wai-iti Farms, Maraekakaho Road, Hastings
Name: Jan Graham and Dick Black   **Telephone:** (06) 879-7951
Beds: 1 Double, 2 Single (2 bedrooms, guest bathroom)
Tariff: B&B $25 per person; Dinner $20; Children half price
Nearest Town: Hastings 12 km, HW50 3 km, HW2 9 km

Last century our house began life as a ploughman's cottage but like Topsy has
grown to gracious and generous proportions.
We have spacious lawns and an attractive garden which hosts a variety of
pets from peacocks to puppies.
Hundreds of school children, parents and teachers visit us every year to enjoy
a variety of farm experiences which our guests would be most welcome to
enjoy also.
Swimming pool and spa pool available.

Hastings
Homestay
Address: Montana Road, RD5, Hastings
Name: Jill and Jock Taylor   **Telephone:** (06) 879-5276
Beds: 1 Double, 2 Single (2 bedrooms, guest bathroom)
Tariff: B&B $25 per person, Dinner $15 by arrangement
Nearest Town: Hastings 10 minutes

Our home is comfortable and welcomes you. Situated in a rural setting 10
minutes from Hastings city and 25 minutes from Napier, we are close to most
of the delights of Hawkes Bay. Within 15 minutes drive are 3 excellent 18 hole
golf courses (2 of these are less than 5 minutes from us) and we can
recommend them all being keen golfers ourselves.
There are of course many reputable wineries which welcome visitors.
The main Hawkes Bay Airport is Napier, 30 minutes away, but close to us is
the Hastings Aerodrome Which offers skydiving, scenic flights, and com-
mercial pilot training.
Visits to farm or orchard can be arranged. If all you need is rest and
relaxation, we are happy to have you and offer good plain food in a quiet
place.
Directions: *Please phone.*

Havelock North
Self-contained Accom B&B
Address: "The Birches",
39 Tanner Street, Havelock North,
Name: Margaret and Geoff Fuller
Telephone: (06) 877-8391
Beds: 2 Single (1 bedroom, guest bathroom)
Tariff: B&B $65 Double, $45 Single
Nearest Town: Havelock North

"The Birches" is situated 1 km from the centre of Havelock North with views towards the mountains.
Havelock North is a very pleasant residential and shopping area, surrounded by orchards and vineyards. The twin cities of Hastings and Napier are within easy driving distance (S.H.2)
Hawkes Bay is an attractive district offering a wide range of activities for visitors, and many types of commercial tours. We are a retired couple who have enjoyed travelling in New Zealand and overseas, and have special interests in the arts. Geoff is an artist/designer.
Our well appointed accommodation is separate and self-contained, with off street parking.
Continental or cooked breakfasts. Packed lunches on request (extra charge). No pets. No smoking inside please.
Directions: *From the centre of Havelock North follow Joll Road to the end, turn left into Tanner Street to number 39. The house is at the top of the drive up the hill. Please phone or write beforehand.*

Havelock North
Homestay
Address: 4 Waikonini Place, Havelock North
Name: Sonia and Martin Heesterman
Telephone: (06) 8774-190
Beds: 1 Double, 2 Single (2 bedrooms, guest bathroom)
Tariff: $25 per person, Children $15
Nearest Town: Hastings

Our spacious sunny home is situated in a quiet cul-de-sac with views to Napier and the coast and only a five minute walk to the Havelock North shopping centre.
We are in our early fifties, two of our three children are married and one lives away from home.
We have travelled extensively overseas using the Bed & Breakfast system. We endeavour to make our guests feel welcome in our home and our beautiful surrounding countryside.
We are close to the twin cities of Hastings and Napier and our area has much to offer the tourist.
We have an inground saline swimming pool, guest sitting room, and off-street parking is available. No smoking in the house.

Hastings / Havelock North
Farmstay
Address: Middle Road, Havelock North
Postal Address: Wharehau, R.D. 11, Hastings
Name: Ros Phillips
Telephone: (06) 877-4111
Beds: 7 Single (4 bedrooms, guest bathroom)
Tariff: B&B $25 Single, $15 Dinner, children 1/2 price (cot & high-chair available), Campervans welcome
Nearest Town: Hastings / Havelock North

About 20 minutes drive from Hastings, Havelock North or Waipawa will find you on a Hereford and Romney stud farm where a welcome awaits. Relax or take advantage of many local attractions. Close to the Tuki Tuki River for keen fisherfolk or a bush walk. Hawkes Bay offers the gannets, performing dolphins or the wine trails.

Havelock North
Farmhouse
Address: "Peak View" Farm, Middle Road, Havelock North
Name: Dianne and Keith Taylor
Telephone: (06) 877-7408
Beds: 1 Double, 2 Single 1 cot (2 bedrooms)
Tariff: B&B Double $55, Single $35; Dinner $15-($20, 3 course); Children half price; Washing facilities avail able
Nearest Town: Havelock North 1 km, Hastings 6 km

We own 25 acres of horticulture land and our house was built in 1900. Our family are the 4th generation to live here. We have recently added a second large living area.
Our home is surrounded by big lawns and trees with a lovely garden which we are presently extending.
One son is married, another son and daughter are presently travelling overseas so we are able to offer hospitality to visitors. We enjoy meeting people – our aim is to provide a pleasant and memorable stay.
We are interested in caravanning, tramping and bushwalks. Keith enjoys fishing, Dianne sewing, gardening and genealogy.
We offer comfortable accommodation with shared amenities. If you have dinner with us be assured of wholesome and generous meals with local wine (our compliments). Afterwards share an evening of relaxation and friendship or browse through our many New Zealand books. We can advise on travel throughout New Zealand from our own family experiences.
We are two minutes away from tennis and squash courts, indoor and outdoor pools. It is only a short drive to Te Mata Peak with panoramic views. Napier is a 20 minute drive away.
No smoking inside please.
Be welcomed with tea or coffee. If travelling by public transport we are happy to meet you for a minimal fee.
Directions: *Please phone.*

Havelock North
Homestay
Address: Please phone
Name: Mrs M Plested
Telephone: (06) 877-4169
Beds: 1 Double (1 bedroom)
Tariff: B&B $35 Double, $20 Single, children under 12 free, $15 Dinner

We have a tastefully furnished English cottage and gardens with pleasant walks to Havelock Village. Close to swimming pool and tennis courts and amongst the best vineyards and well known restaurants.
We have travelled widely and enjoy meeting people. Please no smoking in the house.
Directions: *Please phone.*

Waipukurau
Farmstay
Address: Hinerangi Station,
Hinerangi Road, R.D. 1, Waipukurau
Name: Caroline & Dan von Dadelszen
Telephone: (06) 855-8273
Beds: 1 Double, 2 Single (2 bedrooms, guest bathroom)
Tariff: B&B $60 Double, $35 Single, children 1/2 price, $20 Dinner.
Nearest Town: Takapau 11 km, Waipukurau 20 km.

We live on a 1500 acre station and farm sheep, cattle and deer and we are 6 km off State Highway 2.
We live in a large, comfortable, colonial homestead in which there is a full sized billiard table. There is a swimming pool and tennis court in our garden.
Our home has two guest rooms and a guest bathroom and plenty of extra beds available for children if the need arises as our three children are away at boarding school.
We would be happy to show you and explain whatever is happening on our farm when you come.
There are several large beaches about an hours drive from here and bush walks within half an hour. The Takapau Golf Club is 10 km away.
You may join us for dinner if you wish.
Directions: *please phone.*

Waipukurau
Farmhouse
Address: "Oakworth", Station Road, RD1, Waipukurau
Name: Marilyn and Trevor Jane
Telephone: (06) 855-8255
Beds: 2 Single (1 bedroom)
Tariff: Dinner, Bed and Breakfast – Double $85, Single $50; Children half
price; Campervans $20
Nearest Town: Waipukurau 16 km

*We are 7 km from the small country township of Takapau, and have a mixed
farm, with sheep and cropping, also a small flock of black sheep for spinning.
Our family consists of two working sons who live at home, plus two daugh-
ters who live away from home.*
*We have a large comfortable home, set in an attractive garden with swim-
ming pool. The guest room has twin beds.*
*We are in the midst of an intensive farming area and the rivers nearby are
well known for trout fishing.*
There are several bush walks in the locality.
Dinner with the family will be high quality New Zealand produce.
Directions: *Turn off State Highway 2 at Fraser Road, by "Richmonds" sign,
15 km south of Waipukurau Post Office. Travelling north, 4 km from
Takapau crossroads, turn left at railway line into Station Road, 4th house.*

Takapau
Farmhouse
Address: "Kilbirnie" Byrne Road, Takapau, Central Hawkes Bay
Name: Jill and John Grant
Telephone: (06) 8558- 325
Beds: 1 Double, 1 Single, Cot available (2 bedrooms)
Tariff: B&B Double $50, Single $30, Dinner $15; Campervans $15
Nearest Town: 25 km south of Waipukurau, 32 km north of Dannevirke

*As you enter or leave Hawkes Bay, with its enviable climate, wines, fresh
produce, and beaches, stop over with us while you plan your next move.
Within a few kms are craft, antique and knitwear shops, bushwalks, tennis,
squash and a picturesque 12-hole golf course. Our situation, just off Highway
Two between Wellington an Napier is peaceful but convenient for travellers
using Newmans or Mount Cook buses. We have Dorset Horn sheep and are
happy to demonstrate sheep shearing or other farm activities.*
*Guests have a separate sitting room with its own entrance, open fire, tv and
tea-making facilities. Also available are many books and magazines which
reflect our interest in gardening, cooking, farming, native plants and local
history.*
*We look forward to the opportunity to enrich your holiday while you
recharge your batteries.*
*Directions: Byrne Road is a left turn off Highway Two - 5 km south of
Highway 50 intersection at Takapau or from Wellington 10 km north of
Norsewood on right. A phone call would be appreciated.*

Takapau

Farmhouse
Address: "Tukipo Terraces",
Highway 50, Takapau
Name: Bay and Shona de Lautour
Telephone: (06) 855-6827 Fax (06) 8556-808
Beds: 1 Double, 1 Single (2 bedrooms, guest bathrooms)
Tariff: B&B Double $75, Single $50; Dinner, Bed and Breakfast – Double $112.50, Single $66.50 Children half single rate
Nearest Town: Waipukurau 20 km, Takapau P.O. and general store 8 km

Highway 50 is the alternate route between Takapau and Napier, through attractive Central Hawkes Bay farming country. We are situated approximately 5 km from the southern end on the banks of the Tukipo trout stream, midway between Wellington and Taupo.
Ours is a new home with self-contained guest wing comprising bedroom (with double bed and a single), sitting room and limited cooking facilities.
Beautiful mountain views form a background for farming scenes of deer, goats, sheep, cattle and cropping.
We can show you farming operations on a large scale or small. Lovely native bush walks nearby. Trout fishing day trips by arrangement with professional fisherman.
Members NZ Farm & Home Hosts Inc.
Directions: *If coming from the south drive 30 km north from Dannevirke, turn left onto Highway 50, travel 5 km. We are on the right, just at the end of a long plantation of mature pine trees, and about 500 m in from the road.*

Dannevirke

Homestay
Address: "Inverness", 4 Allan Street, Dannevirke.
Name: Graham & Sally Ramsden
Telephone: (06) 374-7220
Beds: 1 Double, 4 Single (3 bedrooms, guest bathroom off 1)
Tariff: B&B $60 Double, $35 Single, Dinner by arrangement
Nearest Town: Dannevirke

Historic "Inverness" is a picturesque English Cotswald style home, welcoming cosy and comfortable, set in 1/2 an acre cottage style garden with protected trees and a swimming pool.
We are actively involved in hill country sheep and cattle farming and a visit to our farm is easily arranged. Dannevirke and the surrounding area offer a

variety of rural pursuits including fishing, caving, bushwalks plus local crafts, wood-turning, pottery, spinning and weaving.

Directions: *To reach "Inverness" when coming from the North turn right into Cole Street (at North School), then left into Allan Street. When coming from the South, turn left into Miller Street or Allardice Street, then right into Queen Street which later becomes Allan Street.*

Dannevirke
Homestay
Address: 42 Victoria Avenue, Dannevirke
Name: "Glendane"
(Norma and Ian Pedersen)
Telephone: (0653) 46-453,
(06) 374-6453 from Dec 91
Beds: 1 Double, 3 Single (2 bedrooms, guest bathroom)
Tariff: B&B Double $55, Single $35; Dinner $15
Nearest Town: 1 km west of Dannevirke

We have a lovely home approximately ten years old. It is set in one acre of beautiful garden and being on the outskirts of town has a rural view with our Ruahine Ranges in the background. It is very quiet and restful, a great place to break your journey.

We have two bedrooms available, one with two single beds and one with one double and one single and you have your own bathroom and toilet.

You may enjoy dinner with us or bed and breakfast only if you prefer.

Apart from our interests in gardening and farming we make from pure natural wool our own handspun, handmade woollen goods – jerseys, vests, hats, scarves, etc and these original garments are for sale.

Manawatu

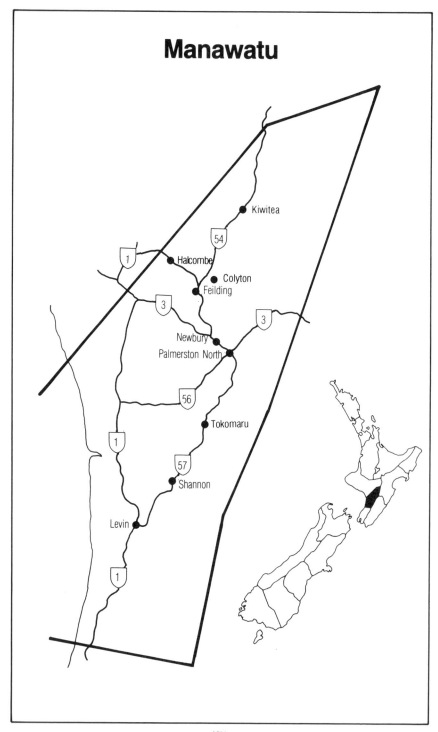

Kiwitea, Feilding

Homestay
Address: "Tirohanga", Kiwitea, RD 7, Feilding
Name: Shirley and John Bird
Telephone: (06) 328 9866
Beds: 4 Single (2 bedrooms, guest bathroom)
Tariff: B&B Double $60, Single $35, Children $15, Dinner $15; Campervans $15
Nearest Town: Feilding

We have 5 acres of land, named "Tirohanga" meaning "View", with a large garden and wonderful views, south to Kapiti Island, and east to the Ruahine and Tararua Ranges. At times we have fabulous sunsets.

We have travelled overseas, especially in Britain, where John's father lived for 21 years before coming to New Zealand to live. In Britain we used bed and breakfast accommodation and decided to open our home for same. Three sons, two daughters (all married) and sixteen grandchildren make up our family. John enjoys helping out on the two Hill Country farms we own with our sons. We could arrange visits to these sheep and beef cattle farms if interested.

John plays bowls at the local green at Kimbolton, and does wood turning as a hobby. I enjoy knitting, reading, jigsaw puzzles, and garden club as well as gardening.

We live 9 km from the well known Cross Hills Gardens, also Kimbolton Rhododendron Park. We are 20 minutes north of Feilding, 2 hours to Wellington and less than 2 hours to Ohakune.

Directions: *23 km north of Feilding PO on SH54. At Cheltenham travel towards Kimbolton, we are 9 km north of Cheltenham.*

Halcombe

Farmstay
Address: Tokorangi Rd., Halcombe
Postal: Bandon, RD 9, Feilding
Name: Richard and Alison Fraser
Telephone: (06) 328-8778
Beds: 4 single (2 bedrooms, guest bathroom)
Tariff: B&B Double $80, Single $40, Children half price, Dinner $20
Nearest Town: 40 km from Palmerston North, 20 km from Bulls, 20 km from Feilding

We have a 32 ha. deer farm on gentle, rolling country just above the river terraces of the Rangitikei River only 15 minutes drive from State Highway 1. Our cedar, ranch-style house looks north to Mt Ruapehu and the garden includes 2 ha. of native bush. As we are close to State Highway 1 and about 2 hours from Wellington we can offer a convenient and relaxing overnight stop with no traffic noise but plenty of bird song. From the house you can watch the deer grazing, 50 m away at the edge of the lawn.

Please phone for directions

159

Colyton, Feilding

Farmstay
Address: "Hiamoe", Waiata Colyton, Feilding
Name: John & Toos Cousins
Telephone: (06) 328-7713 (anytime)
Beds: 1 Double, 2 Single (2 bedrooms, guest bathroom)
Tariff: B&B Double $60, Single $35, children under 14 half price, Dinner $15, Campervans $20
Nearest Town: Feilding (15 minutes), Palmerston North (25 mins)

Our colonial style home is set in a large garden with views of the Ruahine Ranges to the East. Sheep, beef and deer farming is our main activity however we have many other interests and as Holland is Toos recent homeland we are very accustomed to travel and hosting visitors in our home. We look forward to giving you a warm welcome at "Hiamoa" (Maori for sleepy hollow and during your stay it is our aim to make you feel part of a home away from home.
Our location near Feilding places us about half way between Wellington (2 1/2 hours to the south) and Taupo (3 hours to the north)
Directions: *15 minutes drive from Feiding via Colyton but please phone.*

Feilding

Homestay
Address: 5 Wellington Street, Feilding
Name: Beryl Walker
Telephone: (06) 323-4409
Beds: 4 single (2 bedrooms)
Tariff: B&B Double $50, Single $30, Children half price
Nearest Town: 1 km east of Feiding P.O.

A comfortable and sunny family home with open fires in winter. Guests should feel free to use all family rooms and facilities as family members. A chance to catch up with your laundry. A choice of breakfast timed to suit your travel arrangements. Cot and highchair available.
Feilding, only 15 minutes from Highway 1 from Sanson if travelling south or through Rongatea is the centre of a prosperous farming area with many places of natural beauty within reach. It has easy access to the East Coast and is only 15 minutes from the city of Palmerston North. Manfield Racecourse is situated at Feilding.
Feilding has an interesting shopping area and several good restaurants, licensed and unlicensed.
For further directions please ring.

Palmerston North
Homestay
Address: 19 Phoenix Avenue, Hokowhitu, Palmerston North
Name: Vic and Judy Young
Telephone: (06) 356-1156
Beds: 1 Double, 1 Single (2 bedrooms)
Tariff: B&B Double $55, Single $35, Children half price, Dinner $15;
Campervan facilities

We are a couple with a grown family living away from home and live in a pleasant suburb near to parks and fifteen minutes walk from the city centre. We have a cat and a Newfoundland dog.
The main guest room has a comfortable double bed with electric blanket and the bathroom adjoining has a spa bath.
Although a vegetarian household we will provide a meat meal if you wish, also breakfast of your choosing.
We would be happy to meet plane, bus or train.
Directions: *From south (Massey) side, turn off Fitzherbert Avenue right into College Street then take third right (just before Victoria Avenue intersection) into Phoenix Avenue, which is a cul de sac. No. 19 is near the end on the left.*

Newbury, Palmerston North
Farmstay
Address: No 5 RD, Palmerston North
Name: Keith and Margaret Morriss
Telephone: (06) 354-8961
Beds: 1 Double, 2 Single (2 bedrooms)
Tariff: B&B Double $60, Single $35; Dinner $20; Children half price
Nearest Town: 8 km north of Palmerston North on State Highway 3

We enjoy country living, - a short distance from Palmerston North.
A friendly welcome awaits you at "Grinton", our 100-year-old home with family connections with its namesake in Yorkshire, England.
Of our three daughters two are married, this allows us space to offer guests a comfortable stay in pleasant surroundings.
Farming operations consist mainly of beef fattening and calf rearing. Large scale dairying, a llama farm operation, equestrian centre are also in the area.
We both enjoy travel and welcome the stimulation of overseas guests, ensuring them a sampling of some of New Zealand's fine food and complimentary wine and pre-dinner drinks.
Local scenic drives include Massey University, the Esplanade Gardens and trecently opened Pacific Japanese College. A pleasant day trip in Oct/Nov to the world-renowned Cross-Hills Rhododendron Gardens at Kimbolton, or picturesque Pohangina Valley
Our interests include travel, tramping, trout fishing, golf, the Lions Club, music, floral art and dried flowers.

Palmerston North
Homestay
Address: 59 Bryant Street,
Palmerston North
Name: Alison & Jaime
Telephone: (06) 358-9409
Beds: 3 Single (2 bedrooms)
Tariff: B&B $50 Double, $30 Single, $15 Dinner (by arrangement)
Nearest Town: Palmerston North

Our smokefree home is in a quiet street in the centre of the city. It is only one block away from the Sports Stadium, the showgrounds and the Rugby museum and less than ten minutes from the Lido indoor / outdoor swimming centre, Ongley Park sportsgrounds, the Eslanade gardens, walkways and running trails, Massey University and the Awapuni Racetrack.
We are keen athletes with involvement to national and international level. Most of our living is done in the outdoors and we have many contacts for sporting activities, outdoor adventure and recreation.
Our 60 yr old, character home, with modern facilities, is conducive to relaxation and comfort. It is a warm home, gas heated in winter and cooled in summer with fresh air and shade. It has 2 showers and 2 toilets.
The backyard is private, quiet, treelined and picturesque with trees yielding grapefruit, oranges, lemons and mandarins in season. The barbeque is frequently used. Children welcome and a baby's cot is available.

Palmerston North
Homestay
Address: "Kilkenn Down",
143 Victoria Ave, Palmerston North
Name: Keay & Ken McCormack
Telephone: (06) 357-3491
Beds: 3 Single (2 bedrooms, guest bathroom)
Tariff: B&B $55 Double, $35 Single, children 1/2 price, $15 Dinner,
Campervans $20
Nearest Town: Palmerston North

We enjoy welcoming visitors to our 65 year old character home in pleasant surroundings, close to Palmerston North city (10 mins walk). We have a spacious twin bedroom with comfortable beds, electric blankets, and tea / coffee making facilities. Also a small bedroom with single bed.
Our interests are wide and varied - travel, music, theatre and sport. An evening meal is available (prior notice if possible please). Palmerston North is a University and educational city with many cultural activities as well as lovely gardens and walkways.
We have ample off-street parking at rear of house. Campervans are also welcome - electric hook-up available. We are happy to meet any public transport.
Directions: *From the city square travel south in Fitzherbert Avenue to College Street, turn left into College Street and travel approximately 1/2 km, then left into Victoria Avenue. Look for the palm tree in the front garden.* ------

162

Palmerston North
Farmstay
Address: Kelvin Grove Road, RD10, Palmerston North
Name: Terry and Barbara Fryer
Telephone: (063) 54 1295
Beds: 1 Double, 2 Single (2 bedrooms, guest bathroom)
Tariff: B&B Double $60, Single $35; Dinner $20; Children half price;
Campervans $15

*If you are looking for good company, clean, attractive accommodation, a
country setting only a few minutes from Palmerston North township and
good food please give us a call.*
*The house was built 18 years ago on 11 acres. The garden is approximately
one acre and contains many roses of the old-fahioned and the modern types.
On the remaining acreage we run sheep.*
*Transport to and from Palmerston North or the airport will be provided if
required.*
Directions:*There are so many ways you may approach Palmerston North
that it may be advisable to phone. In brief we are on Kelvin Grove Road. In
the fourth dip after Stoney Creek Road coming from Palmerston North along
Tremaine Avenue. At our gateway there are three letterboxes (Jolly, Fryer,
anon.) and we are the first (repeat first) drive immediately after the three
letterboxes.*

Tokomaru, Palmerston North
Homestay in the country
Address: Tokomaru Road, Tokomaru,
RD4, Palmerston North
Name: Claire and Austin Macready
Telephone: (06) 329 8840
Beds: 2 Single (1 bedroom with ensuite)

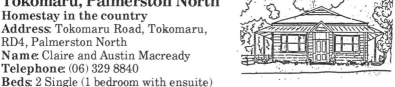

Tariff: B&B Double $50, Single $25, Dinner $15
Nearest Town: South of Palmerston North on SH 57

*Our 90 year old homestead with large verandah has been carefully redeco-
rated by my wife and I. The guest room has its own cosy lounge with wood
burning stove, ensuite and tea & coffee making facilities. The bedroom has
two comfortable single beds with eiderdowns. A second spare bedroom with a
single bed is available if required. Breakfast of your choice is with the family
in our large kitchen / dining area.*
*Tokomaru is a small farming community situated in the foothills of the
Tararuas overlooking the Manawatu. We are adjacent to the well known
Steam Engine Museum with its display of static and live steam engines. A
quiet stroll to the peaceful reserve on the Tokomaru River can be enjoyed, or
perhaps a gumboot equipped expedition around our ten acre patch.*
*We are a middle aged couple with two sons, John and Andrew, one at uni-
versity and one overseas, We often travel abroad and we welcome the opor-
tunity to meet visitors from home and abroad.*
Directions: *From Palmerston North or Levin, Highway 57, the main route
from Wellington to Hawkes Bay passes Massey University – Intercity and
Newmans buses use this route. We are 500m from the Tokomaru village on
the road to Horseshoe Bend.*

Shannon

Farmstay
Address: Hennessey Road, Shannon
Name: Thaddeus's Place
– Colin and Lynn Collecutt
Telephone: (06) 362-7599, 362-7623
Beds: 1 Double, 4 Single (3 bedrooms, guest bathroom)
Tariff: B&B Double $75, Single $40; Dinner $25; Children half price
Nearest Town: 2 km to Shannon, 16 km to Levin, 32 km to Palmerston North

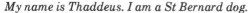

My name is Thaddeus. I am a St Bernard dog.
We have a new Portalok home set in ten hectares of riverland situated below the Tararua Ranges with the Mangahao river meandering through the property.
Colin is the local chemist. His interests are tennis, squash and music. Lynn runs the farmlet. Her interests are animals, gardening, cordon-bleu cooking and music. She trains me and eight of my other farm animal friends for my animal show which we perform on request for groups of 20 or more.
We have a large garden and there is a lawn tennis court. Colin loves having a game with the guests (actually he's not bad for his age!).
The farmlet raises vealer calves, mohair goats, sheep and has a palomino quarter horse. I live outside!
In the Tararua Ranges within three minutes from here there are horse treks, and the historical power station (still working).
The Shannon Golf Club and Bowling Club welcome visitors.
Within 30 minutes drive there are three beaches and Palmerston North (New Zealand's Rose City).
Lynn and Colin enjoy having guests and do their best to make their stay a happy one.

Levin
Homestay
Address: 197 Bath Street, Levin
Name: Robin and Avis Barrie
Telephone: (06) 368-6199 (bus),
368-7266 (home)
Beds: 4 Single (2 bedrooms, guest bathroom)
Tariff: B&B Double $50, Single $25, Children half price; Dinner $15;
Campervans welcome
Nearest Town: Levin. We are adjacent to State Highway 1, situated one
minute from town centre. Wellington 78 km to south (1 hr 15 min),
Palmerston North 46 km to north (35 minutes)

*Levin has an attractive shopping centre, is the hub of a rural farming and
horticulture area and is New Zealand`s second largest textile centre having
many light industries. The Horticultural Research Station is adjacent. The
west coast beaches and the Tararua Forest Park are both five minutes travelling from Levin. Easy bush walks abound. The superb Moutere Golf Links
are approximately 5 minutes by car.*
*We are a family of three, two of the family are now away for tertiary educa-
tion. We are Rotarians and our business interests are Chartered Accountancy
and Sharebroking.*
*Our home has a large and attractive garden _ the guest room two single beds
with own bathroom and toilet. A second room with two single beds is
available (share facilities).*
*We welcome you to share family dinner with us. Bed and breakfast only if
required.*
Directions: *Turn off State Highway 1 in centre of town into Bath Street and
500m towards hills.*

Levin
Homestay
Address: Roberts Place,
Arapaepae Road, Levin
Name: Alec and Noeline Dalton
Telephone: (06) 367-9674
Beds: 2 Single (1 bedroom, guest bathroom)
Tariff: B&B Double $55, Single $35, Dinner available if required
Nearest Town: Levin

*We are a retired couple living in a modern home set in its own delightful
garden of one acre on State Highway 57 – the main route from Palmerston
North to Levin which itself is only one and a half hours drive from
Wellington.*
*Situated in horticultural country but only a few minutes' drive from the
shopping area of Levin, our property is well laid out with lawns, native and
exotic trees and we have ample off-street parking.*
For those interested there is a games room with pool, table tennis and darts.
Directions: *Two hundred metres north of the Queen Street intersection and
on the west side of Arapaepae Road.*

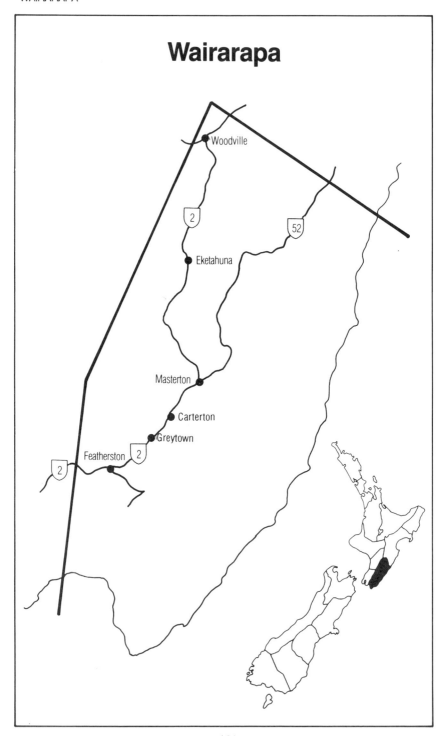

Wairarapa

Eketahuna
Farmstay
Address: "Tidsfordriv",
RD 3, Eketahuna
Name: Ted and Glenys Hansen
Telephone: (06) 375-8474 evenings
(24 hours notice if possible, please)
Beds: 2 Single (1 bedroom)
Tariff: B&B Double $60, Single $35, Dinner $15
Nearest Town: Eketahuna 10 km, Masterton 50 km

It will be worth your while to divert off the main highway to visit us on our 700 acre hill country sheep farm. We are the third generation to live on our farm. Angora goats, black and coloured sheep can also be seen when Ted and Colleen (landgirl-daughter) give you a tour around the farm in a comfortable 4WD vehicle.

Our home is 70 years old, has recently been modernised and is warm and comfortable. The guest room has two single beds. You may have family dinner with us or if you prefer only bed and breakfast - we can provide the breakfast of your choice.

All the family are active members in a waterfowl conservation group - Ducks Unlimited (NZ) Inc. There are many species of waterfowl to be seen in aviaries and on ponds.

We recommend a visit to the National Wildlife Centre at Mt Bruce, just 23 km south on State Highway 2. Glenys is involved with the Centre and is more than happy to talk about the work that is being done there.

Directions: *Turn off SH2 south end of Eketahuna and follow road to Alfredton for 10 km. Good sealed road. Farm name on gate.*

Woodville
Farmstay
Address: River Road, Hopelands, Woodville RD1
Name: Chris and Jo Coats
Telephone: (06) 376 4521
Beds: 4 Single (2 bedrooms)
Tariff: B&B $30 per person, Children half price; Dinner $14
Nearest Town: 12 km North of Woodville on SH 2

We are sheep and cattle farmers on a hill country farm beside the beautiful Manawatu River which is noted for its trout fishing.

The family have fled the nest but return from time to time, seeking quiet from their busy lives, two of them still attending university.

Depending on the time of year, farming activities of possible interest to tourists may be in progress, i.e. mustering, shearing, etc. and you will be very welcome to participate.

Directions: *If travelling on Highway 2 between Woodville and Dannevirke, take the Hopelands Road and follow it until crossing the Manawatu River (6 km). Turn right heading towards Pahiatua, and the fourth house (blue) is where 'Welcome' is on the mat.*

Masterton

Homestay
Address: 2 Keir Crescent, Masterton
Name: David E. Barnes
Telephone: (059) 81-567 (home), 82-345 (bus.)
Beds: 2 Single (1 bedroom)
Tariff: B&B Double $50, Single $30, Children half price; Dinner by arrangement $15
Nearest Town: 41 km south of Eketahuna, 100 km NE of Wellington on State Highway 2

I live in a quiet street which is only 10 minutes walk from our lovely Queen Elizabeth Park and 15–20 minutes walk from the Masterton town centre.
Day trips to Mount Holdsworth, Castlepoint beach, Cape Palliser and the Putangirua Pinnacles, National Wildlife Centre at Mt Bruce, glowworm caves near Martinborough and even Wellington by train can be easily made from Masterton.
I enjoy travel and have recently travelled extensively overseas and within New Zealand.
Bathroom / toilet facilities are on a shared basis.
Directions: *From the north, turn left into Third Street, proceed to the end then turn right into Totara Street; Keir Cres is then first turn left. From the south pass through the town centre heading north on State Highway 2 to Woodville. turn right at Second Street., proceed to the end then turn left into Totara Street, Keir Crescent is second turn right.*

Masterton

Farmstay + Self-Contained Accommodation
Address: Harefield, 147 Upper Plain Road, Masterton
Name: Robert and Marion Ahearn
Telephone: (059) 84-070. (06) 377-4070 from Dec 91
Beds: 1 Double, 1 Single (1 bedroom, guest bathroom); 2 Double and 2 Single in detached, fully equipped, self-contained flat
Tariff: B&B Double $55, Single $30, Children half price, Flat $20 per adult self-catering; Dinner $15; Campervans $15
Nearest Town: Masterton PO 5 km

We are farmers whose family have all left home. Ten years ago we built our cedar house on 13 acres, 5 km from the Post Office and 1 km from Bypass Road.
Our guest room with its own bathroom is well away from ours and the kitchen. A cottage garden surrounds the house and flat, well back from the road.
We look out on to the beautiful Tararua mountains and paddocks with sheep, cattle, deer and free ranging red hens which give us eggs for breakfast!
We have been home hosting for some years and have ourselves been guests in Europe, Australia and New Zealand.
Our interests include travelling and travellers' tales, workshop inventions, Lions Int, wildlife (animals), reading, tramping, walking, gardening, Rose Society, aerobics, painting (oils and watercolour) Probus Club and spinning.
We would be pleased to pick up from the bus depot, railway station or Wairarapa Airlines.
If you stay in the flat you can choose to be self-catering or arrange dinner and

breakfast with us. Guests staying in the house can have dinner or just breakfast. Complimentary tea and coffee at any time. Excellent restaurants 8 minutes away.
Reductions for longer stays.
We are half an hour's drive to the National Wildlife Centre and less than two hour's drive from the Inter-Island Ferry.
We do not smoke — you may.

Lansdowne, Masterton
Homestay
Address: 65 Titoki Street, Lansdowne, Masterton
Name: Gordon and Doreen McNeilage
Telephone: (059) 83-817 After Nov 91 (06) 377 3817
Beds: 1 Double, 2 Single (2 bedrooms, guest bathroom)
Tariff: B&B Double $50, Single $30; Dinner $15; Children half price

We are a family of four, plus one sleepy cat. We are fortunate to live in the beautiful suburb of Lansdowne, about one mile north of the town of Masterton.
Our home is nearly fifty years old and we have altered and improved it to give us more living space. It is surrounded by gardens and has an outdoor court area.
You may have family dinner with us or, if you prefer, only bed and breakfast.
Masterton has a lovely park, attractive shops and restaurants. It is a very appealing town and we wish to extend warm, friendly hospitality.

Carterton
Homestay
Address: "Kowhai Cottage",
1 Rexwood Street, Carterton
Telephone: (0593) 7292
Beds: 2 Single (1 Bedroom)
Tariff: B&B Double $55, Dinner $15, Children half price
Nearest Town: Carterton 5 mins walk, Masterton 15 mins by car

Jim and Carole invite you to share with us warm Kiwi hospitality. Our home is warm and immaculately kept. We are self sufficient with our hot water supply, with a 7 panelled solar water heater made by Jim. He is an A Grade motor engineer and does all our maintenance around our home. Carole's hobbies include embroidery, music, garding and is an experienced cake decorator. We have three adult children - an engineer, a clerical worker and our youngest son who still lives at home is an apprentice jeweller. Carterton is very central to all areas in the Wairarapa, with Wellington City being only 1 1/2 hours scenic train journey or travel by car. Also 45 mins from National Wildlife Centre, 1 1/2 hours to our beaches and historic areas. Masterton offers a beautiful park, swimming complex, crafts, picnic areas.
Being non-smokers ourselves we thank you for not smoking in the house. Tea or coffee on arrival included - Please phone.
Directions: *Rexwood Street is situated about the centre of the township. It is lined with Kowhai trees and there is a red letter box on the corner and is just off the main Highway Two.*

Greytown
Homestay
Address: 40 Kuratawhiti Street, Greytown
Name: Dinah and Max Edridge
Telephone: (0553) 49942
After 29 Nov 1991 (06) 304 9942
Beds: 2 double (1 bedsitting room with ensuite and tea making facilities, and 1 double bedroom) large children's room sleeps 4
Tariff: B&B Double $55, Single $35, Dinner $15, Children $15, under 5 free

... A touch of country ...
... A place of peace ...
Set in 1.6 h amongst historic trees, our pre-1900 brick homestead fully restored, with sunny verandahs complements the generous welcome and care enjoyed by our guests.
Facilities have been specially designed for elderly or disabled.
Our five elder children are now mostly away from home. Our ten year old son shares the delights of our property with his dog and cat, a donkey, some sheep, a trampoline and hot spa.
Every season brings its special delights as you enjoy the picturesque beauty of the southern Wairarapa. Within short distances you can enjoy gentle bush and river walks or serious tramping, canoeing, tennis, cycling (bikes available), swimming, orchards, berry picking, craft and wine making areas, beautiful gardens, surfing, fishing.
We will enjoy sharing your company but will respect your desire for privacy if you wish to 'just be' and relax.
Directions: *please write or phone.*

One of the differences between staying at a hotel and staying at a B&B is that you don't hug the hotel staff when you leave.

Greytown
Guest House
Address: "Bright House",
129 Main Street, Greytown
Name: Paul and Karen Ratcliffe
Telephone: (0553) 48047
After Nov 91 (06) 304 8047
Beds: 1 Double with guest bathroom
Tariff: **B&B** $125 Double

Country charm, comfort and delicious home-baked breakfasts.
Our home has that special appeal being one of New Zealand's oldest inland homes built 1856, with the added bonus of having two of the first Arbour Day trees planted on our front lawn. (beautiful white magnolia and a double pink camellia)
There's lots of cushion filled furniture on our sunny verandah's and comfy outside furniture in our cottage garden for you to enjoy.
Inside our home has an inviting atmosphere with the charm of the past. Your bedroom has a soft nostalgic look - masses of frilled pillows, fluffy quilts, open fire, freshly cut flowers, private bathroom (handmade New Zealand soaps and bubble bath) plus lots more goodies for your enjoyment!
Tariffs include full home-baked breakfast, New Zealand wine, beer or fruit juice on arrival. Freshly ground coffee, tea and home-baked biscuits available at any time.

Featherston
Farmstay
Address: "Waituna", East West Access Road, R.D. 3 Featherson.
Name: Irwin & Kay Luttrell
Telephone: (06) 307-7743
Beds: 1 Double, 2 Single (2 bedrooms, guest bathroom)
Tariff: B&B $60 Double, $35 Single, children 1/2 price, Dinner $25 (3 course with wine)
Nearest Town: Featherson or Martinborough (approx 26 km from either)

We are a farming family with three adult children who all live away from home now. We like meeting people and love to have guests to stay with us. Our home is spacious and quiet with room for our guests to relax. There is a choice of two bedrooms, one with a double bed, one with two single beds. The bathroom is adjacent. Complimentary tea, coffee, milo and home-made biscuits are in each bedroom. I serve breakfast at any time to suit guests. I like to make a picnic style lunch which can be eaten inside or in our large garden. "Waituna" is in a central location to visit several beaches, a seal colony, craft shops, museums, go fishing, walking in the forest park, canoeing or a lovely place to just relax in. At the end of the day we serve a three course dinner with wine or fruit juice which we like to eat with our guests.

171

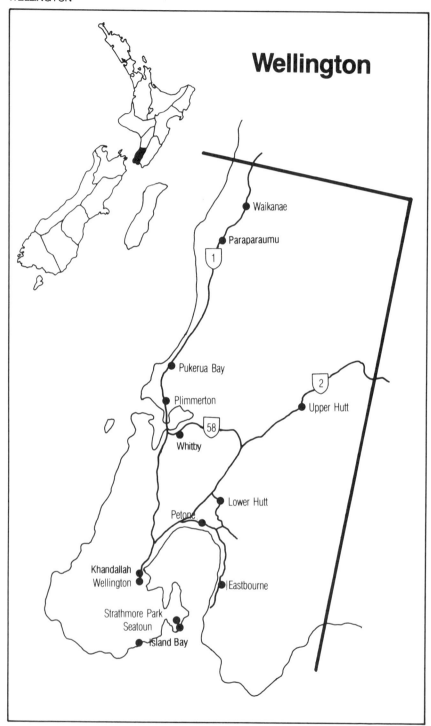

Wellington

Waikanae

Paraparaumu

1

Pukerua Bay

Plimmerton

2 Upper Hutt

58

Whitby

Lower Hutt

Petone

Khandallah
Wellington

Eastbourne

Strathmore Park
Seatoun

Island Bay

Waikanae

Homestay
Address: "Waimoana", 63 Kakariki Grove, Waikanae
Name: Ian and Phyllis Stewart
Telephone: (04) 293-7158
Beds: 2 Double, 2 Single (2 bedrooms, each with private facilities)
Tariff: B&B Double $80, Single $45; 3 course dinner plus cheese board $25 (with complimentary sherry and wine)
Nearest Town: 58 km north of Wellington on State Highway 1

We are a recently retired couple. We have two adult daughters who work and live in the city and come home when they can. Both of them speak German and French. We are non-smokers.
Waikanae is a delightful township, popular for holidays because of its climate. Our centrally-heated home is newly completed and spacious, designed for comfort and warmth. We have only two guest rooms, allowing a friendly, personal atmosphere. Each room has both a queen-size and a single bed and its own basin, shower and toilet. They share a spacious balcony for admiring the fantastic views. An internal swimming pool and conservatory are incorporated as a central part of the living area. Relax around the pool and sun-deck.
Adjacent to our home is a scenic bush reserve with native birds. Enjoy a bush walk before dinner.
Beach and river, bird sanctuary, bush walks, pottery and crafts, Lindale Model Farm and Southward's Car Museum all within easy distance. No pets please.
Directions: *Please telephone.*

Ask your hosts for local information. They are
your own personal travel agent and guide.

173

Waikanae
Homestay
Address: "Ashlea", 7A Andrew Street, Waikanae
Name: Don & Margaret Champion
Telephone: (04) 293 7349
Beds: 2 Single (1 bedroom)
Tariff: B&B $50 Double, $30 Single, $15 Dinner
Nearest Town: Waikanae (10 mins walk to shops), Wellington 45 minute drive.

Our modern home has space for privacy, if wanted, and the twin bedroom opens out onto a conservatory which leads to a pleasant garden with views to the bush clad hills behind Waikanae, and also makes a pleasant place to relax after a busy day. Electric blankets are provided on the comfortable beds. We are keen gardeners and enjoy walking, bowls and travel. The Kapiti Coast caters for all tastes with safe beaches, heated covered swimming pools, fishing, bush walks, craft and pottery, shopping malls, Southward's Car Museum (a must to see), Lindale Farm Complex, Nga Manu Bird Sanctuary. Restaurants abound in the area - but as I enjoy cooking we are pleased to provide extra meals in a friendly relaxed atmosphere, and also an early breakfast for travellers catching the Ferry.
We have travelled throughout New Zealand and enjoy welcoming people to our home and sharing their experiences. Complimentary tea, coffee and biscuits. We are non-smokers.
Directions: *Ring after 5:00 pm or early morning.*

If you find something missing that you are accustomed to, simply ask you hosts for it.

Waikanae
Homestay
Address: Please phone
Name: Madeline Reid
Telephone: (058) 33-689
Beds: 1 Double, 2 Single (2 bedrooms)
Tariff: B&B Double $55, Single $30, Children half price; Dinner $20
Nearest Town: 60 km north of Wellington, 20 km south of Otaki on State Highway 1

My home is situated in quiet surroundings being in the garden area of Waikanae, halfway between Waikanae village and Waikanae beach. I am of English heritage (from North Cornwall) and have lived in New Zealand off and on since 1953. I am a widow with a family of two who are now pursuing their own careers in nursing and film-making respectively.
Waikanae and district has a variety of interesting attractions - fishing, boating, a beautiful beach, arts and crafts, bush walks, agricultural displays, and much more.
I do request that my guests be non-smokers.
Directions: *Please phone.*

Paraparaumu Beach
Guest House
Address: Barnacles Seaside Inn, 3 Marine Parade, Paraparaumu Beach
Name: Kay Ellingham
Telephone: (04) 298-6106
Beds: 14 Double and 14 Single
Tariff: B&B $50 Double, $25 Single, Bed only $15
Nearest Town: Wellington 50 Kms

Barnacles is a lovely old guesthouse which was built in 1923 and has been lovingly restored to its former glory with old oak furnishings and historical photographs of the area. Well worth a stay just to look at all the memorabilia. Barnacles is situated on the most prominent site in Paraparaumu Beach with fantastic views over the sea to the South Island and Kapiti Island. Paraparaumu Beach is a very safe swimming and boating beach and fishing is a favourite pastime around Kapiti Island which is four miles off the coast. Guest rooms all have single beds, electric blankets and a handbasin. Bathrooms are just along the hall and laundry facilities are free. There is also a small kitchen available and also a TV lounge.

Barnacles has a licensed restaurant which operates on Friday, Saturday and Sunday evenings and Sunday lunch.

Directions: *50 Kms North of Wellington - turn left at the lights at Paraparaumu and follow Kapiti Road down two miles (Barnacles on left).*

Plimmerton
Homestay
Address: 12 Roys Road, Plimmerton, Wellington
Name: Cren & Rae Collins
Telephone: (04) 2331-367
Beds: 3 Single (2 bedrooms, guest bathroom)
Tariff: B&B $50 Double, $30 Single, children 1/2 price, $15 Dinner
Nearest Town: Porirua, (10 mins drive South)

We are retired sheepfarmers with a grown up family of three. We enjoy reading, watching TV, tramping, croquet and bridge.
Our house is homely and is set on the hill overlooking Karehana Bay, half an hour's drive from Wellington. We have a great view out to Mana Island and Cook Strait. It is a fifteen minute walk down to Plimmerton Village whose shops provide food and essentials. There is good swimming on the safe beaches and rocks to explore.
Directions: *Please phone*

Whitby
Homestay
Address: 4 The Companionway, Whitby
Name: Nola and Vance Russell
Telephone: (04) 234-8851
Beds: 1 Double, 2 Single (2 bedrooms)
Tariff: B&B Double $55, Single $30, Dinner $16, Campervans $15 for 2, $5 each extra
Nearest Town: 8kms from Porirua, 25km from Wellington

Whitby village is situated 3 kms east of the Paremata bridge, on the Pauatahanui Inlet, set in rolling countryside with a network of interesting walkways.
Our home offers a quiet, comfortable sunny stopover featuring a sheltered private patio and an interesting studio wing.
Centrally located for sightseeing, being equally 25 km from Wellington City, Hutt Valley and Paraparaumu, also well placed for travellers joining or leaving the Cook Strait Ferry. Several Golf Courses are within easy distance. For bird lovers a sanctuary with hides 5 km from our home has a wide range of species.
Vance is a full-time artist, a realist working mainly in watercolour and he welcomes visitors into the studio.
Your hosts are ardent travellers and we enjoy sharing our home with fellow travellers and meeting people from different countries.

Petone
Homestay
Address: 1 Bolton Street, Petone
Name: Anne and Reg Cotter
Telephone: (04) 568 6960
Beds: 2 Single (1 bedroom)
Tariff: B&B $25 per person, Dinner $15 per person
Nearest Town: Lower Hutt 5 km, Wellington 8 km

We have an older type home by the beach which we have modernised. It has three bedrooms, a large lounge, diningroom, kitchen, bathroom with shower and bath.
We are two minutes from the museum on the beach, two minutes from the shops and the bus route into the city. A restaurant is only two minutes away also.
We have three children, two girls and a son who have left home.
We offer two single beds with room for one extra or a child's cot which is available. Children would be very welcome as we have several children's play things in the back yard.
Laundry facilities available.
My husband is a keen amateur ornithologist and he goes to the Chatham Islands with an expedition trying to find the nesting place of the Taiko _ a rare sea bird which is on the endangered list. We are keen to show any folk interested in birds the local places of interest.
He is also a member of the genealogy society. We have an old 1937 Austin 10 Car and belong to the Austin Vintage Club.
We are 10 minutes by road to the Picton ferry.

Some homes share the bathroom, others have bathrooms
exclusively for guests - they are indicated in the listing.

Eastbourne
Self-Contained Accommodation
Address: Please phone
Name: Carole and John Fisher
Telephone: (04) 687-549
Beds: 1Double (1bedroom, guest bathroom)
Tariff: B&B Double $60, Single $40, Dinner $15
Nearest Town: Lower Hutt 10 km, Wellington 20 km

Eastbourne is a very pleasant seaside village 20 minutes drive from Wellington. Our home in York Bay has a lovely view of the harbour and is close to the bus route into Lower Hutt and the city.
My husband is a computer consultant and we live upstairs with our two cats. Downstairs we have a small self-contained flat which consists of one double bedroom, lounge, kitchen and shower. Non-smokers preferred. You are most welcome to join us for dinner or there are good restaurants nearby.
Directions: please phone.

Eastbourne
Homestay
Address: 27 Marine Drive,
Mahina Bay, Eastbourne
Name: Janete and Jim Thomas
Telephone: (04) 562-8990
Beds: 2 Single (1 bedroom, guest bathroom)
Tariff: B&B Double $60, Single $40, Dinner $20
Nearest Town: Wellington city 20 mins by car or ferry

We are in an ideal situation for you to stay on your way to or from the South Island. Our home is right beside the ocean, with a marvellous view of Wellington which is only twenty minutes away.
Your room is a large bed sitting room (with television and phone) and the beds have electric blankets, woollen underlays and fluffy duvets. French doors open onto the garden with the sea just beyond.
You are welcome to use the laundry.
Breakfast is usually home made muesli, fresh fruit, muffins, and freshly brewed coffee.
We have a small publishing business and also restore old houses. We love music of all kinds, theatre, anything old, and our city.
Directions: *please phone.*

Khandallah, Wellington
Homestay
Address: 10A Izard Road, Khandallah, Wellington
Name: Genevieve and Peter Young
Telephone: (04) 795-036 Home, 774-444 Peter (work)
Beds: 5 Single, (3 bedrooms, guest bathroom, spa pool, pool table)
Tariff: B&B Double $60, Single $30; Dinner by arrangement

We are a couple who enjoy relaxing and meeting people and our particular interests are travel, sport, food, wine, and the Arts. Our family of 3 girls have left home, and while we both work, we are able to take time off to show guests our beautiful harbour city. Khandallah is a hillside suburb handy to all the attractions of the capital, with a village atmosphere and a ten minute bus or train ride to town.
We look forward to making your stay an enjoyable one.
Directions: *please phone and we will arrange to pick you up.*

Wellington City
Homestay / Self-contained Accom
Address: 33 Mortimer Tce, Mitchelltown, Wellington
Name: Elfi & Nelson Wattie
Telephone: (04) 853-667
Beds: 1 Double for B&B. 1 Double & 1 sofa-bed (double) in self-contained flat with kitchen & bathroom
Tariff: B&B $60 Double, $40 Single - Flat $75 Double. Dinner by arrangement

Come and enjoy with us our lovely old house with the ever-changing view of Wellington harbour! We look across the water to the mountains beyond - the Rimutakas and the Orongorongos. Like its neighbours, our house was built in the 1920's and it looks out on the Victorian settlement of the Aro Valley. We are within walking distance (up hill) of the city centre with its shops, theatres, cinemas and museums, and close to the University and the National Museum and Art Gallery.
Elfi has been making quilts for more than ten years and you will be able to see some of them. She also makes smaller items, like jackets and other garments. Being an Austrian she also likes cooking and baking and you will have home-made bread for breakfast.
Nelson is a New Zealander and is interested in literature, theatre and music. We both speak German and English. We love the fresh Wellington air and are non-smokers.

Mt Victoria, Wellington City
Homestay
Address: 58 Pirie Street, Mt Victoria, Wellington
Name: Robert and Elizabeth McGuigan
Telephone: (04) 385 8512
Beds: 1 Queen, 3 Single (3 bedrooms, 2 guest bathrooms)
Tariff: B&B Double $60, Single $40

We are a family of five, our three teenage children still living at home. Our 100-year-old Victorian 2-storey home is situated in Mount Victoria, an historic and quaint suburb, just a few minutes easy walk from the city.
We live upstairs and have our own facilities while downstairs is for guests. Downstairs a TV lounge and a dining room with tea and coffee making facilities. There are three bedrooms and two bathrooms – one queensize ensuite, a twin room and a single room. We request guests not to smoke in the house.
Wellington area has a lot to offer — good restaurants and shopping and a good public transport system. A beautiful coastline with wonderful views from Mt Victoria and up the cable car and through the botanic gardens. We also have parliament buildings, museums, art galleries and live theatre.
Directions: *Off motorway into Ghuznee Street, Taranaki Street, Vivian Street, across Kent Terrace and up Pirie Street to No. 58. From Airport take Airport bus to Kentucky Fried Chicken. From Railway Station take city bus no. 2 or 5 (2 sections), ask driver.*

Wellingon City
Bed & Breakfast Guest House
Address: 182 Tinakori Road, Thorndon, Wellington
Name: 'Tinakori Lodge' – Hosts, Mel and John Ainsworth
Telephone: (04) 473 3478. **Fax** (04) 472 5554
Beds: 8 Double, 12 single (13 bedrooms, guest bathrooms)
Tariff: B&B Double $77, Single $66, Triple $88, Prices include GST

New Zealand's
Federation of Bed &
Breakfast Hotels

It is our pleasure to welcome you to 'Tinakori Lodge", our home, and we hope your home away from home during your stay in Wellington.
The Tinakori Lodge is a two storeyed, one hundred year old house, conveniently situated in historic Thorndon within walking distance of the central shopping and commercial areas, transport services, botanical gardens and government centre.
Whether you are in Wellington on holiday or business we endeavour to provide a warm, comfortable atmosphere with the emphasis on relaxation.
All rooms are equipped with wash basins, TV, electric blankets and additional heaters. Ample shared bathroom facilities are located on each floor. Guest laundry facilities.
Our tariff includes a lavish breakfast buffet, twenty-four hour 'serve yourself' tea, coffee, hot chocolate, soup, cookies, morning and evening newspapers.
A home cooked evening meal is available (by arrangement) or you may wish to eat out at one of the nearby restaurants.
Tinakori Lodge provides quality Bed and Breakfast accommodation where the little things mean a lot.

Please let the hosts know if you have to cancel.
They will have spent time preparing for you.

Mt Cook, Wellington City
Homestay
Address: Please phone
Name: Miss Jamie Bull
Telephone: (04) 384-6505
Beds: 1 Double (1 bedroom)
Tariff: B&B Double $60, Single $40; Dinner by arrangement
Nearest Town: Wellington inner city

I am a self-employed choreographer, performer and tutor of dance. Consequently my work takes me around the country (which I love and know well) but when I'm at home I really enjoy sharing my home and my energy with others.
I live in an ninety-year-old inner-city cottage which I am gradually restoring. I think it has character as well as comfort.
It is a 15–20 minute walk to the heart of the city, there are buses nearby and the National Art Gallery and Museum is virtually on the doorstep.
Directions: *Please phone.*

Seatoun
Homestay
Address: 10 Monro Street, Seatoun, Wellington
Name: Frances Drewell
Telephone: (04) 388 6719
Beds: 3 Single (2 bedrooms, guest bathroom)
Tariff: $35 per person
Nearest Town: Wellington City 10 mins (9 km)

Enjoy a comfortable night's rest before setting off on the next stage of your journey. Only five minutes from the Wellington Domestic and International Airport or a one minute walk from the bus stop. 5 minutes to Wellington Aquatic centre.
Several good restaurants are within 5 minutes drive. You are welcome to use the kitchen to make tea or coffee and the microwave for a quick meal. There is a writing desk and TV in the lounge and a sunny conservatory to relax in. Auto washing machine and dryer available for small extra charge.
Being semi retired my leisure time is mainly occupied in the garden or playing golf at the nearby links three minutes drive away. I have travelled over most roads in New Zealand and Australia. Non-smokers preferred.

Some hosts are away from home during the day. It will
help if you phone them the evening before you want to stay.

Strathmore Park
Self-Contained Accommodation
Address: Please phone
Name: "Treetops"
Telephone: (04) 388-6923
Beds: 1 Double, 1 Single (in en-suite cabin), Electric blankets, lambswool underlays, narrow foldaway bed on request
Tariff: B&B Double $75, Single $50, 3 course dinner by prior arrangement $25 (includes pre-dinner drinks and wine with dinner)
Nearest Town: Wellington city 10 minutes (9 km)

We are on the main bus route to the city and 1 km from Wellington Domestic and International Airport and could pick you up by prior arrangement.
We are a home-loving couple whose children are now independent. However our large, friendly dog keeps us in trim by demanding his daily walk around Wellington's rugged coastline at the harbour entrance or on the hills above the sea — you would be most welcome to join us. We would also be happy to take you on a short, local sightseeing drive. We love travelling ourselves and thoroughly enjoy talking to everybody.
Although only one room, our comfortable cabin is spacious and has its own bathroom, fridge, toaster, tea-making facilities, frypan, microwave, radio, \ television and two comfortable chairs. Make your own breakfast at your leisure, or if you prefer come down to the house.
If you don't feel like joining us for lively conversation over dinner, then two minutes' walk to the local shops provides cold cuts and salad to bring back to your cabin or perhaps the favourite New Zealand takeaway, fish and chips (Chinese takeaway two minutes' drive). As another dinner choice we keep a home-made casserole in our freezer for your microwave.
The closest licensed restaurants are five minutes' drive away. Seatoun beach and Miramar Golf Course are two minutes' drive or an easy walk. Wellington Aquatic Centre 5 minutes' drive.
We look forward to your visit. "There are no strangers here – only friends we haven't met."
Directions: *Please phone.*

Send us a comment form to tell us about your B&B vacation.
Forms are in this book and are also obtainable from hosts.

Island Bay, Wellington
Homestay
Address: 52 High Street,
Island Bay, Wellington 6002
Name: Theresa and Jack Stokes
Telephone: (04) 3835-169
Beds: 2 Double, 2 Single (3 bedrooms, guest bathroom)
Tariff: B&B $50 Double, $30 Single, children (under 13) 1/2 price, $15
Dinner, Campervans $20 (incl power)
Nearest Town: Wellington

*A modern, four year old Lockwood house standing in a very private three
acre section with probably the finest view in Wellington. We overlook Island
Bay harbour with its fishing boats - the entrance to Port Nicholson
(Wellington's harbour) - the Cook Strait with its ferries and cargo vessels on
the move day and night.*
*Five minutes down the hill (a good ten minutes up again!) to Island Bay
beach with its safe swimming. Ten minutes drive from the town centre. Ten
minutes walk to the bus terminal. Transport to and from the Interisland Ferry
can be arranged.*
Directions: *From the Fire Station in Wellington follow Kent Terrace, round
the Basin Reserve and continue along Adelaide Road. Up the hill, leaving
Athletic Park on your left and the road becomes The Parade. Keep going until
you reach the sea and then turn SHARP right, left and left again. We are up
the private road at the end of High Street. Plenty of parking.*

New Zealand is known as the friendliest country in the world and
our hosts will live up to that reputation.

Nelson, Marlborough

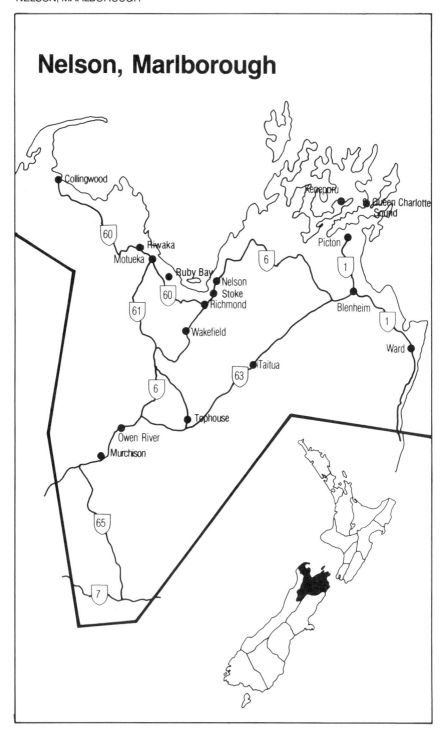

Queen Charlotte Sounds

Homestay
Address: "Craglee", Bay of Many Coves, Private Bag, Picton
Name: Anne & Robin Perret
Telephone: (03) 5799223
Beds: 1 Double, 2 Single (2 bedrooms, guest bathroom)
Tariff: B&B $60 Double, $30 Single, children (under 12) 1/2 price, $20 Dinner, $12 Lunch
Nearest Town: Picton - 17 kms by water - no road access.

Our modern home in a secluded bay in the Marlborough Sounds, is warm, comfortable and spacious, with breathtaking views over the bay and surrounding native bush. Awake to the chorus of Bellbirds.
Our guest rooms have electric blankets, guest bathroom and guest lounge with TV, Radio, tea and coffee facilities, a cot is available and laundry.
A large deck overlooking the bay has a heated spa for you to enjoy on a starry moonlit night.
You may wish to see bird life, glow-worms, go on bush or beach walks, tramping, fishing, diving, swimming, rowing, canoeing - Dinghy or Canoe available for small charge. Fishing trips can be arranged.
Our family's interests include: boating, fishing, gardening, entertaining, amateur radio, cooking, brewing.
Our meals will include local fare which includes local wine and home brewed beer.
We share our home with our 9 year old son and Toby our Terrier. Children are most welcome. Booking essential (don't be disappointed).
Directions: *Fly Float Plane, from Picton or Wellington 20 mins or Water Taxi from Picton 35 mins. Car storage can be arranged.*

Kenepuru Sound

Farmstay
Address: "The Reef", RD2, Picton
Name: Robyn and Jim Jenkins
Telephone: (03) 573 4342
Beds: 1 Double, 1 Single, (1 bedroom, guest bathroom)
Tariff: B&B Double $60, Single $50, Dinner $15, Lunch $8, Children half price
Nearest Town: Picton and Havelock, 1 hour drive to wharf

Our 50 acre farmlet is located adjacent to the sea in a bush-clad setting. Our property is very secluded on Kenepuru Sound and offers a special relaxed environment for people wishing a break from the usual tourist route. We have a new log style home with splendid sea views and we wish to share our living with travellers who enjoy farm activities and animals (goats and horses). We offer as an extra, early rider training and horse care on a one-to-one basis. Saltwater swimming and fishing are right at our doorstep.
We have three children, one son thirteen at boarding school, and two daughters eleven and eight at home.
We can be reached easily from Wellington via Skyferry (Outdoor Aviation) fly to Nopera Airstrip, or from Picton, via water taxi or by road access.
Because of our location we are best suited as as a farmstay destination lodging rather than as en route one night accommodation.
We request no smoking in our home.

Kenepuru Sound
Guest House
Address: St Omer House, Kenepuru Sound, RD2, Picton, Marlborough
Name: Flora and George Robb
Telephone: (03) 573 4086
Beds: 5 Double, 5 Twin (others with 3 or 4 bunks) (16 bedrooms)
Tariff: $23 per person; Campervans, caravans, tent sites $12 per person per day; Dinner $25, Lunch $12, Breakfast $10 (Continental $5.50); Children under 2 no charge, Children under 12 half price
For longer stays $65 per day all meals supplied, $25 in self contained cottages
Nearest Town: Picton or Havelock, 2 hours by road

A peaceful bay, a fifty-year-old, family-run guest house with plenty of historic interest is where my husband and I and two adult daughters welcome you. Our family are the fifth generation in the area.
The Marlborough Sounds are a maze of waterways – you can cruise, yacht, canoe, row, dive, swim, fish, water ski or explore beaches and wrecks, climb bush-clad hills, tramp walkways, see farmland (sheep, cattle, deer, goats), hunt deer and wild pigs.
Nearby are mussel and salmon farms, bird sanctuaries, shag colonies and glowworm walks.
Our dining room has a BYO licence, we cater for all meals and tastes – venison, wild pork, shellfish, fish, fresh eggs, vegetables and fruit locally grown are on our menu.
The games room is large enough for dancing – has piano, table tennis, TV, etc. mini golf on lawn and tennis court.
Travel: By car – part-metalled road, 2 hrs from Havelock or Picton. Fly float plane from Picton or Porirua or small plane from Wellington, 20 minutes. Watertaxi from Picton or Havelock.

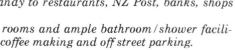

Picton
Guest House
Address: 22 Waikawa Road, Picton
Name: Admirals Lodge
Telephone: (03) 573 6590. Fax: (03) 573 8318
Beds: 4 Double 12 Single (8 bedrooms, guest bathroom)
Tariff: B&B Triple $90, Double/Twin $72, Single $45. Quote this book for a 10% discount

A friendly welcome awaits you when you arrive in Picton at our centrally located guest house, which is handy to restaurants, NZ Post, banks, shops and launch trips.
We provide individually heated rooms and ample bathroom/shower facilities, along with 24 hour tea and coffee making and off street parking.
Some rooms available with private facilities. Tariff on request.
Our courtesy car will pick you up from bus/train/ferry terminals if you telephone on arrival.
All rates include a full menu breakfast. _____

Picton
Country Lodge
Address: Linkwater Lodge, Queen Charlotte Scenic Drive, Linkwater R.D. 1
Picton
Name: Tony Furness & John Howard
Telephone: (03) 574-2507
Beds: 2 Double, 2 Single (3 bedrooms, guest bathroom)
Tariff: B&B $75 Double, $52.50 Single, Restaurant meals.
Nearest Town: Picton 25 km, Havelock 15 km

Greetings from Linkwater Lodge, an historic homestead set in the original house garden of two acres on Marlborough's picturesque Queen Charlotte Scenic Drive.
The house, restored to its period by hosts John Howard and Tony Furness offers the comforts of orthapedic beds, electric blankets, fluffy duvets, open fires, electric and gas heating. Furnished with crystal chandeliers, antiques, art deco carpets and comfortable period furnishings, the lodge offers the charm and romance of yesteryear combined with the comforts of today.
At night the main house restaurant glitters with chandeliers, silver service and the flicker of antique table lanterns - the menu features Marlborough's superb products - venison, salmon, lamb fillets, poultry, fresh fruit, vegetables and herbs.
We do not accept children under twelve years and request guests not to smoke in the bedrooms.
The Lodge has been reported both in New Zealand and overseas but the comment we appreciate most is recorded through our visitors book - Home again.
Directions: *From Picton, 25 kms Queen Charlotte Drive, opposite the service station. From Blenheim, turn off Nelson highway before Havelock at Queen Charlotte Drive sign - 15 kms to Linkwater.*

Picton

Self-Contained Accommodation

Address: 'Bridgend Cottage', 36 York Street, Picton
Name: Len and Billie Fortune
Telephone: (03) 573 6734
Beds: 1 Double, 2 Single (2 bedrooms, both with ensuite facilities). All beds with 'Slumbertime' mattresses
Tariff: B&B Double $55, Single $35, Four people $100, 4 course dinner $ 20

We welcome you to Picton at the top of the Queen Charlotte Sound. The most beautiful waterway in the world for boating, fishing and walks.
Our property is situated within easy walking distance of all activities in Picton. The accommodation is fully self contained including colour TV, tea/coffee making facilities, full cooked menu breakfast which is included in the price. Breakfast arranged for early inter-island ferry passengers.
Dinner is a four course gourmet meal with wine featuring local salmon, seafoods, venison.
Safe and secure off street parking, sun deck, transport provided from buses, train or inter-island ferry by prior arrangement.

Always telephone ahead to enquire about a B&B. It is a nuisance for you if you simply arrive to find someone already staying there. And besides hosts need a litle time to prepare.

Picton

Homestay, Baystay
Address: Moenui Bay, Queen Charlotte Drive, RD1, Picton (near Havelock end of Drive)
Name: "Ribbonwood"
Telephone: (03) 5742 217
Beds: 1 Double (ensuite, spa bath), 2 Single (guest bathroom)
Tariff: B&B Double $50, (ensuite $55), Single $35; Dinner $15
Nearest Town: Blenheim 32 kms, Picton 32 kms

This is a Resting site, bush sheltered. Cross the Queen's chain to swimming beach, in Pelorus Sound. Dinghy, lifejackets and fishing rods available. Barbecue dinner, if preferred. Breakfast cooked or as preferred. Guests are welcome to stay for more than one night.
An ideal base for tripping about the Marlborough Scene.
My interests are very wide. I have both travelled and worked overseas for the past twenty years. This was my beach house which I have now doubled in size to become my retirement home.
Sorry, no smoking or animals.
Directions: *From Blenheim, turn off Nelson Highway before Havelock, at 'Queen Charlotte Drive' sign. Moenui Bay, first sign on left, after 10 minute drive. The name 'Ribbonwood' is on side of letterbox, at top of driveway, as your vehicle completes turning around road circle.*

Picton

Self-Contained Accommodation
Address: 11 Dorset Street, Picton
Name: Please phone
Telephone: (03) 573 7177
Beds: 1 Double, 2+ Single (1 bedroom, bed-settee in living room, guest bathroom)
Tariff: B&B Double $45, Single $30, Children $15, Dinner $18, (+ $5 surcharge for one night stay)

Welcome to our home with views over Picton's lovely harbour, bushclad hills and farmland. Your home here will be a comfortably furnished ground floor apartment where you can relax on a sun deck overlooking gardens, small swimming pool and barbecue area. The living room has a small kitchen area, dining corner, bed settees and TV. The bathroom has a shower, toilet and handbasin.
Our family has varied interests but in particular we enjoy sailing, vintage car restoration and rallying, travel, folk music and meeting people.
We provide a comprehensive continental style breakfast. This is usually prepared and placed in your apartment so you can breakfast at your leisure. If you prefer you may do your own catering (discount tariff).
We enjoy assisting travellers with their itineraries and will meet most ferry, train and bus services.
Please phone for directions.
Don't just pass through Picton - STOP - relax and enjoy the marvellous Marlborough Province with its wineries, scenery, waterways and walks!!

Picton

Homestay + Self-Contained Accommodation
Address: PO Box 256, Picton
Name: Ron and Wendy Gabites
Telephone: (03) 573 6491
Beds: 1 Double, 2 Single (2 bedrooms, guest bathroom)
Tariff: B&B Double $65, Single $40, Children under 12 half price; dinner $20

Picton is the main centre for the beautiful Marlborough Sounds, with its lovely bays and scenic views of water and bush-clad hills.
Our new home is situated by the sea in Waikawa Bay (three minutes from Picton). The property has an expansive view over the Bay and Queen

Charlotte Sound where we can watch the inter-island ferries, pleasure yachts and launches.
A safe swimming beach, children's playground, boat launching ramp and general store are close by.
We have a fully self-contained and separate apartment downstairs which sleeps four with all facilities. It is very suitable for longer holidays.
Our family of four sons are all away from home and we now have time to pursue our own interests which include sailing, fishing, golfing, leathercraft, gardening and meeting people.
Relax for a few days with us in the beautiful Marlborough Sounds, enjoy sailing, sightseeing, bushwalking, fishing, picnics or a game of golf.
We are happy to meet and provide transport from buses, train or inter-island ferries.

Blenheim
Homestay
Address: "Mirfield",
722 Severne Street, Blenheim
Name: Pam & Charles Hamilton
Telephone: (03) 578-8220
Beds: 4 Single (2 bedrooms, guest bathroom)
Tariff: **B&B** $22.50 Single, children under 12 1/2 price, $12.50 Dinner, campervans welcome
Nearest Town: Blenheim

Welcome to our home. We love to meet people from round the world. Situated on the town boundary, our home is 5 minute's drive from town. Being a three generation household, our home is large and spacious, with a separate guests' bathroom / toilet, and two bedrooms each with 2 single beds. A private lounge is available for relaxing or TV viewing.
We are flexible and sensitive to the needs of a wide age-range of guests, and can offer you an evening meal with the family or just bed & breakfast.
"Mirfield" is a convenient stopping place for those using the Cook Strait Ferries, arriving at Blenheim Airport, or travelling to Nelson, West Coast or Christchurch. By arrangement, transport may be provided to and from local departure points.
Make Marlborough a highlight - make our home your home.
Directions: *Take Highway 6 from Blenheim to Nelson. Severne Street is the next on the left after you pass the Shell Service Station.*

Blenheim
Farmstay
Address: Maxwell Pass, Blenheim
Name: Jean and John Leslie
Telephone: (03) 578 1941
Beds: 4 Single (3 bedrooms, guest bathroom)
Tariff: B&B Double $55, Single $30, Children half price; Dinner $15
Nearest Town: Blenheim 8 km

We live 8 km from Blenheim on a 1500 acre hill country property (ranch) running sheep and cattle.
Our home is a modern two-storeyed house set in spacious grounds with a swimming pool and grass tennis court.
All beds have electric blankets and guests have own bathroom.
Now that our family have left home we enjoy spending time with guests.
Marlborough is a major grape growing area with several wineries plus horticulture, agriculture and livestock farming from high country to the coast.
Marlborough Sounds is nearby either by sea or road. Trout fishing is also close at hand and there is a ski field 1 1/2 hours drive. Blenheim has a golf course, croquet green and hard and grass tennis court.
Directions: *Please phone.*

Blenheim
Homestay in the country
Address: "Green Gables", St Andrews, R.D.4, Blenheim
Name: Raelene and Bill Rainbird
Telephone: (03) 578 1869
Beds: 2 Double, 2 Single (3 bedrooms, guest bathroom)
Tariff: B&B Double $50, Single $27, Dinner $15, Children $10
Nearest Town: 1.5 km east of Blenheim

Our spacious ,modern, two storey, 3000 sq ft home is set in 4 acres of gardens.
Accommodation is spacious with own bathroom, glass doors opening onto the terrace with a panoramic view of Blenheim.
Breakfast is of your choice, cooked or Continental.
Marlborough has the highest sunshine hours in New Zealand and offers a variety of very good restaurants. Spend a day on a wine trail at our world renowned vineyards and wineries, the cherry orchards, salmon farms, mussel farms, the beautiful Marlborough Sounds, and the picturesque Rainbow Skifield, all within easy driving distance from our home.
Having travelled extensively around the world and enjoying the hospitality of many people we would like to offer our New Zealand hospitality and look forward to making new friends.
We are a few minutes from town and will happily collect you if required.

Blenheim

Farmstay
Address: Ugbrooke, Blenheim
Name: Hugh and Belinda Vavasour
Telephone: (03) 575 7259
Beds: 1 Double, 4 Single (4 bedrooms, guest bathroom)
Tariff: Dinner, Bed and Breakfast – Double $135, Single $90, Children 10 and under no charge
Nearest Town: 26 km south of Blenheim

Ugbrooke is a large, old family home, listed with the Historic Places Trust. It is situated in the Awatere Valley, 26 km from Blenheim. The farm is 850 acres mainly running sheep and some very friendly angora goats.

We have two comfortable sitting rooms, billiard room and TV room. The bedrooms have comfortable beds with electric blankets, bedside lamps and electric heaters. Our guests have their own bathroom.

We have a tennis court, swimming pool and croquet lawn. Or you may just want to relax on our long verandah and admire the view across Cook Strait. The gardens are extensive and well-maintained.

Meals may feature farm-killed lamb, and the freshest fruit and vegetables available according to the season.

Freshly ground coffee is a specialty, at Ugbrooke.

Ugbrooke is just 5 km from the main south road and so we are ideally situated for those travelling on the ferries. We enjoy having guests and sharing our lovely old family home with you. We are happy to show you over our farm and take pride in telling you about the district.

Directions: *Please phone.*

As distances in New Zealand are not great check out the maps of the neighbouring provinces for other B&Bs nearby.

Blenheim
Homestay
Address: 30 Glenroy Crescent, Blenheim
Name: Barbara and Nicolaas Mels
Telephone: (03) 578 2704
Beds: 2 Single, also foldaway for 1 child (1 bedroom, guest bathroom)
Tariff: B&B Double $55, Single $30 Dinner $15, Children free
Nearest Town: Blenheim
Sleepout (garden cottage) with shower and toilet. Situated in a semi-rural neighbourhood. You can park the car alongside and 20 mtrs to lounge and dining room. TV, tea and coffee making facilities are also there but guests are most welcome to spend their evenings in conversation in the lounge. We are in our early fifties with no children at home. Have travelled ourselves and know what a comfortable sleep means to the next day's travel. If guests are travelling by road, rail, or air we are happy to fetch and carry. To get to the centre of town via parks is an easy and pleasant walk.
Directions - *Off the Old Renwick Road, near the racecourse.*

Blenheim
Farmstay
Address: "Taitua", State Highway 63, RD1 Blenheim
Name: Robin and Cathie Young
Telephone: (03) 572 2816
Beds: 1 Double, 2 Single (2 bedrooms, guest bathroom)
Tariff: B&B Double $55, Single $38.50; Dinner $18; Campervans $20, Children half price

We have a new ranch-style house on a 440-acre sheep farm midway between Blenheim and Nelson Lakes National Park (50 km from each).
Robin is a kiwi (Crocodile-Dundee-type), Cathie an American (California, Pennsylvania, Massachusetts).
We have one daughter of 20 who is sometimes at home, 2 cats – 1 black, 1 colourpoint Himalayan.
We are keen card players – bridge, piquet, cribbage, pinochle, and more. Cathie collects antiques and books.
Robin will provide a free farm tour by Landrover and a sheep-shearing demonstration (he does all his own).
There is trout-fishing nearby, a heated swimming pool (open Oct.– April) and many walks.
Breakfast features waffles, pancakes, omelettes, muffins, fresh (or home-bottled) fruit. Dinner featuring home-killed lamb by arrangement, cut lunches available.
Directions: *On the main highway between Blenheim and St Arnaud (Lake Rotoiti), 16 km past Wairau Valley village.*

Blenheim

Farmstay + Self-contained Accom
Address: Watsons Road, R.D. 3, Grovetown, Blenheim
Name: Robert & Lynne Kennedy
Telephone: (03) 570 5475
Beds: 4 Single (1 bedroom, guest bathroom)
Tariff: B&B $60 Double, $40 Single, $5 Children, $15 Dinner,
Campervans $15
Nearest Town: Blenheim

Our fully self contained flat is a new building, semi-detached from our modern Farmstay. It has one bedroom, bathroom and large kitchenette / lounge with settee. Colour TV and good heating.
We are a married couple with three teenage children, one at university ad one at boarding school.
We are very proud of our Province of Marlborough and enjoy showing it off to others.
We have both travelled extensively and enjoy meeting people from other countries, having employed numerous overseas students on our 18 hectare orchard and market gardening unit comprising of apples, stonefruit, kiwifruit, garlic and vegetables.
We are ideally situated just off the main highway, 15 minutes drive from Picton and 5 minutes from Blenheim. By arrangement we can provide boating day trips in the nearby Marlborough Sounds. We are also happy to provide transport from buses, trains and interisland ferries.

Blenheim

Homestay
Address: "Waterlea Lodge",
84 McLauchlan St, Blenheim
Name: Ian & Rosemary Douglas
Telephone: (03) 578-8238
Beds: 3 Single (2 bedrooms, guest bathroom)
Tariff: B&B $60 Double, $35 Single, $20 Dinner
Nearest Town: Blenheim

We are a married couple whose 2 daughters have now left home. Our large cat, Boswell, and Corgi dog Emma, share our lives.
Our home is a warm, comfortable Kauri villa, approx 90 years old and situated 2 kms from the town centre and only a few minutes walk to Waterlea Racecourse, Pollard Park and a 9-hole golf course.
We offer quiet, friendly hospitality with your choice of breakfast. We can provide dinner by arrangement or, if you prefer, Blenheim offers a wide choice of excellent restaurants.
Our guest rooms are spacious and are provided with electric blankets and bedside lamps. The single room has a sun-room annexe for your enjoyment.
Tea and coffee, magazines and a daily newspaper are freely available. We respectfully request that you do not smoke indoors.
We look forward to welcoming you.
Directions: *We are located directly off Nelson St. (State Highway 6) but please phone before arrival if possible.*

Blenheim
Homestay
Address: 191 Redwood Street, Blenheim
Name: Alan and Mary Stevenson   **Telephone:** (03) 578 9091
Beds: 1 Double, 5 Single, Cot available (3 bedrooms, guest bathroom, room with double bed also has a single bed, all beds have electric blankets)
Tariff: B&B Double $65, Single $40, Children $5; Dinner $17; Campervans $5 per person

We have a lovely warm brick home on the rise at the southern end of Redwood Street (opp. Safe Street). We were farming at Seddon until our son's marriage (early 1984) and we are still very interested in everything pertaining to farming and community work.
As the house is built back from the street, ours is a very quiet, restful home.
We really enjoy meeting people from overseas. We have travelled a little and are members of the Marlborough Travel Club.
Our guest area has its own bathroom with bath, separate shower and separate toilet. There is a small swimming pool and a pool table available. Ample off-street parking. On request early morning tea or coffee provided. We are happy to provide transport to and from coaches, train or plane; and if desired can take guests on a sort tour of our area.
Directions: *Travel to railway crossing on Main Street (State Highway 1), turn between siding and main line into Redwood Street and travel approximately 2.7 km.*

Blenheim
Homestay
Address: Please phone   **Telephone:** (03) 578 9562
Beds: 1 Double, 4 Single (3 bedrooms, guest bathroom)
Tariff: B&B Double $55, Single $35 (less 10% if prebooked by night before); Dinner by arrangement.
Nearest Town: Blenheim 3 km from town centre

Your hosts are a married couple with a grown up family offering a spacious, modern home in a quiet, southern suburb of Blenheim. We have one double and two twin bedrooms available – all beds with electric blankets. Guests have their own toilet / bathroom.
This landscaped property includes sundeck, pool, barbecue and parking.
The host is an airline pilot with interests in all aspects of aviation from models to homebuilts and gliding – also builds miniature steam locomotives. The hostess loves cooking and will serve wine with meals. She is also a spinner and woolcraft hobbyist. Both enjoy sharing travel experiences. We have a 1929 Model A Ford vintage car – soft top tourer – and offer guests the chance to ride and be photographed in it. Can also arrange sightseeing flights around Marlborough.
We can assure you of personal attention and a warm, friendly atmosphere, but should you require privacy that too will be respected. We are non-smokers but don'tt mind if you do. There are no household pets.
Nearby attractions include 2 hour Wither Hills walk, Brayshaw Historical Park and Vintage Farm Museum, vineyards and winery trail, salt works, skifields, Nelson Lakes National Park, Marlborough Sounds Maritime Park.

Ward
Farmstay
Address: "Weld Cone", Ward, Marlborough
Name: Charlie and Audrey Chambers
Telephone: (03) 575 6816
Beds: 4 Single (2 bedrooms, top quality woolrest sleep- ers,guest bathroom)
Tariff: B&B Double $60, Single $38; Dinner $16; Campervans $15; Children half price; Morning and afternoon teas free
Nearest Town: 45 km south from Blenheim on State Highway 1

We are a family of four with two teenage children. We have a sheep and cattle farm 1,570 acres near Ward beach which is a great place for "rock hounds".
Our home is about 80 years old with lovely leadlight windows and doors. It is a large gracious house with ample space for you to relax and have a restful time if you so desire.
Our farm is part of the early "Flaxbourne Settlement". The Historic Places Trust have an information noticeboard by our woolshed.
Our garden is very large, about 1 acre, with over 200 rhododendrons, camellias and azaleas plus roses and lots of lovely trees and birds.
Directions: *Our farm is 2.5 km from State Highway 1. Turn opposite "Fuel Plus Tearooms" along Seddon Street over railway line and bridge, "Weld Cone" on your right. We will pick up visitors who travel by bus.*
Happy Holidays.

If you find something missing that you are
accustomed to, simply ask you hosts for it.

Nelson

Farmstay
- separate self-contained cottage
Address: Dovedale, R.D. 2, Wakefield
Name: Heather & "Brad" Bradley
Telephone: (03) 5433-685 (let phone ring or phone evenings)
Beds: 1 Double, (1 bedroom, guest bathroom)
Tariff: **B&B** $60 Double, $30 Single, Dinner $17
Nearest Town: Motueka 25 km, Richmond 36 km (nearest restaurants)

Situated on 40 acres of picturesque farmland in the Dove River Valley. Fully furnished cottage built 1912. One double bedroom, lounge, kitchen and bathroom. Spacious restored homestead in the same era, set amid century old oaks. Stylish dining, character and charm. Main house and cottage surrounded by large grounds.

You are welcome to eat with us or bring your own food and cook for yourselves. Evening meal by prior arrangement. We grow our own vegetables and herbs, and raise hens for fresh eggs.

A relaxed rural environment and peaceful surroundings. There is a special farmyard atmosphere on our free-range organic poultry farm. Turkeys, peacocks, hens, ducks and other animals roam free.

Ample recreational pursuits including trout fishing, bushwalking, one hour to Nelson Lakes and skifields, beautiful rivers and picnic spots, excellent vineyards and potteries nearby. Hunting and fishing guides can be arranged.

Hosts have travelled extensively and lived in several countries. Interests include music, literature, films, gardening and bushwalking. Guests will be warmly welcomed.

   Cut here 165

Directions: *Take inland highway from Nelson towards Motueka, 2 km past Upper Moutere, turn left at Prices Corner. Proceed for 10 km. Turn left at Thorn Road. Go for 2 km over ford. Turn left at "T" intersection. Driveway entrance 200m on left, 50m past letterbox.*

Nelson

Homestay
Address: Please Phone
Name: Elaine & Peter Cooke
Telephone: (03) 548 1261
Beds: 2 Single (1 bedroom, guest bathroom)
Tariff: **B&B** $60 Double, $35 Single, $20 Dinner, Campervans $20
Nearest Town: Nelson

Situated on Britania Heights overlooking the entrance to Nelson harbour with extensive views of Tasman Bay, from the Airport to Separation Point.

From our modern home you are within 5 minutes of Nelson City, interesting port area and the renowned Tahuna Beach.

We are an active retired couple with interests in golf, yachting, sea fishing and travel.

Our swimming pool reaches pleasant temperatures in summer months while underfloor heating ensures cosy living in winter.
A sunporch with two single beds provides an occasional extra bedroom.
No young children please.
Nelson has much to offer within the district and we recommend a trip over the marble mountain to explore Golden Bay. Spend a night there, make the fabulous trip to Farewell Spit. Return to our home for dinner if you wish, a comfortable night's rest and a good breakfast to continue your travels on.
Directions: *We will pick you up from the Airport or town. Please phone.*

Central Nelson
Guest House
Address: Collingwood House, 174 Collingwood Street, Nelson
Name: Cecile and Alan Strang
Telephone: (03) 5484-481
Beds: 1 Double, 5 Single (3 bedrooms, guest bathroom)
Tariff: B&B $30 share per person, Single $40, Children half price; Dinner $15
Nearest Town: Walking distance from city centre

After travelling extensively overseas and enjoying meeting so many people, we returned home, retired early and found our lovely old New Zealand home from which we offer bed and breakfast in the best British tradition. We found "Collingwood House" – with its big guest rooms, each having lovely views of the city; and bathroom with separate shower and bath – to be central and quiet.
We have now welcomed many guests and can say with confidence we are catering for their needs, providing great breakfasts, plenty of hot showers and washing facilities. We are familiar with our many great restaurants which are within easy walking distance and we are also happy to make suggestions of places to visit. This we have found to be appreciated by our guests who come to tramp in our national parks, tour in our region, or just relax and stay at home to relax from travel.
As we love Nelson's Tasman district and Golden Bay we have lots of ideas for day's outings including our fabulous beaches such as Kaiteriteri.
For those arriving by coach, phone us and we will collect you. The airways bus brings you to our door.

Nelson

Bed & Breakfast Inn
Address: 29 Collingwood Street, Nelson
Name: California House
Telephone: (03) 548-4173
Beds: 2 Queen, 2 Double, 2 Twin (4 bedrooms, private or shared bathrooms)
Tariff: B&B $95 - $135 Double, $78 Single (Special Winter Rates)
Nearest Town: Nelson - 3 blocks from town centre.

Your hosts Neil & Shelley Johnstone invite you to discover a unique bed and breakfast experience in their historic Nelson home. Built in 1893 and classified by the New Zealand Historic Places Trust for its historical and architectural significance, California House features original English oak panelling, 24 stained glass windows, open fires, spacious rooms and wide sunny verandahs overlooking the lawns and garden. The house is set wellback from the street in a quiet residential area just 5 minutes walk from the centre of town.

We offer a peaceful and relaxing atmosphere with warm and friendly hospitality and the feeling of being a guest in an historic home. Guest rooms are furnished with comfortable antique beds, period furnishings, fluffy quilts, memorabilia and fresh flowers.

Unique to California House are its speciality breakfasts, which in true Californian style may include freshly squeezed orange juice, fresh fruits, berries and cream, ham and sour cream omelettes, delicious muffins, Finnish pancakes served with strawberries, cream and pure Canadian maple syrup and freshly ground coffee amongst other things to tempt you.

Bicycles and beach towels are available for guest use. No smoking in the house.

Courtesy transport is available to and from bus depots. An airport shuttle bus will deliver you to our door.

Tariffs include GST, full speciality breakfast, wine, beer or fruit juice on arrival and tea, coffee, sherry and biscuits available at any time.

Tell other travellers about your favourite homes.

Nelson City
Homestay
Address: 15 Riverside, Nelson
Name: Hunts Home Hosts - David & Edith Hunt
Telephone: (03) 548-0123
Beds: 1 Double, 2 Single (2 bedrooms, guest bathroom)
Tariff: B&B $55 Double, $40 Single, children 1/2 price, $17.50 Dinner
Nearest Town: Nelson city

Take a break in sunny Nelson - the geographical centre of New Zealand - with your Home Hosts, David & Edith Hunt at their beautiful home by the crystal clear River Maitai in the centre of the city. Sightseeing, excursions, picnics, barbecues, fishing, gold panning, visits to local potteries and weavers, museums, theatres - all within easy reach.
Bed and cooked breakfast and meals as required including packed lunches. Guest suite with one twin, one double bedroom. Guest lounge with colour TV, private facilities, kitchenette, lock-up garage.
Our service car is available to pick up guests from the Airport or Bus Depot or for sightseeing trips, etc. My wife speaks English, German & Czech.
Our upstairs quarters always have a warm welcome for those who want our company. Our brochure with city plan shows the way to our sunny home.
We want our guests to feel comfortable and at home - and a little spoilt. We are looking back over 11 years of happy home-hosting with an ever increasing circle of friends.

Nelson
Homestay
Address: Please phone
Name: Claire and Brian Higgins
Telephone: (03) 548-6323
Beds: 2 Double (2 bedrooms)
Tariff: B&B Double $60, Single $35, Dinner $20
Nearest Town: Nelson

We would like to welcome you to Nelson, the fruit bowl of the South Island. We are nestled in a sunny secluded spot on the Tahuna hillside, overlooking the busy entrance to Nelson Harbour. Our home is in perfect order with every comfort for discriminating guests who are non-smokers.
We are five minutes from Nelson Airport and will be happy to pick up travellers if required. Our interests include rugby, golf, walking and cooking.
We will be happy to share our million dollar view of Tasman Bay, our very comfortable home and excellent cuisine.
Directions: *please phone.*

Nelson

Intimate Hotel
Address: 7 Cambria Street, Nelson
Name: Cambria House
Telephone: (03) 548 4681. Fax (03) 546 6649
Beds: 2 Queen, 2 Double, 1 Twin (5 bedrooms, all with ensuite facilities)
Tariff: Double $85–$125, Single $65–$95

Cambria House is an original Nelson homestead dating back some 125 years and has a wealth of features typical of that period with beautiful fireplaces, panelling and original doors in rimu and kauri. The owners, Bill and Catherine Vincent have sought to create a warm friendly atmosphere in this lovely old home which is only 5 minutes walk from the city centre, yet offers peace and tranquility.

All five guest rooms are luxuriously appointed with top quality beds and antiques and each room has its own ensuite. For winter, all rooms have the added comfort of heating and electric blankets. A comfortable guest lounge with log fire opens onto a private courtyard and delightful cottage garden.

Whether you prefer a light healthy breakfast of home preserves, muesli and yoghourt or a leisurely traditional feast of farm fresh eggs, bacon, tomatoes and mushrooms served with your choice of tea or freshly ground coffee, we know that your breakfast will be an enjoyable experience.

If you wish to make Cambria House your base to explore the beautiful Nelson region, special rates are available for longer stays.

Tariffs include full breakfast, tea, coffee, fruit juice or wine on arrival.

New Zealand is known as the friendliest country in the world
and we expect our hosts will live up to that reputation.

Nelson
Homestay
Address: 585 Waimea Road, Nelson
Name: Maureen & Ramon Box
Telephone: (054) 73622
Beds: 1 Double, 2 Single (2 bedrooms, double brm has a toilet)
Tariff: B&B $50 Double, $25 Single, $10 Children, $15 Dinner
Nearest Town: Nelson

We live 5 minutes from Nelson City in a large 4 bedroom modern home with wide views of Tasman Bay and panoramic mountains, we are close to the airport and 2 minutes from the beach.
Our family of 4 daughters, only the youngest living at home, are all outdoor people with many interests - tramping, ski-ing, mountain biking, running, yachting, but most of all meeting poeple with a warm welcome to Nelson.
Directions: *Please phone.*

Nelson
Homestay
Address: Please phone
Name: Dorothy and Bob Brown
Telephone: (03) 5484-751
Beds: 2 Single (1 bedroom, guest bathroom)
Tariff: B&B Double $60, Single $40
Nearest Town: Nelson (5 minute walk)

My husband and I are a retired couple and we would like to welcome you to our comfortable, modern home which is in a garden setting on the banks of the Maitai River and close to the Queens Gardens, just five minutes' walk to the city centre, shops and restaurants, art gallery, cinema and covered heated swimming pool and spa. Central yet quiet. Off-street parking.
The guest room has two single beds and you have your own bathroom, also your own sitting room with colour TV, fridge and tea and coffee making facilities. Or you may prefer to join us in our lounge and just sit and talk, maybe share a common interest, travel. Why not spend a few days exploring the wonderful Nelson area?
We just love meeting people and making new friends. We are non-smokers.
Directions: *Please phone.*

Nelson
Homestay
Address: Sussex House, 238 Bridge Street, Nelson
Name: Mrs Ida Hunt
Telephone: (054) 89972
Beds: 1 Queen/Dble, 2 Single (2 bedrooms)
Tariff: **B&B** $75 Double, $45 Single, $15 Children, $15 Dinner
Nearest Town: Nelson

A fine character home built around 1900, Susses House is situated on the banks of Nelson's scenic Maitai River within easy walking distance of the Queen's Gardens, the Suter Art Gallery and Botanical Hill.
The house features two large sunny bedrooms which overlook the river. There is a swimming pool and the secluded garden area allows you to relax and enjoy the quiet surroundings.
Breakfast may include fresh fruit juices, fresh berries or fruit, French toast, puffy fruit omelette, savoury mushrooms and home-made jams and marmalades. Excellent home-cooked dinner may be available on request, Chinese food a speciality.
No smoking in the house.
Your host, Ida Hunt, comes from Sussex, England.

Nelson
Guest House
Address: Abbey Lodge, 84 Grove Street, Nelson
Name: Peter Nuttall
Telephone: (03) 548 8816 Fax: (03) 548 3368
Beds: 2 Double, 14 Single (8 bedrooms, guest bathrooms)
Tariff: **B&B** $55 Double, $35 Single, $15 Dinner
Nearest Town: Blenheim/Picton 2 hours, Greymouth 5 hours.

We welcome international visitors to Nelson on their way to Abel Tasman National Park, Kaikoura Whale Watch or West Coast glaciers. Tours pick up and set down at the front door. We provide courtesy car from bus depots and are 500 metres form main shopping area of the city.
Our guests appreciate the clean, comfortable accommodation with colour TV, coffee and tea facilities, hot & cold water handbasins, and electric blankets in all rooms.
We have off street parking, laundry facilities, telephone and guests' lounge (TV-free and Smoke-free).
Directions: *400 metres from Information Centre*

Nelson
Homestay
Address: 20 Martin Street, Monaco, Nelson
Name: Jean and Jack Anderson
Telephone: (03) 547-6739
Beds: 1 Double, 2 Single (2 bedrooms)
Tariff: B&B Double $48, Single $25, Children half price; Dinner $12.50
Nearest Town: Nelson

We are a couple who like meeting people. We are members of Friendship Force International and have made lasting friendships with overseas visitors staying with us.

We live beside the sea where it is lovely to walk or put your boat in for a leisurely cruise. Waterskiing is prominent here in the summertime.

Shopping is close at Nelson, Stoke or Richmond. Also very near to historic houses, museum, gardens and craft habitat. In the winter time it is only about an hour's drive to the skifields.

We are near the airport and will meet planes or buses at depots. A phone call or a letter would be appreciated before arrival.

Directions: *Take the road from Nelson to Stoke. Turn right at the lights into Songer Street. Travel right to the bottom of Songer Street around the bay into Monaco turning in front of the Monaco Boat Club into Martin Street.*

Nelson
Homestay
Address: 201a Annesbrook Drive, Nelson
Name: Jim & Audrey McMahon
Telephone: (03) 548-5146
Beds: 4 Single (2 bedrooms, guest bathroom)
Tariff: B&B $50-60 Double, $40 Single
Nearest Town: 5 km South-West of Nelson city on Highway 6

Our home is newish, sunny and comfortable with pleasant rural and sea views. You will find us easy to locate, our driveway being directly off Highway 6 (West Coast - Picton route). A few minutes drive from the city centre, bus stop is handy.

Guests tell us we "have the ideal bed & breakfast set up", "good beds, excellent food and great conversation" - frequent comments in guest book. Your accommodation is spacious and spotless with own bathroom, fridge, coffee, tea, muffins, phone, books etc. Breakfast is your choice - varied selection of cooked and continental. Good coffee! Main bedroom has comfortable chairs, TV and glass door to garden, second bedroom available (share facilities).

Tahunanui Beach (swimming, tennis, golf & fishing) is close by, also village shops and restaurants.

Your hosts, a well travelled retired couple, have wide ranging interests and genuinely enjoy visitors of all nationalities. A friendly relaxed atmosphere awaits you.

Directions: *We'll happily collect you from nearby airport or bus - just ring.*

Nelson
Homestay
Address: 28 Devon Street, Stoke, Nelson
Name: Ralph and Reigh Robinson
Telephone: (03) 547 7442
Beds: 4 Single (2 bedrooms, guest bathroom)
Tariff: B&B Double $55, Single $30, Dinner by arrangement
Nearest Town: 8 km south of Nelson, 8 km north of Richmond on SH6

We are a retired couple who have been home hosting guests from Europe, North America, Africa, Asia and Australia for eight years.
The twin bedded double bedrooms open onto a balcony with mountain views. The beds have electric blankets and innersprung mattresses. The house is situated 1 km off SH6 at Stoke. It adjoins an historic home, open to the public and a flood-lit rose garden. Pick-up available from buses and airport. Special interest tours can be arranged.
'Superb hospitality. A highlight of our trip' - J & M O'F. Canada
'The company comfort and cuisine all rate 5 star' - P & A N, USA.
'Delightful and very comfortable' - E S, South Africa.
'Great evening. Beautiful meal' - M & J L, Australia.
'Thanks for all' - O & M B, Germany.
'Thank you for good company, good food and your lovely home' - J A, UK.

Wakefield, Nelson
Homestay
Address: 6 Anslow Place, Wakefield, Nelson
Name: Ngaire and Norman Lochhead
Telephone: (03) 541 8321
Beds: 4 Single (2 bedrooms, guest bathroom)
Tariff: B&B Double $55, Single $35, Children half price; Dinner $15; Campervans welcome
Nearest Town: Nelson 32 km, Richmond 16 km

Our house is situated about two minutes off the main road in a cul-de-sac, quiet area.
Recently we have retired to Wakefield after enjoying a farming life. We both enjoy meeting people and like to think we make them very welcome.
The village of Wakefield is surrounded by mixed farming, also logging activities.
We have a steam museum, very good golf course, tramping available, snow skiing one hour away.
In our village we are very lucky to have a Post Office, large supermarket, chemist and two takeaway/dairies.
We are a very caring and sharing village.

Wakefield, Nelson

Homestay
Address: Whitby Lodge, 212 Whitby Road, Wakefield, Nelson
Name: Marion and Buster Stringer
Telephone: (03) 541 8117
Beds: 1 Double, 2 Single (2 bedrooms)
Tariff: B&B Double $60, Single $35, Dinner $15; Campervan facilities
Nearest Town: Richmond 15 km, Nelson 30 km

Our home is very easy to find just 1 km north of Wakefield Village. We are in the centre of Nelson Province, an ideal base for visiting lakes, mountains, and beaches, or following wine and pottery trails. A golf course is handy, also the local steam museum and historic church.
We are a well-travelled couple with a very comfortable home, complete with open fire in winter and swimming pool in summer. Our interests include trail-bike riding, spinning and embroidery.
We serve substantial home-cooked meals and invite you to enjoy our hospitality (non-smokers please).
Directions - *please phone.*

Stoke, Nelson

Homestay
Address: "Treeview",
7 Titoki Street, Stoke,
Nelson
Name: Kathie and Laurence Carr
Telephone: (03) 547-6307

Beds: 1 Double, 2 Single (2 bedrooms, guest bathroom)
Tariff: B&B Double $55, Single $30, Children half price, Dinner $20
Nearest Town: Nelson 5 km, 10 minutes to city

Our comfortable home is ideally situated with view towards the mountains. The breakfast room gets the morning sun. Relaxed atmosphere. We welcome you to this attractive area, within walking distance to Stoke Centre on Highway 6 with all facilities. Isel Park and Broadgreen Rose Gardens, historic homes and museum. By car a short distance to restaurants, beaches, walkways, bowling greens, golf links.
Two guest rooms, one double with TV and one with two singles. Shower room with hand basin. Separate lounge.
Kathie a country girl at heart, Laurence likes a game of golf and very knowledgeable of Port Nelson (retired tugmaster). Non-smokers, we like walking with our Cocker Spaniel dog.
Directions: *From Nelson to Stoke on Highway 6, turn left at traffic lights into Songer Street. Titoki Street is last street on right before the hill. From Richmond on Highway 6 turn right at the lights into Songer Street.*
A shuttle service from Airport or City Visitors Centre can bring you to our door.

Richmond, Nelson

Homestay
Address: 37 Kihilla Road, Richmond
Name: Ray and Janice O'Loughlin
Telephone: (03) 544 6541
Beds: 3 Single (2 bedrooms, guest bathroom)
Tariff: B&B Double $55, Single $30, Dinner $15, Children $20
Nearest Town: Nelson

Richmond is a small town 13 km south of Nelson. Our large, spacious four year old home is built on three levels, making the most of the sun in every room and the panoramic views of the mountains in the SW and the sea to the north. We have two guest rooms, one with twin beds and the other with one single bed. Guests have their own toilet and large bathroom including a spa bath for two.
We have enjoyed extensive travel and the company of many families in their homes. Now we would like to extend our hospitality to visitors to our area and share our home with them.
We have a friendly cocker spaniel and a cat and Ray has a large aviary with many varieties of finches and canaries. Guests will awake to their song in the morning. Our large colourful garden demands quite a lot of our time. We also find time to enjoy the beautiful beaches which are only fifteen minutes from our home.
After a busy day you may enjoy relaxing with us over a family dinner or you may prefer just bed and breakfast.
We will do our best to make your stay enjoyable.

Richmond, Nelson

Homestay
Address: Edens Road, Hope R.D. 1, Richmond, Nelson
Name: Laurie & Pat Rainbow
Telephone: (03) 544-5766
Beds: 3 Single (2 bedrooms)
Tariff: **B&B** $25 Single, children 1/2 price, $10 Dinner, Campervans welcome
Nearest Town: Richmond (8mins), Nelson (20mins)

Laurie loves old cars, Fords in particular, and wood working, stamps and taking photos.
Pat loves sewing, weddings are special, pottery and of necessity the very large garden area of our 10 acre block, where we have a small flock of sheep and grow peas.
We live in a cream, splitstone boomarang shaped home built to the sun, where we would enjoy making you one of the family, especially now we have only one of our family living at home.
Cosy beds with electric blankets and you share our toilet facilities.
We would really enjoy hearing your holiday adventures and seeing photos of your home and family.
Directions: *Travelling South through Richmond carry on 4 km from traffic lights to Edens Road, and turn right (Aniseed Valley Road goes left and can be confusing). Travelling North from Brightwater, pass over Wairoa River and at second crossroad turn left. You are in Edens Road.* _____

Appleby, Nelson

Homestay
Address: Seachange Farm, Appleby, Richmond R.D. 1, Nelson
Name: Dot & Dave Wills
Telephone: (03) 544-2702
Beds: 1 Double, 2 Single (2 bedrooms)
Tariff: B&B $50 Double, $30 Single, $15 Dinner
Nearest Town: Richmond (7 km), Nelson (22 km)

Welcome to Seachange Farm. We abandoned city life and are now developing a small vineyard and winery in sunny Appleby. We also have our own sheep and hens and enjoy all home grown produce from our orchard and garden.
You will enjoy your stay in our cosy, comfortable home.
Directions: *State Highway 60 from Richmond, cross the Waimea River (Appleby Bridge), take second turning on the left at Peaviner Corner. We are 200 metres on left.*

Thorpe, Nelson

Farmstay +
Self-Contained Accommodation
Address: Thorpe, RD 2 Wakefield,
Dovedale-Woodstock Road, Nelson
Name: Robert and Joan Panzer
Telephone: (03) 543 3825
Beds: 1 Double (1 bedroom): 1 Double, 1 Single (self-contained)
Tariff: B&B Double $55, Single $35, Dinner $15
For longer stay and self-contained accommodation, please inquire

Thorpe is halfway between Nelson and Motueka, with plenty of nearby options for tramping (Abel Tasman, Northwest Nelson and Mt Arthur); fishing (Motueka River 3 minutes away); or the local crafts and vineyards.
We offer a peaceful, rural retreat with the sunny Nelson climate, view of Mt Arthur, good food, and international Kiwi hosts. Our 70 year old farmhouse surrounded by rolling hills, forests and rivers, is in the middle of 20 acres planted in timber, fruit, and nut trees, plus sheep, pigs, chooks, geese, cats and a dog. Situated along the Dove River, guests arrive at our door by foot crossing over our own swing bridge or by driving over a vehicle bridge.
Robert is from Holland and involved in tourism, backpacking and organised tours, and along with Joan from the United States, are happy to advise, assist or even guide you in your travel plans. We are both frequently in Nelson so can easily arrange transport to and from there.

Ruby Bay, Nelson
Private Hotel
Address: "Holton", Coastal Highway, Ruby Bay, Nelson
Name: Lynda & Hilary Blundell
Telephone: (03) 540-2269
Beds: 1 Double, 2 Single (2 bedrooms, ensuite bathrooms)
Tariff: B&B $80 Double, $60 Single, $25 Dinner
Nearest Town: Motueka (10 mins), Richmond (20 mins)

*Holton has been a landmark in Nelson for 125 years. With it's unusual red
and white facade, high-pitched gables and slate roof, this historic house sits
tranquilly amid majestic trees on the hillside overlooking Ruby Bay.*
*The house has been recently restored, with due respect paid to it's original
character, warmth and charm. Antique furniture, polished wood, open fires
and tapestries enhance the sense of timelessness and romance which is part of
this gracious old home. The garden has many interesting and rare plants, old-
fashioned roses, specimen trees, and giant eucalypts.*
*There are two double attic bedrooms (with ensuite bathrooms), tastefully and
comfortably furnished. Downstairs, your private sitting/dining room opens
onto a conservatory and secluded side garden. The covered verandah,
framed by an ancient wisteria, offers a vista down to the sea.*
*Breakfast is a la carte and dinner is available by arrangement. All meals
feature imaginative use of fresh local produce, organic vegetables, fruit and
herbs from our garden, and free-range eggs from our hens. Local wines are
complimentary with dinner.*
*On the Coastal Highway, 30 minutes from Nelson, Holton is a convenient base
from which to visit Abel Tasman Park, beaches, wineries and the craft trail.*
*No TV disturbs the peaceful atmosphere, and the inside of the house is a
"smoke-free area" for the comfort of all guests.*
*Because we have only two guest rooms, we have time to spend with our
visitors, and can assure you of friendly, personal attention. We look forward
to meeting you and sharing our little piece of paradise.*
Directions: *On the Coastal Highway at Ruby Bay between Richmond and
Motueka.*

210

Motueka
Guest House

Address: Whites Guest House, 430 High Street, Motueka (just south of junction Highway 60 and 61)
Name: Laddie and Rachael White
Telephone: (03) 528-7318
Beds: 3 Double, 2 Twin, 2 Single (7 bedrooms 3 guest bathrooms)
Tariff: B&B Double $67.50, Single $45 (Winter Discounts, May–Aug, for 2 nights or more); Dinner by arrangement $18
Nearest Town: Motueka 1.6 km

Rachael and Laddie offer quality hospitality and personal service in a no smoking atmosphere, in their freshly renovated home. Room to relax in the spacious lounge and garden. Sleep in quality inner-sprung beds. Enjoy a home-cooked evening meal served with fresh garden vegetables. Rachael's meals are cooked and presented with flair and pride. (For optimum satisfaction meals should be ordered by 4 pm).

Books on New Zealand and up-to-date local information is displayed. Laddie has the knowledge and is happy to advise and assist with your ongoing travel plans.

Both Skyline and Newmans bus services will set you down near the Guest House on request. This will save a walk back from Motueka centre (which is only 1.6 km).

Off-street parking is available for your car.

Should you be walking the Abel Tasman Park we can store your car or belongings. A limited amount of tramping gear is available for hire.

A laundry service is also available at a small charge.

Tea and coffee facilities are self-service at all times.

The sunny Motueka area offers beautiful beaches, wine and crafts trail, horticulture tours and the unique and peaceful Abel Tasman Park.

Forward booking is advisable December through March in this area.

211

Motueka

Farmstay
+ Self-Contained Accommodation
Address: Kairuru, State Highway 60,
Takaka Hill, Motueka
Name: David and Wendy Henderson
Telephone: (03) 528 8091

Beds: 2 Double, 2 Single (2 bedrooms, guest bathroom)
Tariff: B&B Double $70, Single $35, Children half price; Dinner $15
Nearest Town: 17 km from Motueka on the Takaka Hill on State Highway 60

We are a farming family of four (two girls aged 12 and 5 years). We farm sheep and cattle on our 4000 acre hill country property called Kairuru.
Our farm is handy to Kaiteriteri beach, Golden Bay and Abel Tasman National Park.
We are offering to travellers a modern, fully-equipped two-bedroom cottage with open plan living, and its own bathroom and laundry. The cottage has wonderful views, is wooden inside and outside giving a rustic but warm feeling. A good selection for breakfast is supplied, but made by yourselves at your leisure in your own fully-equipped kitchen. Your accommodation is handy to ours for dinner and socialising.
We enjoy visitors from allover the world and look forward to your stay.
Directions: *From Motueka take the road to Takaka (State Highway 60). 'Kairuru' is 11 km up the hill on the right hand side.*

Riwaka, Motueka

Bed & Breakfast
Address: Main Road, Riwaka,
RD3, Motueka
Name: "Hillview"
Telephone: (03) 528-6042

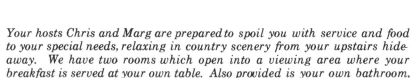

Beds: 1 Double, 2 Single (2 bedrooms, guest bathroom)
Tariff: B&B (Continental Breakfast) Double $60, Single $45, (Cooked Breakfast) Double $66, Single $48
Nearest Town: Motueka 5 mins

Your hosts Chris and Marg are prepared to spoil you with service and food to your special needs, relaxing in country scenery from your upstairs hideaway. We have two rooms which open into a viewing area where your breakfast is served at your own table. Also provided is your own bathroom, fridge and tea/coffee making facilities.
Marg has spent several years in the motel industry which has taught her the importance of cleanliness and giving the homely touch to your rooms, also enjoys craft making and cooking. Try one of her omelettes for breakfast. Chris has spent most of her life in the area and has a great love and knowledge of our lovely countryside and can guide you to all the little beauty spots. We endeavour to treat our guests as we would our friends which could include a social drink in our living room. Good licenced restaurants close by, including takeaway food shops within walking distance.
Riwaka is situated only 5 to 15 mins from such pleasures as a golf course,

caving, horse trekking, trout fishing, tramping, Able Tasman National Park or just a stroll along the golden sands of Kaiteriteri Beach.
Directions: *From Motueka take the road to Takaka (SH60) reaching Riwaka approx 5 mins where you will see our sign on your left.*

Riwaka, Motueka
Homestay
Address: "Sea Haven", Green Tree Road, Riwaka, RD3, Motueka
Name: Dennis and Maureen Farrer   **Telephone:** (03) 528-6219
Beds: 1 Double, 3 Single (1 bedroom, guest bathroom)
Tariff: B&B Double $55, each extra $22, Single $40, Dinner $15, Children under 12 discount
Nearest Town: Motueka 5 km, Nelson 55 km

Riwaka is a rural settlement, the heart of hop, tobacco and kiwifruit growing. We overlook the tidal estuary at Riwaka wharf with sea views across Tasman Bay to D'Urville Island. Close by is the Abel Tasman National Park and the beaches of Stephens Bay, Marahau and Kaiteriteri and trout fishing in the Motueka River.
The guest accommodation in our new two storey home is on the ground floor and consists of lounge/dining room with double bed settee, single divan, TV and tea/coffee making facilities, one twin bedroom and separate toilet and bathroom. Packed lunches are available, also dinner which can be served in the guest accommodation or with us.
Directions: *by car leave Motueka by main highway to Takaka, after crossing Motueka River Bridge turn right into Lodder Lane. At the end of Lodder Lane, turn left into School Road, then right into Green Tree Road. When arriving by Newmans or Skyline bus at Motueka or through Motueka airport, please phone.*

Motueka
Self-contained Cottage
Address: Southtrack Farm, Pokororo, R.D. 1, Motueka
Name: Gail & Don Barrier   **Telephone:** (03) 526-8630
Beds: 8 Single (3 bedrooms, guest bathroom)
Tariff: **B&B** Double $50, Single $25, children 1/2 price, $15 Dinner. (For bed only i.e. self-catering $20 per person but a discount for larger groups.)
Nearest Town: Motueka

Our 140 hectare farm is in the Graham Valley on the road to Mt Arthur and the North West Nelson Forest Park. We have a comfortable self-contained farm cottage available. It has a lounge with an open fireplace and large kitchen with coal range, three bedrooms and can accommodate eight people. You may bring you own food and cook for yourselves or we will be pleased to provide any meals you require. Wild pork, venison, duck or seafood may be served if requested, with local wines, or vegetarian meals if preferred.
The forest park is only a few kilometres away and noted for its diverse landscape, beech forests, birdlife and well maintained tracks and huts.
The Motueka River is two minutes away and offers very good trout fishing. Guided tramps and fishing trips can be arranged.
We enjoy meeting people from New Zealand and overseas. Families welcome.
Directions: *Please phone.*

Motueka
Homestay
Address: Doone Cottage, R.D. 1, Motueka, Nelson
Name: Stan & Glen Davenport
Telephone: (03) 5268 740
Beds: 2 Double, 2 Single (2 Bedrooms, guest bathroom)
Tariff: B&B $80 Double, $45 Single, $25 Dinner
Nearest Town: Motueka (28 km), Nelson (64 km)

Homely hospitality, peace and tranquility, trout fishing, beautiful garden and bush setting, native birds, goats, sheep, chickens, ducks, donkey and pet pig, weaving studio - all abound at Doone Cottage. A lovely 100 year old home, comfortably furnished cottage style in an attractive 2 acre setting of garden, native trees and ferns, lawns and shrubs, which have a beautiful outlook across the Motueka Valley to the Mt Arthur range. Double and twin accommodation available with private bathroom facilities for guests and own private verandah. Home cooked meals, home made bread, fresh garden vegetables, free range eggs etc. Fishermen's "out of hours" meals also catered for.

Your hostess spins wool from the raw fleece and has her own weaving studio where you can see the finished garments, blankets, wallhangings, rugs etc.

There is much to interest the tourist and fisherman. The Motueka River is at the gate, with several others closeby, providing the opportunity to fish some of the best brown trout rivers in the South Island. Fishing licences and a local guide are available. Wilderness trips can be arranged. Excellent day trips include the Nelson Lakes and Abel Tasman National Parks, Kaiteriteri beaches, Northwest Nelson Forest Park, Golden Bay and Nelson.

This is one of New Zealand's main fruit producing regions where the sun shines over 2,400 hours annually. The region is rich in crafts of all descriptions.

We are very fortunate to live in this beautiful corner of New Zealand and we enjoy sharing our home and surroundings with visitors from all over the world.

Collingwood
Bed & Breakfast
Address: Hakea Hill House,
Parapara, R.D. 2 Takaka, Golden Bay
Postal: P O Box 35, Collingwood
Name: Vic and Liza Eastman
Telephone & Fax: (03) 524-8467
Beds: 2 Double, 2 Single (a bunk-bed) - up to 5 people (2 bedrooms, guest bathroom)
Tariff: B&B $95 Double B&B, $60 Single, children 1/2 price, boxed lunches available.
Nearest Town: Takaka 20 km and Collingwood 10 km

Hakea Hill rises above the South side of the Parapara estuary on the Golden Bay coastlinee and allows a view of the entire bay including Farewell Spit and its lighthouse. We usually can see D'Urville Island beyond Separation Point and are treated to Mount Taranaki on the North Island occasionally.
Our new home is designed to encompass the view from every room. One guest bedroom has its own balcony, overlooking the estuary and bay. Both American and New Zealand electrical outlets are installed.
Vic is a physician specialised in emergency medicine and family practice. His hobbies include astronomy, and guests are welcome to explore the dark skies with a Questar 3.5 or an Odessey 17.5 telescope. Liza, besides homemaker and expert cook, is interested in sailing, horse riding, and machine quilt making. We have three teenage children.
Golden Bay is renowned for its tourist attractions such as Waikoropupu Springs, Farewell Spit safari tours, Aorere gold fields, limestone caves, settlers' museums, numerous pottery and craft outlets, pleasant sandy beaches, bush walks and the beginning of the famous Heaphy Track to Karamea.
Directions: *Reservations are necessary. Please phone.*

The standard of accommodation in *The New Zealand Bed and Breakfast Book* ranges from homely to luxurious, but you can always be sure of superior hospitality.

Tophouse

Farmstay Tourism Award Winner
Address: Tophouse, RD2, Nelson
Name: Melody and Mike Nicholls
Telephone: (03) 521 1848
Beds: 2 Double, 8 Single (5 bedrooms, guest bathrooms)
Tariff: B&B Double $60, Single $30, Dinner $15; Children negotiable
Nearest Town: Blenheim 98 km, Murchison 57 km, Nelson 72 km, St Arnaud 9km

We, Melody and Mike Nicholls, with our two young sons, invite you to share our unique home with its huge open fires, lovely setting and homely atmosphere.

Tophouse, a cob (mud) building, dating from the 1880's when it was a hotel, and reopened in 1989 as a Farm Guest House, has that 'good old days' feel about it.

Situated on 300 ha (730 acres) of picturesque high country farm running goats and cattle, with much native bush and an abundance of bird life, Tophouse is only 9 km from St Arnaud.

St Arnaud, gateway to Nelson Lakes National Park, is nestled on the shore of Lake Rotoiti, a popular holiday spot for its peace and beauty, bush walks, fishing etc and in the winter becomes a ski village serving the two local fields, Rainbow and Mt Robert.

A typical farmhouse dinner is taken with the family and since the fire's going, 'real' toast for breakfast.

Directions: *Just off State Highway 63 between Blenheim and Murchison and 9 km from St Arnaud is Tophouse, that`s us! The area took its name from the building. If travelling from Nelson, leave State Highway 6 at Belgrove and travel towards St Arnaud, we're signposted from the main road and looking forward to your visit.*

Owen River, Nelson

Farmstay
Address: 'Strathowen', Owen River, Nelson
Name: Peter and Rankeilor Arnott   **Telephone:** (03) 523 9075
Beds: 4 Single (2 bedrooms)
Tariff: B&B Double $60, Single $40, Children half price; Dinner $20
Nearest Town: 18 km east of Murchison, 1 hour 30 mins from Nelson, 2 hrs 30 min from Picton

Strathowen is situated in a beautiful area in the Owen River valley, 1 km drive from the only highway to the west coast from Nelson and Blenheim. Being surrounded by native reserves, rivers and lakes, we are ideally situated for those interested in the many activities and scenery that this beautiful area provides, or for the travel-weary, guests may like to relax in our attractive garden overlooking the Owen River.

We provide two comfortable bedrooms, guests' bathroom and a separate sitting room.

We enjoy entertaining trout fishermen and their wives who may like to explore the many rivers in the area. Guides are available locally.

Guests are welcome to take part in farm life, and walk the bush tracks in the area. Horse trekking and white water rafting are also available locally.

We are a farming family with three teenage children currently at boarding school and university.

We look forward to welcoming you to 'Strathowen'.

Directions: *1 km drive off main highway at Owen River. Signposted.*

Murchison
Farmstay
Address: "Awapiriti",
Highway 65, Maruia Valley,
Private Bag, Murchison
Name: David & Irene Free
Telephone: (03) 523-9466
Beds: 2 Double, 2 Single (3 bedrooms, guest bathroom)
Tariff: B&B $60 Double, $40 Single, $20 Dinner
Nearest Town: Murchison 18 kms

Our farm is situated in the beautiful Maruia Valley. We have the Maruia River (well known for fishing) as our boundary with a swing foot bridge and road bridge to the property. The farm has native bush and offers many interesting places to walk and relax with lovely scenery for the artistic. We mostly farm deer with some cattle and sheep, grow all our own vegetables organically, keep poultry and milk a house cow. We are a couple on our own with a grown up family with interests in gardening, hunting, native birds and animals. Hunting trips on the place by arrangement. Wild pork is served frequently as a speciality for evening meals. Murchison offers many activities for visitors including Kayaking, white water rafting on the Buller River and has a very good golf course. We are happy to involve visitors in our daily activities on the farm and to share our interests.

Directions: *Please ring.*

Westland

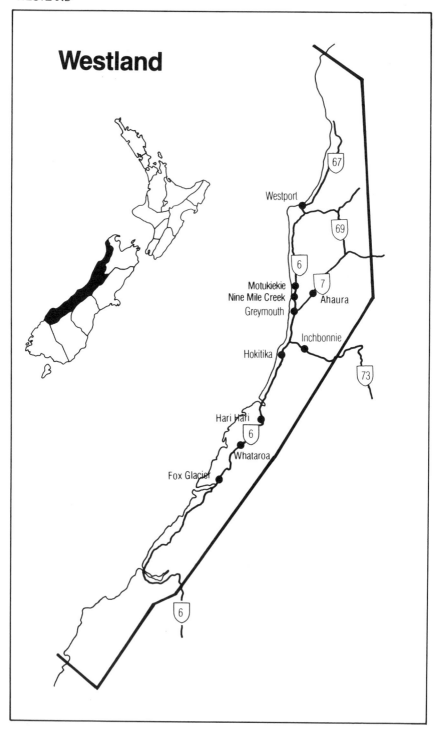

Westport

67

69

6

Motukiekie
Nine Mile Creek
Greymouth

7

Ahaura

Inchbonnie

Hokitika

73

Hari Hari

6

Whataroa

Fox Glacier

6

Westport
Homestay
Address: "Wynyard" Fairdown Beach, PO Box 127, Westport
Telephone: (0289) 27-860 before 9 am or after 5 pm
Beds: 1 Double, 2 Single (2 bedrooms, guest bathroom)
Tariff: B&B Double $65, Single $40; Dinner $20; Campervans $24
Nearest Town: 11 km north of Westport on the Karamea Highway

Forget pollution and noise. Watch the breakers roll, enjoy the peace of native bush - or how about just lazing? Come and enjoy the hospitality and scenery of the West Coast. Westport, where friendly people live, has much to offer - jet boating, caving, white and black water rafting. You tell us where your interest lies and we will try to help.

"Wynyard" is designed so that those with disabilities, paraplegics or simply needing a quiet rest can enjoy this peaceful environment. Should you need a special diet, need transport from airport, to be met or taken to the Heaphy Track, we at "Wynyard" can help – comfortable, warm, and friendly hospitality assured.

It is advisable to make a reservation. Please phone before 9 am or in the evening.

Ahaura
Homestay
Address: "The Acadamy",
Main Road, Ahaura
Name: Felix & Glenda Pickering
Telephone: (03) 732-3731
Beds: 1 Double, 4 Single (3 bedrooms)

Tariff: **B&B** $60 Double, $30 Single, children (under 14) 1/2 price, $15 Dinner, Campervans welcome
Nearest Town: Greymouth - 34 km South

Your hosts Felix and Glenda welcome you to our modern two storey home, nestled on 14 acres beside the Ahaura River.

We have raised a family of three and are now alone, and are keen to welcome you with genuine West Coast hospitality.

Enjoy the peace and quiet of a rural life-style, but with all the amenities of the local village within walking distance, eg. squash, tennis, gun-club. To this can be added great trout fishing, bush walking, gold panning.

If less than inclined to physical pursuits, quietly explore numerous small valleys, hidden lakes, and historical sites.

We are centrally situated and within a few hours travel of all major tourist attractions the "Coast" has to offer.

EXPECT THE MOST

Motukiekie, Coast Road,
Homestay
Address: Tigger's House,
Motukiekie Rocks, 12 Mile Bluff,
R.D. 1, Runanga, Westland
Name: Jenny Greene
Telephone: (03) 762-7654
Beds: 2 Double, 1 Single (2 bedrooms - extra 2 singles if req'd)
Tariff: B&B $40 Double, $20 Single, $15 Dinner
Nearest Town: 20 km North of Greymouth, 25 km South of Punakaiki
(Pancake Rocks)

"Tigger's House" is a quaint historic miner's cottage on the Coast Road, near the Paparoa National Park. A cosy, comfortable, wooden home with a new extension that blends into the beautiful bush surroundings.
My cottage has unique charm and is a peaceful retreat on a spectacular headland with superb views of mountains and the rugged coastline. There are fascinating beach and river walks and old coal-mines to explore nearby.
I enjoy having people to stay and provide warm, friendly hospitality. I have travelled extensively and have an interesting library. I also offer a wealth of tourist information and enjoy preparing delicious food.
Facilities are shared, cooking facilities are available by arrangement.
I also earn my living weaving, tutoring creative drama and movement, teaching English to foreigners, editing books, writing brochures and calling for barn dances.
Transport can be arranged from Greymouth or Punakaiki on request. Please telephone first to make a booking.
Directions: *From Punakaiki through Barrytown to 13 Mile Creek then 2.3 km on top of hill, Motukiekie B&B sign on right. Last house up drive. From Greymouth, through Rapahoe to 10 Mile Creek then 1.5 km on top of hill, B&B sign on left.*

Nine Mile Creek
Homestay
Address: Nine Mile Creek,
Highway 6, Coast Road, Westland
Name: Tony & Ib Pupich
Telephone: (03) 762-7743
Beds: 1 Double, 2 Single (2 bedrooms, guest bathroom)
Tariff: B&B $60 Double, $30 Single, children 1/2 price, $20 Dinner
Nearest Town: Greymouth

We are retired farmers in our mid fifties who offer warm hospitality in our lovely home set in two acres of garden and native bush overlooking the Tasman Sea and adjoining the Paparoa National Park.
We have two guest bedrooms, one double with ensuite and one twin. Both have fantastic views. The sunsets are unbelievably beautiful.

Breakfast is served at your convenience. A three course dinner isserved with New Zealand wines.

There is a lot for you to do in the area. Punakaiki Blowholes and Pancake Rocks, Helicopter hikes, caves, rafting, and many bush walks. We are one hundred metres from the beach where you can fossick for green stone, go shellfishing or surfcasting.

Directions: *9 miles North of Greymouth on Highway 6 at 9 Mile Creek, Coast Road. Our house is signposted with our name.*

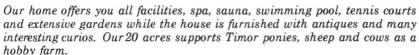

Coal Creek, Greymouth
Prestigious Homestay
Address: "Oak Lodge", Coal Creek, Greymouth
Name: Roy and Zelda Anderson
Telephone: (03) 768 6832
Beds: 2 Double, 2 Single (3 bedrooms, guest bathroom)
Tariff: B&B $50 per person, Dinner $20
Nearest Town: Greymouth 3 km

Our home offers you all facilities, spa, sauna, swimming pool, tennis courts and extensive gardens while the house is furnished with antiques and many interesting curios. Our 20 acres supports Timor ponies, sheep and cows as a hobby farm.

We have both lived in Greymouth for twenty five years and have a good knowledge of the many interesting features of the area and New Zealand. Roy an active Rotarian. We have vintage cars to view in the barn.

We have also travelled extensively and appreciate you may like time out in your own lounge or join us around the fire in our living room. Traditional home made soups and sweets accompanies roast lamb, venison, or fish.

Allow a couple of days at least to visit Punakiki Blow Holes, Shanty Town, abandoned Coke Ovens, greenstone manufacturing, fishing and the many interesting walks especially Woods Creek.

A small cottage (all facilities) sleeping four also available at $50 a night.

Directions: *State Highway 6 main north road to Westport. 4 km from town centre.*

Greymouth
Homestay
Address: "Ardwyn House",
48 Chapel Street, Greymouth
Name: Alun and Mary Owen
Telephone: (03) 768-6107
Beds: 1 Double, 4 Single (3 bedrooms)
Tariff: B&B Double $55, Single $33, Children half price

Ardwyn House is three minutes walk from the town centre in a quiet garden setting of two acres offering sea, river and town views.
The house was built in the 1920s and is a fine example of an imposing residence with fine woodwork and leadlight windows, whilst being a comfortable and friendly home.
We are ideally situated for travellers touring the west coast as Greymouth is central and a popular stopover.
We offer a courtesy car service to and from local travel centres and also provide off-street parking.

Greymouth
Guest House
Address: Golden Coast Guest House, 10 Smith Street, Greymouth
Name: Gladys Roche
Telephone: (03) 768 7839
Beds: 2 Double, 1 Queen, 2 Twin (5 bedrooms)
Tariff: B&B Double $60 (continental breakfast), $66 (cooked breakfast), Single $42; Children half price; Backpackers room with facilities $15 per person

Gladys Roche is the hostess at the Golden Coast Guest House and has been for the last 25 years. It is two minutes from town Railway Station and buses but there is no noise from trains. It is built on a slight rise with lovely gardens and barbecue area. There is a TV lounge and tea and coffee making facilities and laundry. There is also off-street parking. Electric blankets and heaters in all rooms. I offer a courtesy car to and from buses and train.
Your comfort is my business.
Directions: *Main highway to South Road above Railway Station.*

Inchbonnie
Farmstay +
Self-Contained Accommodation
Address: Inchbonnie, RD1,
Kumara, Westland 7871
Name: Russell and Jean Adams
Telephone: (03) 738-0153
Beds: 1 Double, 4 Single (2 bedrooms, guest bathroom)
Tariff: B&B Double $60, Single $35, Dinner by arrangement $15,
Children $10; Campervan facilities
Nearest Town: Inchbonnie is 70 km from Greymouth and Hokitika, and is easily accessible from Canterbury especially via Arthur's Pass

We offer a fully furnished cottage in a scenic rural retreat. The cottage is on our property and we farm sheep, beef and deer. We are situated in the midst of some of the best trout fishing in the South Island - Lake Brunner and Lake Poerua and rivers within 10 minutes travel. Abundant bird life and good scenic walks nearby.
Our home was built about 1916 and is set in a large English style garden. Russell is the farmer, Jean handspins, handknits and sells her work and also gardens. Our young adults live away but come home weekends. Craig is a keen fisherman and also shoots, Janine loves riding and enjoys needlepoint Inchbonnie is a great place to relax and 'catch up'.
Directions: *we are 10 km from Jacksons turnoff (S.H. 73) on Inchbonnie-Mitchells Road. Please phone for details.*

Hokitika
Homestay
Address: 70 Tudor Sreet, Hokitika
Name: Brian and Berna
Telephone: (0288) 57 599
Beds: 4 Single (2 bedrooms, guest bathroom)
Tariff: B&B Double $60, Single $30, Dinner $ 15

We are a semi-retired couple living in a fifteen year old split level home within one kilometere of the business area and the airport. We have been home hosting for five years and enjoy meeting people. Our interests are golf, (4 km to golf course) bowls, whitebaiting in season and gold prospecting.
Our sons operate an alluvial gold claim 8 km from here which most guests enjoy seeing. The glow-worm dell is 5 minutes walk away
Hokitika has 3 greenstone shops where you can watch the artifacts being made, several good craft shops, a gold room and a glass blowing studio.
Directions: *when coming into Hokitika from Greymouth take first turn on left. We are the third house on the left. Travelling from south Westland take last turn on right (Tudor Street), third house on left. Follow airport sign from SH6 from either direction.*

Hokitika

Homestay
Address: "Rossendale",
234 Gibson Quay, Hokitika
Name: Vi and Arthur Haworth
Telephone: (0288) 56620
Beds: 1 Double, 2 Single (2 bedrooms, guest bathroom and toilet)
Tariff: B&B Double $50, Single 30, Dinner $15, Children half price

We are a semi retired couple with a grown up family who are now married. We have travelled extensively both within NZ and overseas and enjoy meeting people from other countries, also fellow New Zealanders.
We offer hospitality in a spacious home situated at the edge of town on the banks of the Hokitika River. We are 1 km from the centre of town with full view of the Southern Alps and with off street parking. We have two guest bedrooms, one double with H & C, and one twin. All beds have electric blankets. Guests have their own bathroom.
We offer a full cooked breakfast or a continental, whichever you prefer. Dinner by arrangement.
Our hobbies are gardening, fishing, bush walks, gold panning and meeting people.
Hokitika is within easy reach of all 'West Coast' main attractions, from the beaches to the Alps, together with pleasant bush walks, and scenic drives.
We will meet the plane or bus.

Hokitika

Guest House
Address: 20 Hamilton Street, Hokitika
Name: Central Guest House – Joanna and Brent Williamson
Telephone: (0288) 58-232 until late 1991
Beds: 6 Double/Twin, 1 Single, 1 Quad (9 rooms, ample bathroom and shower facilities.
Tariff: B&B Double/Twin $59, Single $39; Dinner $19; Full English breakfast available $5 extra per person
Nearest Town: Central Hokitika

Our 1920s character home is centrally located in Hokitika. Hokitika is a pleasant, small town, once "the capital of the goldfields" and in recent years it has seen a resurgence in gold-mining activity.
The goldroom, greenstone factory, craft co-operative, museum, Tweed factory, three superb restaurants and banks are all within two minutes walk. Those who have a little more time may like to take a scenic drive around Lake Kaniere to the Hokitika Gorge, shanty-town – the authentic recreation of an 1880s goldrush town or the local glow-worm dell. For the more energetic

Hokitika is surrounded by many walkways, gold panning, hunting, fishing, whitebaiting (in season) and rafting areas.
Both of us have travelled extensively and enjoy meeting others from around New Zealand and overseas.
We look forward to sharing the many wonderful features that made us choose Hokitika as our home.
We are only too happy to meet anyone arriving by bus or plane.
Hokitika is 30 minutes from Shantytown, 1 hour from Punakaiki Blowholes, 30 minutes from Greymouth, 5 hours from Picton, 4 hours from Christchurch, 6 hours from Wanaka, 7 hours from Queenstown, 2 hours from the glaciers, 5 hours from Nelson.
Directions: *Turn left at town clock and take first street to right.*

Evans Creek, Hari Hari
Farmhouse +
Self Contained Accommodation
Address: Evans Creek,
Private Bag, Hokitika
Name: Joanne & Jon Duindam
Telephone: (03) 288-33028
Beds: 1 Double, 2 Single, plus self contained farm cottage
Tariff: B&B $25 per person, $15 Dinner per person
Nearest Town: Hokitika

Your hosts are Joanne & Jon Duindam, who with their oldest son Jon, farm 1200 acres as a Dairy Unit.
Close to native bush - your hosts will provide trout fishing / hunting excursions - and should you have the time, there are many bush / beach walks closeby. Easy commuting distance to the FRANZ JOSEF GLACIER and FOX GLACIER. Your hosts have travelled extensively and you are assured of a warm welcome.
Directions: *Take State Highway 6 from Hokitika, travel through Ross - continue through native bush areas past Lake Ianthe. Watch for Evans Creek Bridge - Our homestead is on the left.*

Hari Hari, South Westland

Farmstay
Address: Please phone
Name: Bev and Grant Muir
Telephone & Fax: (0288) 33074. After Sept 92 (03) 753 3074
Beds: 1 Queen, 1 Double, 3 Single (3 bedrooms, 1 ensuite, 1 guest bathroom)
Tariff: B&B Double $70, Single $40, Dinner $20, Children half price
Nearest Town: Hari Hari 6 kms on SH6

Our modern home is warm and comfortable with spacious indoor/outdoor living areas. A natural stone courtyard is enclosed by beautiful native bush gardens which attract many delightful birds. Accommodation is deluxe standard throughout featuring a large double room downstairs with separate bathroom facilities. The family sized ensuite and another attractively furnished twin room are located upstairs.

A recent change to drystock farming allows us to spend more time with guests and other tourism activities. South Westland is now part of the designated World Heritage Area and is renowned for its scenic beauty. There are spectacular views of mountains, glaciers, lakes, rivers and rainforests – a photographer's paradise! Close by are historic goldfields, the White Heron Sanctuary, a seal colony, bush walks, horse treks, white water rafting, boating and glowworms.

We now offer personally guided fishing trips for brown trout and salmon.

We can also arrange photography, birdwatching, bushwalking and hunting trips. (Prices on request.)

We are the ideal stopover on S.H.6 between Picton/Christchurch and Queenstown, and offer a base for exploring the glaciers and surrounding region at leisure.

You will be hosted by two friendly Kiwis who enjoy meeting people and who will endeavour to make your stay one of the highlights of your New Zealand holiday.

No smoking in the house please.

At least 24 hours notice is advised to avoid disappointment.

FARM STAY

Whataroa, South Westland

Farmhouse
Address: "Matai Lodge", Whataroa, South Westland
Name: Jim and Glenice Purcell
Telephone: (0288) 34-156
Beds: 2 Double, 2 Single (3 bedrooms, 2 guest bathrooms, 1 spa bath)
Tariff: B&B $50 per person, Dinner $20
Nearest Town: Hokitika (north), Franz Joseph S.H.6 (south)

We are situated 20 mins from the world famous Franz Josef Glacier and live in the Westland National Park, on a 350 acre farm of sheep, deer and horses.
Our modern home has been designed to give the farmstay guests their own area of bedrooms, bathroom and lounge upstairs. There is a backdrop of native bush and you look out to the Southern Alps.
We offer a warm friendly and relaxed atmosphere with plentiful home cooked meals. Now our family has grown up we enjoy entertaining guests from all over the world. Watch wool from sheep spun into yarn and have a go!
I speak Japanese and have taught spinning, weaving and felting in Japan. My husband and I also play golf and tennis.
Other activities in the area are salmon and trout fishing in the lakes and rivers, jet boating, horse treks, and a highlight from November-February is a visit to the White Heron bird sanctuary.
Transport: daily.
Train and bus from Christchurch to Whataroa.
Bus from Queenstown and Wanaka to Franz Josef.
Plane from Christchurch to Hokitika bus Whataroa.
We will be happy to meet bus at Franz Josef for reasonable rate.

Fox Glacier
Homestay
Address: PO Box 42, Fox Glacier
Name: Jan and John Scott
Telephone: (028830) 834
Beds: 1 Double, 1 Single, cot available, (1 bedroom, guest bathroom)
Tariff: B&B Double $60, Single $40, Children under 12 $5-10
Nearest Town: Hokitika

Our modern colonial home has a rural outlook and is situated off SH6 on the road to Lake Matheson just a few 100 metres from the Fox Glacier township.
We are a young couple with a small child and enjoy welcoming visitors to our area and making them feel comfortable in our home. Our guest bedroom is cosy and warm with an ensuite bathroom. We offer a double bed and one single and have a cot available if required.
From the guest room is a picturesque view of Mt Cook and the surrounding mountains. The Fox Glacier itself is a mere 6 km away and we are also the same distance away from the world famous Lake Matheson with its unique reflections of New Zealand's highest peaks, Mt Cook and Mt Tasman. Gillespie's Beach is 16 km away which is renowned for its rugged West Coast beach line and is steeped in gold mining history.
Evening dining can be enjoyed at either of the local hotels or restaurants which are within walking distance.
We do request visitors not to smoke in our home.
We can help you with any arrangements of the various sightseeing activities you may wish to do and can help with transport if necessary.

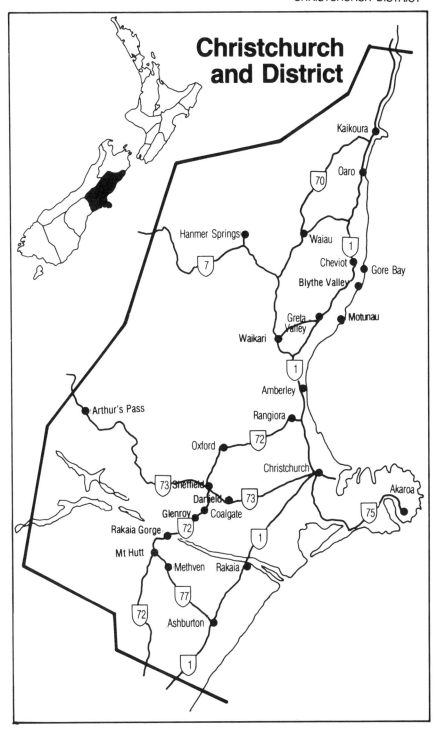

Christchurch and District

Kaikoura

Homestay
Address: "Bevron",
196 Esplanade, Kaikoura
Name: Bev and Ron Barr
Telephone: (03) 3195-432
Beds: 2 Double, 4 Single (4 bedrooms, guest bathroom)
Tariff: B&B Double $50, Single $30, Children half price
Nearest Town: 130 km south of Blenheim, 183 km north of Christchurch

We are a semi-retired couple and have a wonderful two storeyed home on the Esplanade in Kaikoura. The view from our balcony is breathtaking and gives an unobstructed view of the bay and mountain ranges. We are situated opposite a safe swimming beach and a children's playground.
Kaikoura is well endowed with tourist attractions, eg dolphin trips, whale watching, scuba diving, nature walks, coastal as well as bush.
We can offer a double bedroom or single rooms, or a family room consisting of a double bed and 2 single beds.
We are a friendly couple and look forward to extending our hospitality to you.

Kaikoura

Self-Contained Accommodation
Address: "Bayview",
296 Scarborough Street, Kaikoura
Name: Bob and Margaret Woodill
Telephone: (03) 319-5480 If no reply (03) 319-5379
Beds: 2 Double, 2 Single (3 bedrooms)
Tariff: Double $55, Single $35; Dinner $15
Nearest Town: 130 km south of Blenheim, 183 km north of Christchurch

We are a retired couple with four grown children and five grandchildren. Between us we have many interests including golf, lawn bowls, woodwork, cake icing and stretch sewing. We are keen gardeners and grow tomatoes and cucumbers under glass. We also make our own bread.
Our home on an acre of land is high on the Kaikoura Peninsula, about 3 km from the township, and we have a splendid view of the mountains and sea.

The accommodation attached to our home is a completely self-contained unit with a large double, a small double and a twin bedroom. We have a guest lounge, bathroom, laundry and kitchen facilities for tea/coffee making. We offer both bed and breakfast and evening meal with us.

We have our own swimming pool, recreational activities in the district include golfing, seaside and bush walks, beach swimming, native bird watching, museum, Maori fortifications, aquarium, fishing, wharves, seal colony, nature watch sea trips to view whales, dolphins, seals and numerous sea birds, natural limestone caves and many more.

We offer transport for visitors travelling by train or bus.

Directions: *Scarborough Street, the access to the Peninsula, is off the main highway on the south side of the town.*

Oaro, Kaikoura
Farmhouse
Address: Oaro, RD2, Kaikoura
Name: Kathleen and Peter King
Telephone: (03) 319 5494
Beds: 2 Single (1 bedroom, guest bathroom)
Tariff: B&B Double $55, Single $28, Children half price; Dinner $12
Nearest Town: 22 km south of Kaikoura

We are semi-retired living on 48 acres having sold our hill-country property. Our three daughters all live away from home now. One is married with four children.

This is a mild climate and we are experimenting in a small way with citrus and subtropical fruits, predominantly feijoas.

Oaro is close to the sea and we have a fine view north along the Kaikoura coast. A walk south along the coast is always popular.

We enjoy sharing our home with visitors and assure you of a warm welcome.

We are happy for you to join us for dinner but if you prefer there is a restaurant 2 km north where they have takeaways as well as meals.

Directions: *We are 22 km south of Kaikoura on a side road just a short distance off the main north-south highway.*

Hanmer Springs
Bed and Breakfast
Address: 'Percival Bed and Breakfast', Hanmer Springs, North Canterbury
Name: June and Michael Manion
Telephone and Fax: (03) 3157-062
Beds: 2 Double, 2 Single (3 bedrooms, guest bathroom). Also bunkhouse accommodation, semi-furnished, sleeps 6;
Tariff: B&B Double $50, Single $25: Children and Campervans, by arrangement. Bunkhouse: Adults $10, children$5. Credit cards accepted.
Nearest Town: 4 kms before Hanmer Springs township on the main road. Sign opposite the gate

Percival is centrally situated in the Hanmer Basin with panoramic views of the surrounding hills, mountains and forest. It was part of the historic 'St Helens' station, a well known early run in Canterbury, before becoming part of Molesworth.
At present the property is running beef cattle, Romney sheep and deer.
We are a family of three and live in the homestead which is warm, spacious and comfortable. There is a solar heated swimming pool and grass tennis court in the grounds.
Having owned and operated our own hotel for sixteen years we all enjoy meeting visitors and sharing our home and farm with them. We are interested in most sports but fishing, skiing, shooting and tramping are our favourites. There are good fishing streams and rivers in the area with salmon as well as trout.
Hanmer Springs is a unique alpine thermal resort which is famous through New Zealand for its thermal swimming pools, forest walks and tranquil environment.
Our guest accommodation is adjacent to the homestead and with its own private facilities including tea and coffee.
All guests will be warmly welcomed at Percival.

Many homes have facilities for campervans. The ideal camping spot with electricity, bathroom, laundry and friendly hospitality. Tell campervanners about this when you see them.

Blythe Valley, Cheviot

Homestay
Address: RD3 Cheviot
Name: Pamela and Paul Lagan   **Telephone:** (05138) 315
Beds: 1 Single, 1 Set Bunks (1 bedroom)
Tariff: B&B $20 per person, Children under 12 half price; Dinner $15 vegetarians especially welcome; Campervans $15 for 2 people, $5 each additional
Nearest Town: Cheviot 25 km north, Christchurch 100 km south

We would like to welcome you to our comfortable home set on 5 acres in the picturesque Blythe Valley and share the peace, tranquility and beautiful scenery of the surrounding farmland with you.
The guest room has a single bed, two bunks beds, electric blankets, heater and wonderful views of the valley, sea, trees and garden. The guest lounge has a Kent log fire and television.
We have lived and travelled overseas, are keen gardeners. Our property is of mixed terrain and has a large area of lawn and organic ornamental and vegetable garden. As well as cats. dogs and peacocks we have a assortment of other animals and birds.
As W.W.O.O.F.er hosts (Willing Workers on Organic Farms) hosts there is usually work in exchange for short stays. (No preschool children). Booking essential. No smoking please.
Directions: *A twenty minute detour off State Highway 1, south of Cheviot or north of Greta Valley brings you to the Blythe Valley. We are near the Nape Nape scenic reserve (surf casting), Hurunui river mouth (fishing), and Gore Bay (swimming and surfing). Please phone for directions.*

Gore Bay, Cheviot

Homestay
Address: "Saltburn", Gore Bay, Cheviot RD3, Canterbury
Name: Dorothy and Les Jefferson   **Telephone:** (05138) 686
Beds: 1 Double, 2 Single (2 bedrooms, electric blankets)
Tariff: B&B Double $45, Single $25, Children half price; Dinner by arrangement $12
Nearest Town: Cheviot 9 km

Originally from England, my husband and I have retired to the house we have built overlooking the bay in this attractive area.
We have travelled extensively, both in New Zealand and overseas, and thoroughly enjoy meeting people from other countries.
At home we are keen gardeners and appreciate the mild climate we experience here.
We also enjoy tramping and there are many walking tracks, delightful views and a safe surfing and swimming beach.
Native birds abound and a seal colony lies a short walk along the coast to the north, while a walkway follows the coastline southward through natural bush to the Hurunui River mouth. an excellent fishing spot.
Cheviot, the nearest shopping area is 1 hour 30 mins drive north of Christchurch on State Highway One and 1 hours drive south from Kaikoura.

Greta Valley & Waikari
Farmhouse
Address: Foxdown, Greta Valley. Postal: Amberley, RD3
Name: Alison and Peter Fox
Telephone: (03) 314 3704 Fax: (03) 314 3401
Beds: 2 Double (1 queen), 3 Single (3 bedrooms, guest bathroom)
Tariff: B&B Double $60, Single $40; Dinner $18
Nearest Town: Farm is situated 1 1/4 hours drive north of Christchurch (90 km) on a valley road between Highways 1 and 7. 16 km from Greta Valley and 19 km from Waikari. 4 hours drive from Picton.

Foxdown is a farm of 1400 hectares (3500 acres) carrying 5500 sheep and 250 cattle in the rolling to steep North Canterbury hills. It has been in the Fox family for over 115 years.
Our home is a large, modern, two-storeyed homestead with own facilities for guests. If you wish you will be able to join in farm activities, be taken for a tour of the farm or relax, whichever you wish.
Foxdown has a swimming pool, trampoline, tennis court, pool table for guests' use. Many walks are within easy distance of homestead.
In the area are fishing, golf, bowls, squash, walkway, beach (33 km), Hamner Springs Hot Pools (84 km) and Skiing (2 hours).
Our farm is run by Peter and son Andrew with some casual help. Our interests are contract bridge, local history, travel and meeting overseas people and fellow New Zealanders, farm forestry, wool, and machine knitting.
Directions: *End of Foxdown Road which is off Waikari–Greta Valley Road.*

Greta Valley
Farmhouse
Address: "Gorrie Downs", Greta Valley, RD, North Canterbury
Name: Janette and Rod McKenzie
Telephone: (03) 314 3475. Fax: (03) 314 8291
Beds: 1 Double, 1 Single (1 bedrooms guest bathroom) plus spare twin room in house.
Tariff: B&B Double $70, Single $35, Children half price; Dinner by arrangement; Campervans welcome, but no power available
Nearest Town: Cheviot 30 mins north, Amberley 30 mins south, Christchurch 1 hr south, Picton 4 hrs north

Our home is a very comfortable 40-year-old house, with established garden and trees, situated in a peaceful valley with magnificent views of the countryside.
The guest wing has a separate entrance, one double bed and one single bed, with own bathroom. Furnishings are designed with your comfort in mind and good heating is available. A second twin room is available in our house.

Having both travelled extensively overseas we enjoy meeting people from other countries.
We are involved in numerous business activities which we run from our 1000 acre farm. These include the farming of Friesian bulls, raising black and coloured sheep for handcraft wool and export, and international consultancy. Between us we are involved in golf, spinning, gardening and tennis.
Delicious home-cooked meals are offered and a cooked breakfast if required.
We are ideally situated for those travelling the Picton–Christchurch route, and we are only five minutes off the highway. Likewise we are five minutes from a quiet, safe swimming beach.
You are guaranteed a quality and memorable stay when you break the journey with us.
Directions: *Please phone or write for directions and reservations.*

Please let your hosts know if you have to cancel.
They will have spent time preparing for you.

Motunau, North Canterbury
Farmstay
Address: "Seaward Downs", Greta Valley R.D., North Canterbury
Name: Julie & Jonathan Douglas
Telephone: (03) 3143-489
Beds: 1 Double, 2 Single, (2 bedrooms, guest bathroom)
Tariff: **B&B** $60 Double, $35 Single, children (under 12) 1/2 price, $15 Dinner
Nearest Town: Greta Valley 20 km

We welcome you to our 1200 acre sheep and beef farm on the sea coast of North Canterbury, 20 kms from Greta Valley (Highway 1), 1 hour 30 mins from the popular Hamner Springs resort or the Whales at Kaikoura.
We are a family of 4 with 2 schoolchildren who enjoy meeting people form all over the world. We welcome you to join us in farming activities and hobbies such as gardening, craft, golf and horse-riding. Fishing available close by (sea or river).
Our house is nestled in a large landscaped garden with un-interrupted views of the mountains to the West and the sea to the East, Motunau Beach only minutes away.
We offer a guest room with double bed, own bathroom and private entrance or a twin room by request. All beds have electric blankets. Transport can be arranged for a small charge from the Greta Valley bus stop.
Directions: *Please phone*

Amberley

Guest House
Address: RD1, Amberley
Name: Harleston Guest House
Telephone: (03) 312 9806
Beds: 5 Double, 1 Single (6 bedrooms, own bathrooms)
Tariff: B&B Double $74, Single $37; Dinner $24; Children half price, under 5 free; Campervans $20 per vehicle

We are very proud of the history associated with our 127-year-old farmhouse which is a North Canterbury landmark protected by the NZ Historic Places Trust.
Harleston is ideally situated for travellers wishing to use the inter-island ferries. Going north you can enjoy a half-hour start on city dwellers and for southbound travellers, instead of wearily trying to find accommodation in a strange city late in the day, you can stay with us and after a hearty breakfast drive to Christchurch with the advantages a new day brings.
Our home is welcoming, comfortably unpretentious and has a great deal of character.
Guests can enjoy acclaimed cuisine, the nearby (usually deserted) beach or perhaps visit a local vineyard, catch a fish, explore the varying countryside or simply relax in our garden.
Your hosts are Liz and Les and as Liz has worked in international tourism until recently she completely understands the needs of her guests and enjoys caring for them. Les will happily discuss horses and the races they never won, farming in general and after lengthy encouragement may even sing a song!
Directions: *State Highway 1, 40 km north of Christchurch, 10 km south of Amberley, sign at gate.*

Rangiora

Homestay
Address: 29 Victoria Street, Rangiora
Name: Chris & Wendy Carmody   **Telephone:** (03) 313-8378
Beds: 1 Double, 3 Single (4 bedrooms, guest bathroom, lounge)
Tariff: B&B $40 Double, $22 Single, family discount available on request. Wheelchair access.
Nearest Town: Rangiora

"Glowing sky at sunset, fine weather after bad, place of peace" these translations for Rangiora reflect the quintessence character of accommodation we seek to provide. A stay in our home could be just the escape from the hurly burly pace of city living you seek whilst holidaying!! Indeed our guest house is a little different from most. Up until two years ago it was a convent, and we believe that even now it continues to "ooze" a sense of peaceful well being and spiritual tranquility - the result of it being for many years a house of prayer.
Our family enjoys living in this historic dwelling. Guests are most welcome to share our family life. Or a separate lounge is available to "escape to" or for entertaining your own visitors.
Directions: *Rangiora is 20 minutes motorway driving North of Christchurch. Given 24 hour prior notification we will pick-up/drop off guests at Christchurch bus, train or airport termini.*

Ashley, Rangiora
Farmstay
Address: "Woolly Meadows Farmyard",
Cones Road, Ashley, Rangiora R.D. 2,
Name: John & Lynda van Beek
Telephone: (03) 313-5387
Beds: 1 Double, 3 Single (3 bedrooms)
Tariff: B&B $55 Double, $35 Single, $15 Dinner, $20 Campervans (own toilet & shower)
Nearest Town: Rangiora (5 mins) Christchurch (25 mins)

Our new 4 bedroomed home is on 40 acres, 5 km from Rangiora, 5 km from State Highway 72, 12 km from State Highway 1.
John was born in Holland, came to New Zealand with his family in the early 50's, Lynda has always lived in the Rangiora district.
We developed Woolly Meadows Farmyard in Oct '86 and is now our main form of income off the farm. In the complex we have built, day visitors eg. school children, senior citizens, overseas travellers came and enjoy the farm animals we have here. You too can do the activities like feeding chickens, rabbits, hens, pig, turkeys, guinea pigs, ducks, milking the cow and feeding milk to the pet lambs, goats and calves.
We use an antique separator to get cream and sometimes make our own butter and ice-cream. Dinner is always available, use our answerphone if necessary. We can meet the bus in Rangiora. Near our farm are the usual services eg. golf, restaurants etc.

Oxford
Homestay + Self-Contained Accommodation
Address: 37 High Street, Oxford
Name: Norton and Helen Dunn
Telephone: (03) 312 4167
Beds: 3 double bedrooms, (one brm has guest shower, toilet, sitting room, kitchen facilities, verandah entrance) others bathroom is handy
Tariff: B&B Double $50, Single $25, Dinner $15 if required, Children $12, under 5 no charge
Nearest Town: Walking distance to the shops, 55 km from Christchurch

Our house is 60 years old and has a spacious garden – warm and sunny.
We are a contented married couple with a family of three grown-up sons.
We retired from Dunedin to live in Oxford – a charming, restful town and a friendly community. Oxford offers scenic walks, horse treks, homecrafts, pottery, herbs, basket making and home spun hand-knitted garments, bowls, tennis, squash, restaurant, golf and bridge club handy.
Directions: *High Street is off the Main Road – left – sign outside the gate.*

Oxford
Farmhouse
Address: "Thornton", Main Oxford Road (HW72), Oxford, North Canterbury
Name: Robin and Micky Leech
Telephone: (03) 312 4035
Beds: 1 Double, 2 Single (3 bedrooms, guest bathroom)
Tariff: B&B Double $50, Single $30
Nearest Town: Oxford 5 km

Travelling through the South Island? Then HW72 is the route for you. It follows our beautiful Alps down the centre of the Island, through our most breathtaking scenery.

Our farm is situated on HW72, 35 minutes west of Christchurch and 5 km from Oxford, a charming country town nestled under the hills. Salmon fishing, skiing, horse trekking and tramping are just a few of the activities found in this area.

If the house is deserted, you will probably find me in the garden! We have extensive grounds, with over 50 rhododendrons, swimming pool and many beautiful native shrubs and trees.

The farm is becoming more like "Old McDonalds" every day, with sheep, Angora goat stud and now deer added to the list. Visitors are most welcome to look around.

Our house is spacious, clean and comfortable, and visitors may choose privacy, or joining the family circle, whichever they prefer.

We have made several trips overseas, and also know New Zealand intimately. We love our country, and enjoy helping to make overseas visitors' trips here happy and memorable. _____

Christchurch City
Homestay
Address: 7 Selwyn Street, Christchurch 2
Name: Jaap and Riet van Hamelsveld
Telephone: (03) 332-8141
Beds: 1 Single room, 1 Twin room
Tariff: B&B $22 per person, children $12

We have a lovely seventy year old home. It is within a half hour to the city centre, one minute to the bus stop and a ten minute walk to the Cashmere Hills.

Christchurch has much to offer visitors and public transport is handy. There are many lovely walkways on our hills.

Daily departures by air and road to the Southern Alps and lakes.

Our family of five children have grown up so there is just my husband and me to warmly welcome you. We are looking forward to meeting you.
Directions: *Please phone.* _____

Christchurch City
Private Hotel
Address: 52 Armagh Street, Christchurch
Name: Windsor Private Hotel
Telephone: (03) 661-503, or 662-707. Fax (03) 669-796
From July 92 (03) 336 1503 or 366 2707, Fax (03) 366 9796
Beds: 40 bedrooms
Tariff: B&B Double $78, Single $50, Children under 12 years $15. Quote this book for 10% discount. (Includes Full Menu Breakfast)

"The Windsor", originally named Warwick House, was built at the turn of the century. Located in the quiet northwest situation of Cranmer Square, we are within easy walking distance of the Art Centre, museum, gardens, theatre, town hall and Cathedral Square (our city centre), with its banks, buses, shopping arcades and excellent restaurants.

Guests are greeted on arrival and shown around our charming colonial style home. Our nicely furnished bedrooms, all with a small posie of flowers and an original water colour by local artist Denise McCulloch, lend charm to the warm and cosy bedrooms which are all individually heated. The dining room where our generous morning menu includes juice, fresh fruit and cereals, followed by a choice of bacon and eggs, sausages, tomatoes, toast and marmalade. The lounge where we serve tea, coffee and biscuits each evening at 9.00 pm is where everyone gathers to watch television and have a chat. There are 24 hour tea, coffee and laundry facilities along with off-street parking for the motorist. For the comfort and convenience of our guests we encourage non-smoking.

Christchurch City
Bed & Breakfast

Address: "Turret House", 435 Durham Street North, Christchurch
Name: Robin and Gayle Chambers
Telephone: (03) 653-900, Fax (03) 655-601
Beds: 6 Double, 1 Single (7 bedrooms, guest bathrooms) 2 suites, 1 apartment all with private bathrooms
Tariff: B&B Double from $78, Single from $56, extra adult $15, children under 12 yrs $10, all credit cards accepted

Turret House is a gracious superior bed and breakfast accommodation located in downtown Christchurch. It is within easy walking distance of Cathedral Square, the Botanical Gardens, museum, art gallery, the arts centre and Hagley Park 18 hole golf course.

Built in 1885 this historic residence is one of only three in the area protected by the New Zealand Historic Places Trust. It has been extensively restored to capture the original character and charm. Situated within the grounds is one of Christchurch's best examples of our native kauri tree.

Elaborately decorated bedrooms with heaters and electric blankets combine comfort and old world elegance with private bathrooms including bath and shower, all offering a totally relaxed and comfortable environment. A redecorated apartment (has private lounge and kitchen) is also available, as well as a bedroom with an orthopedic bed for those with back problems.

Tariffs include a full continental breakfast. Cots and highchairs are also available. There is a licensed restaurant next door.

If you're looking for a place to stay where the accommodation is superior and the atmosphere friendly – experience Turret House.

Directions: *just 15 minutes from Christchurch Airport. Situated on the corner of Bealey Ave and Durham Street.*

Can't contact your host? Ring 018 for directory assistance.

Christchurch City
Homestay / B&B
Address: Cranmer Lodge
& Chester House, 26 Cranmer
Square, Christchurch 1
Name: Dennis & Margaret Cottle
Telephone: (03) 797-864
Cranmer Lodge
Beds: 1 Double, 4 Single
Tariff: B&B $65 Double, $45 Single - includes continental breakfast, other meals are available with the family by arrangement.
Chester House
Beds: 1 Double, 2 Singles (one twin is large & can accommodate extra beds for children)
Tariff: B&B $50 Double, $30 Single, $12 for children under 12 in same room as parents. Includes self service continental breakfast.

Cranmer Lodge is a distinctive 100 year old family home overlooking Cranmer Square. Chester House is a quiet 75 year old house featuring wood panelling and leadlights. Cranmer Lodge provides homestay accommodation while Chester House provides budget bed and breakfast. They are adjoining properties in a pleasant inner city residential area, 5 minutes' walk from shops, buses, restaurants and tourist attractions.
Dennis & Margaret enjoy talking to visitors and are pleased to discuss travel plans and help with bookings.
Cranmer Lodge and Chester House are non-smoking.

Christchurch City
Homestay
Address: Please phone
Name: Elspeth & Ken
Telephone: Withdrawn
Beds: 1 Double, 2 Single (3 bedrooms)
Tariff: B&B $55 Double, $35 Single
Nearest Town: Christchurch

We are a couple in our fifties, a Scots/New Zealand partnership who have done some overseas travelling and enjoy meeting people. Our home is situated in a quiet street on the banks of the Heathcote River in a very pleasant suburb. We are just a short distance from the city centre, close to all amenities including bus stops and the terminus for both road and rail transport services. There are some very pretty walks around our area. Christchurch is known as the Garden City, the City that Shines and we hope you have included it in your itinerary.
We can offer comfortable accommodation and would like to say welcome to our world.
Directions: *3 km South of city centre. Please phone.*

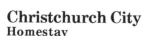

Christchurch City
Homestay
Address: 59 Ngaio Street, Christchurch
Name: Gerda de Kleyne & Hans van den Bos
Telephone: (03) 332 2896
Beds: 1 Double, 2 Single (2 bedrooms, guest bathroom & lounge)
Tariff: B&B $25 per person, children 1/2 price,$15 Dinner or $10 for Pancake Dinner
Nearest Town: 3 1/2 km to Christchurch city centre

Our two guestrooms are private, pleasant and quiet. Guest have the solo use of the lounge and bathroom. We have a characteristic home in a cul-de-sac street on the foot of the Port Hills. Drive or walk up the Port Hills and you will have a magnificent view.
Our meals are homecooked and on your request we cater for any type of diet. If you like we'll cook a special pancake dinner. Ask!
The garden is lovely and well established with a barbeque area. We preserve fruit, make jams and bake bread.
For your convenience we have composed a folder about Christchurch which can work as a real timesaver.
We are in our late thirties, have one son and your hostess works as a registered nurse. We do not have family in New Zealand and having guests is to us a little like having family come to stay. We enjoy having guests and look forward to meeting you.
Directions: *By car - stay on SH1 until intersection Brougham and Waltham Road. Head towards St Martins. After 1 1/2 km turn right into Gamblings Road, then first left.*
From city centre and railway station - take bus 12, off at Gamblings Rd, 2 minute walk. From Airport - take airport bus then change to 12.
You are welcome to ring for further directions.

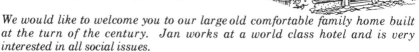

Christchurch City
Homestay
Address: 12 Dublin Street, Christchurch
Name: Jan & Mike Cann
Telephone: (03) 661-861
Beds: 4 Single (2 bedrooms)
Tariff: B&B $60 Double, $30 Single

We would like to welcome you to our large old comfortable family home built at the turn of the century. Jan works at a world class hotel and is very interested in all social issues.
Our house is situated in the city, 100m from the Avon River and Hagley Park, and only minutes walk from the Cathedral Square, Arts Centre, City Mall, Botanical Gardens, major hotels, restaurants, nightclubs and top class vegetarian restaurant and pizza house.
We are on all main bus routes, including to Airport and beach. Car hire is available around the corner and also a petrol station, whilst a few minutes walk takes you to an up-market shopping centre - Merivale. In fact we have everything on our doorstep.

Christchurch City
Homestay
Address: Fendalton Road, Christchurch 1
Name: Moira & David
Telephone: (03) 3555-661
Beds: 1 Double, 4 Single (3 bedrooms, 2 guest bathrooms ensuite)
Tariff: B&B $70 Double, $40 Single, children 25% off, $20 Dinner
Airport: 10 mins on main route, City 5 mins, bus at gate

We have been home hosting for more than six years and enjoy sharing our home and city with overseas visitors. Our new home has just been completed and is ideally situated adjacent to some of Christchurch's most beautiful parks. You may even wish to walk downtown, across the golf course, and past the lake - 25 mins.
There are several excellent restaurants close to our home - within 2 kms.
We are in our fifties, retired, with interests including golf, sailing and antiques. We are non smokers, have an aging cat, five children and three grand children. Our extensive knowledge of the South Island's scenic attractions has often been of assistance to those visitors seeking information for their stay here. We can meet flights for those arriving in New Zealand and assist, where necessary, with rental car hire and local tours. Other transfers by arrangement at a cost of $5 per head.

Always telephone ahead to enquire about a B&B.
It is a nuisance for you if you simply arrive
to find someone is already staying there.
And besides, hosts need a little time to prepare.

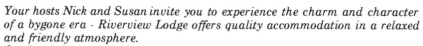

Christchurch City
Homestay
Address: "Riverview Lodge",
361 Cambridge Terrace, Christchurch
Name: Nick & Susan Bray
Telephone: (03) 652-860
Beds: 2 Double, 3 Single (4 bedrooms, 3 guest bathrooms)
Tariff: B&B $70 Double, $40 Single, children negotiable
Nearest Town: Christchurch

Your hosts Nick and Susan invite you to experience the charm and character of a bygone era - Riverview Lodge offers quality accommodation in a relaxed and friendly atmosphere.
Our house is a restored Edwardian residence that reflects the grace and style of the period with some fine carved Kauri and Rimu features.
It is ideally situated on the banks of the Avon River in a tranquil setting, surrounded by an old English garden with mature trees.
The city centre will all its attractions is a ten minutes walk along the river side.
Guest rooms are elegant, combining modern facilities with colonial furnishings. All rooms have colour televisions and heating, balconies provide a superb river view.
Tea and coffee making facilities are available at all times. Breakfast is a house speciality with a wide choice of cooked and continental fare.
A canoe and bicycles are available for guests to use.
Directions: *From city, follow Salisbury St (one way) to Avon River, turn left into Cambridge Terrace - we are 300 metres on the left on the corner of Churchill Street.*

Christchurch
Homestay
Address: 15 Charlesworth Street, Ferrymead, Christchurch 6
Name: Joan & Barrie Shakes
Telephone: (03) 384-3147
Beds: 3 Single (2 bedrooms)
Tariff: B&B $55 Double, $35 Single, children 1/2 price, Dinner $15
Nearest Town: Christchurch

We live in a quiet semi rural area but within close proximity to the sea, and only 8 minutes from the central city. Our interests are travel, music and gardening. Christchurch is renowned for its lovely parks, gardens and river, live theatres and choirs. Barrie helps in the restoration and driving of early trams at the nearby Ferrymead Historic Park (a place of interest for tourists).
We are on the scenic route to the Bays and the attractive village of Sumner is nearby. You may have dinner with us if you wish though Sumner can boast excellent restaurants.
Directions: *Please phone*

Christchurch

Homestay
Address: please phone
Name: John & Joan Elder
Telephone: (03) 384-9344
Beds: 2 Single (1 bedroom)
Tariff: B&B $55 Double, $35 Single, $12 Dinner
Nearest Town: Christchurch

We are a recently retired couple, with a grown and flown family of three. Our two storey home is modern and spacious, on the Port Hills with extensive views of the mountains, Eastern Christchurch, the estuary and Pegasus Bay.
All bedrooms open on to the lower balcony, leading directly to our swimming pool. The living areas have a sunny upper balcony and conservatory. The area is quiet and private. Off street parking is available. Small campervans no problem but no power available.
Our interests are mainly golf, landscape painting, flower gardening, contract bridge and travelling.
The local facilities range from beaches to indoor sports centre, Ferrymead Park to yacht clubs. City centre or Lyttelton are ten minutes away by car, the city 20 minutes by bus (morning and afternoon, two buses stop at our drive).
We extend a warm welcome to all, but especially to overseas visitors.
Evening meals at home can often be arranged.

Cashmere, Christchurch

Homestay
Address: 41 Kidson Terrace, Cashmere, Christchurch 2
Name: Bette and Brian Palmer
Telephone: (03) 3370-263
Beds: 1 Double, 2 Single (2 bedrooms, guest bathroom)
Tariff: B&B Double $70, Single $40, Dinner $20
Nearest Town: Christchurch, 5 minute drive

We have a large home, nestled in the Cashmere Hills, with panoramic views over the city. The house is centrally heated. In summer breakfast can be served on the balcony. We also have a kauri spa tub available to guests. Bedrooms are attractive and own facilities available. Gourmet cooking is my speciality. Breakfast of your choice and any favourites will be catered for dinner. There are many walks around the hills and golf can be arranged. A courtesy car is available. Please phone for reservations. We have an answerphone. Please leave your request and contact number.

Fendalton, Christchurch

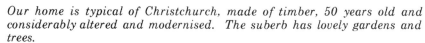

Homestay
Address: 50 Clifford Avenue,
Fendalton, Christchurch
Name: Pam Rattray
Telephone: (03) 355-4298
Beds: 1 Double, 2 Single (2 bedrooms, guest bathroom)
Tariff: B&B $65 Double, $35 Single

Our home is typical of Christchurch, made of timber, 50 years old and considerably altered and modernised. The suberb has lovely gardens and trees.
There is a swimming pool in the private back garden and a little stream where we feed the ducks.
The big conservatory warms the house on sunny days and gets closed off at night and in the winter.
Skiing has always been very much part of the family's life and Christchurch has 2 commercial ski fields 1 - 2 hours drive away. We have an Olympic skier and a computer scientist in the family although both the children have left home and reappear only occasionally.
The centre of town is a walk of about 15-20 minutes and we are a 10 minute drive from the airport. The well known garden of Mona Vale with boats for punting is 5 minutes walk. ───────────────

Bryndwr, Christchurch

Homestay
Address: "Allisford",
1/61 Aorangi Road,
Bryndwr, Christchurch
Name: Allison Crawford
Telephone: (03) 3517-742
Beds: 2 Single (1 bedroom)
Tariff: B&B Double $55, Single $35; Dinner $12
Nearest Town: 5 km from Christchurch central post office

"Allisford" is a private residence in a choice area where warm friendly hospitality is offered in comfortable surroundings.
A large twin bedroom is available for guests, also a comfortable lounge opening onto lawn and garden.
There is also off-street parking.
The nearest No. 17B Wairakei Rd bus stop is only three minutes walk away and this bus passes the Arts Centre, the Museum, the Botanical Gardens and the McDougall Art Gallery on the way into the city centre.
Allisford is situated about halfway between the Airport and the city centre and is also easily reached from north, south and west main highways.
You may have the breakfast of your choice and are welcome to have dinner by arrangement.
Directions: Please phone. ───────────────

Bryndwr, Christchurch
Homestay
Address: Please Phone
Name: Doreen and Ruth
Telephone: (03) 351 6858
Beds: 2 Single (1 bedroom)
Tariff: B&B Double $50, Single $30
Nearest Town: 5 km NW of City Centre

Our comfortable red brick home is situated in a quiet street and we offer a double room with two single beds. Also for your use is a large sunny lounge with open fire in winter. This room has colour TV and tea making facilities. We are 7 minutes from Christchurch International Airport, 2 minutes from the main highway north and approximately 15 minutes from the main highway south.
Close by is an outdoor swimming pool complex and a covered heated pool for winter swimming, also within close proximity to us are shopping malls and restaurants. The bus stop to the city centre is a 5 minute walk. Your hosts - two working ladies who enjoy meeting people. We have both travelled throughout New Zealand and overseas. Our interests include gardening and tramping.

Opawa, Christchurch
Homestay
Address: 41 Opawa Road, Christchurch 8002
Name: Carolyn and Stephen Mangan
Telephone: (03) 653-718
Beds: 1 Queensize waterbed, 1 foldaway, + cot (1 bedroom, guest bathroom)
Tariff: $30 per person, Children under 12 half price, pre-schoolers free, Dinner $15, Special Dinner with wine $20

We have a large, old comfortable family home built in 1870. A warm welcome, a comfortable bed and a good breakfast await our guests.
Rates quoted are for one night. Longer stays are discounted accordingly. We offer a generous three course meal with NZ wines.
We are on the main bus route from the airport and only 4 km from the city where some of Christchurch's best restaurants are.
Full laundry and drying facilities available at a small charge. Tea and coffee making facility available. We will be only too happy to help you with your holiday plans during your stay in Christchurch.

Sumner, Christchurch
Homestay
Address: "The Digbys", Ocean View Terrace, Sumner, Christchurch
Name: Robin & Jenny Digby
Telephone: (03) 265-634
Beds: 2 Double, 1 Single (2 bedrooms, guest bathroom)
Tariff: B&B $35 per person, Dinner $20
Nearest Town: Christchurch "the city that shines"

At the "Gateway to Banks Peninsula" we have chosen to build our new home, on a few acres of hillside.
Robin is a builder, Jenny cooks breakfast. We're both in the "Roaring 40's" and the family is all grown up, so you can relax with us on a comfortable chair on our verandah and enjoy the lovely view across this popular seaside suberb, out to sea.
Our immediate area has many wonderful walkways with spectacular views and there are some superb day trips to be made around Banks Peninsula. 15-20 minutes will see you in Cathedral Square, downtown (if you have to go). 5 minutes to the beach.
"The Digbys", a brand new homestead, where we guarantee comfort, with hosts who have been accommodating the travelling public for almost 20 years.
Directions: *Please ring first for location instructions.*

Spreydon, Christchurch
Self-contained Accommodation
Address: 105 Lyttelton Street, Christchurch
Name: Bev & Kerry Bloomfield
Telephone: (03) 332-5360
Beds: 1 Double, 2 Single (2 bedrooms, guest bathroom)
Tariff: B&B $50 Double, $10 each extra person
Nearest Town: Christchurch

If you wish peace and quiet in the city, we have a modern two bedrooms self contained flat which is situated on a back section.
It is separated from our house by a carport. It has a private phone, TV, washing machine and your own front lawn.
We are a 10 minute drive from the centre of the city and a 5 minute drive from a big shopping mall (Riccarton Mall). All beds have electric blankets.
Directions: *Please phone.*

Akaroa
Homestay B&B
Address: 83 Rue Lavaud, Akaroa
Name: "Lavaud House"
Telephone: (03) 304-7121
Beds: 6 Single, 1 Double (4 bedrooms)
Tariff: B&B Double $60, Single $30
Nearest Town: Christchurch 80 kms

For relaxation and nostalgia, try Lavaud House, a bed and breakfast homestay. Our large, French designed historic home overlooks the main beach and harbour, and is warm, comfortable and peaceful with three separate living areas. Within easy walking distance there are seven restaurants.
Relax in our spacious colourful garden, enjoy the birds and glorious harbour and rural views, walk along the beach, browse in the shops, or stroll around the historic French streets. Our mild climate makes Akaroa a year round resort.
Retired farmers, we have travelled widely, and enjoy meeting people.
Tariff includes a full continental breakfast plus tea and coffee making facilities, usually with home baking.
"A warm welcome awaits you"
Directions: *We are centrally situated in the main street, opposite the war memorial.*

Akaroa

Farmstay, Chalet with en-suite
Address: Bayview, Main Akaroa Highway 75, Barrys Bay
Postal: Private Bag, Little River
Name: Jacqui & Martin
Telephone: (03) 304-5875
Beds: 1 Double, 5 Single (3 bedrooms, guest bathrooms)
Tariff: B&B $30 per person, Children half price, Dinner $20, $70 per
person for 24 hour stay (3 meals); campervans welcome,
Nearest Town: Christchurch

*Your chance to stay on a New Zealand farm and participate in farming
activities. We farm 500 acres of steep hill country rising from 400-2600 feet.
We have 1500 Romney sheep, cattle and an assortment of "farmyard"
animals. You are welcome to join in milking the cow, mustering, trekking
over the hills or through native bush, or just relaxing on our verandah,
enjoying the beautiful scenery. We have a comfortable home and promise
you a warm welcome. We serve a farmstyle breakfast. Three course
dinners consist of farm roasts with home-grown vegetables, local cheeses
and local wines, preceded by pre-dinner drinks of your choice. Guests have
their own bathrooms.*
*Golf, tennis or horse trekking are nearby and a trip to historic Akaroa is a
must. We recommend a 24 hour stay.*
Directions: *Situated in Barry's Bay, 2 kms below the Hilltop Tavern.
Bayview is the first farmhouse on the right on Highway 75 going to Akaroa.
Buses will stop at our gate.*

Akaroa
Homestay
Address: "Glencarrig",
7 Percy Street, Akaroa,
Banks Peninsula
Name: Mike and Kaye Stokes
Telephone: (03) 304-7008
Beds: 2 Double, 2 Single (3 bedrooms guest bathroom)
Tariff B&B Double $80, Single $40
Nearest Town: Akaroa, 80 km from Christchurch

We live in the town of Akaroa, on one and a half acres with vistas over lawn to the harbour. One of the boundaries is along the Aylmer Stream with a waterwheel (under restoration) and across from 2 acres of bush reserve.
The house was built by Rev. Aylmer in 1851 with a spacious country warmth. There is a large dining room with a casual sitting area and 2 other large sitting rooms.
With french doors opening to the verandah are a double room (with hand-basin) and a single (or twin) room. The other double room has a double and a single bed. We also have an antique cot and child's bed.
One bathroom solely for guests and another we share. Showers and bath available. Wheelchair access to bathroom and house.
Rooms are centrally heated by modern hot water radiators run from the Rayburn stove in the kitchen. Breakfast is served in the sunny country kitchen with french doors opening to kitchen garden and swimming pool.
A few minutes walk to restaurants, the jetty and the village.

Akaroa
Homestay
Address: Please phone
Name: Gwen and Murray Manhire
Telephone: (03) 304-7127
Beds: 2 Single (1 bedroom, guest bathroom)
Tariff: B&B Double $60, Single $35, Dinner $15
Nearest Town: Akaroa

Our home stands in the sunshine in an acre of bush and well-established garden, just about two minutes walk from the beach on the shore of the incomparable Akaroa harbour. The view is magnificent. The sea and shoreline are everchanging in colour, always lovely. Birdlife and birdsong are ever-present – wood pigeons, fantails and bellbirds as well as many seabirds nearby.
We offer tranquility and peace.
We are recently retired with an adult family. Truly rural, we enjoy sharing the country life. We love our garden and have home-grown vegetables all the year round as well as our own honey and fresh eggs from our contented brown chooks.
Our home is modern colonial and our guest accommodation consists of a twin-bedded room and adjacent private bathroom. We hope guests will feel at home and make tea or coffee when they choose.
Akaroa township is less than five minutes away – an excellent variety of craftshops, activities and our well-known herb farm and boat and fishing trips offer a wonderful holiday.

Akaroa
Cottage
Address: Tree Crop Fram, Grehan Valley, Akaroa
Postal: PO Box 9, Akaroa
Name: Lynne Alexander
Telephone: (0304) 7158 (early morning or evenings)
Beds: 1 Double (1 bedroom, private entrance)
Tariff: Dinner, B&B $50 per person includes pre-dinner drinks, expresso coffee, fruit bowl, walnuts, flowers and candles in room, open fires
Nearest Town: Akaroa 2 km, Christchurch 80 km

Tree Crop Farm is a small, quaint lifestyle farm with a stream running tthrough the gardens beside a150-year-old wood and sod cottage - very English looking with dry stone walls. Lots of walnut trees and other nut trees plus wandering vegetable and flower gardens and walk tracks all over the farm.

The accommodation is a rustic, sunny, private, detached double room with French doors onto a brick courtyard and guest carpark. Shared shower, bath and toilet facilities are also separate from the house.
The farm has a flock of black sheep grown for skins and organic meat for the table.
Horses are available for hire to experienced riders, and a qualified riding instructor can be booked for private lessons.
Masseuse and naturopath available at nearby Herb Farm.
Specialities of the house include home-made fruit icecreams, soups fresh laid eggs, vast green salads, farm meat and local fresh fish in season.

Barrys Bay, Akaroa
Homestay, Farmhouse
Address: Oihitu Estate,
Barrys Bay, Akaroa
Name: Lynette and Ross Curry
Telephone: (03) 304-5804
Beds: 2 Double, 1 Single (3 bedrooms, guest bathroom)
Tariff: B&B Double $90, Single $60, Children negotiable, Dinner $12.50
Nearest Town: Akaroa 12 km

We are fortunate to live in an extremely old home by New Zealand standards, finished in 1870. The house is set amid the rolling hills of Banks Peninsula with a view of the harbour.
We have a 315 acre dairy farm which also runs deer, pigs and the many pets including horses for you to ride if desired.
You'll be accommodated in luxury rooms with private amenities and furnished in antiques of the period. You will receive traditional farm fare from the wood stove, bacon, egg and toast cooked on the embers, also fruit from our own orchard for breakfast. For dinner a farm style roast with home grown vegetables. Pre-dinner drinks and wine are also included. Tea, coffee and home baking are always available.
We have both travelled and enjoy meeting people. We also enjoy socialising whether it be relaxing in front of the open fire, on the large verandah or playing croquet on the front lawn.
Directions: We are conveniently situated on the Akaroa Highway with our sign "Oihitu Estate" on the harbour's edge, just before the Barry's Bay cheese factory.

Wainui, Akaroa

Farmstay
Address: Wainui,
Akaroa R.D.
Banks Peninsula
Name: Rod and Kate Shaw
Telephone: (03) 304 8409
Beds: 2 Double, 3 Single (3 bedrooms guest bathroom)
Tariff: B&B Double $70, Single $40, Dinner $20, 24 hour stay includes 3 meals, $75 per person. Plus GST on all charges. Children half price; Campervan facilities but no power.

Your hosts, Rod and Kate Shaw, live in a large colonial style home situated at Wainui in Akaroa Harbour. Our property is a 900 acre hill country sheep and cattle farm with 3 miles of coastline which offers spectacular views and walks.
Become involved in day to day farm activities, shearing demonstrations, explore penguin caves on our farm relax in our home and garden.
Trips to historic Akaroa (harbour cruises available) and surrounding bays, golf course nearby. We recommend you stay at least 24 hours.
Directions: *take main Akaroa highway, when you meet the sea turn right at Barrys Bay to Wainui (approx 8 km), drive through Wainui until you reach our farm on your left with a notice 'Kowhai Vale' at our driveway. If you are not travelling by car come on public transport to Barrys Bay where we will collect you, for a small fee.*

Paua Bay, Banks Peninsula

Farmstay
Address: Paua Bay
Postal Address: C/o 113 Beach Road, Akaroa, Banks Peninsula
Name: Murray & Sue Johns
Telephone: (03) 304-8511
Beds: 1 Double (1 bedroom, guest bathroom)
Tariff: B&B $50 Double, $25 Single, $15 Dinner
Nearest Town: Akaroa

We are a family of four, our two children are Primary School age. We have a sheep, cattle and deer farm of 900 acres at Paua Bay, surrounded by coast-line with valleys of native bush and streams. Those interested in taking a stroll can enjoy the unique scenery including seal and penguin colonies which are a twenty minute walk from the house.
You would be most welcome to participate in any farm activity that occurs during your stay. Imagine returning home with a photo of yourself shearing a sheep!
Our cosy home is nestled against native bush surrounded by a large cottage garden including a swimming pool.
The farm is a twenty minute drive from picturesque Akaroa which is a French-style harbour village.
Directions: *Please phone.*

Le Bons Bay, Banks Peninsula

Farmstay +
Self-contained Accom
Address: Le Bons Bay,
R.D. 3, Akaroa, Canterbury
Name: Anne & Gerhard ten Hove
Telephone: (03) 304-8529
Beds: 4 Single (2 bedrooms)
Tariff: B&B $55 Double, $30 Single, children (under 12) 1/2 price, $20 Dinner
Tariff for self-contained cottage: $25 for 2 persons per day, $5 for each extra adult, children (under 15) 1/2 price.
Nearest Town: Akaroa 20 km

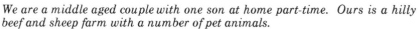

We are a middle aged couple with one son at home part-time. Ours is a hilly beef and sheep farm with a number of pet animals.
Our house was built in 1880, set in extensive gardens and shrubbery for your enjoyment. We have two comfortable twin rooms. Electric blankets on beds and heaters in both rooms. One room on ground floor, toilet and shower shared with family.
Enjoy our home cooking. All meat, vegetables, most fruit home grown. We have free range hens and our own honey. Explore the beauty of Banks Peninsula. From Akaroa take a cruise to view Hectors Dolphins. Bush walks and Okains Maori and Colonial Museum close by. 3 kms to safe sandy beach. Two bicycles available.
Self-contained cottage has 1 bedroom, 4 bunks and 1 bed. Detached sleepout - 2 single beds. Cot available. Everything supplied but food. Dinner by arrangement. 3 km from main house and beach. More suitable for summer months.
Directions: *Please phone.*

Arthur's Pass

Homestay / Self-contained Accom
Address: Highway 73, P O Box 3, Arthurs Pass, Canterbury
Name: John & Judy Charles
Telephone: (0516) 89-238
Beds: 2 Singles (1 bedroom)
Tariff: B&B $55 Double, $30 Single
Nearest Town: Arthur's Pass Village

We are a couple in our late forties with a friendly dog and a son and daughter living away from home. Our two-storeyed house which we built ourselves is at the east end of Arthur's Pass Village on State Highway 73. Our guest bedroom has two single beds and you share facilities, whilst our cabin has a double bed, two bunks, shower, toilet and cooking facilities.
We are surrounded by a National Park which offers a variety of walks and mountain climbs and you may reach us by car, Trans-alpine train which we can meet or Coast-to-Coast Shuttle (0800-800-847).
John is a former National Park Ranger with Antarctic experience, we both have travelled overseas and have a wide range of interests and enjoy meeting people and helping them discover our part of New Zealand. We would prefer non-smokers and 24 hours notice would be appreciated.

Sheffield

Homestay
Address: "Galloway Braes", Malvern Hills Road, Sheffield, Canterbury
Name: Molly Ramsay
Telephone: (051) 638-833
Beds: 1 Double, 3 Single (3 bedrooms) Cot & highchair available
Tariff: B&B $50 Double, $26 Single, $15 children, $12 Dinner (by arrangement)
Nearest Town: Darfield (12 kms) Christchurch (56 km)

Sheffield Township is very small comprising approximately 50 households, a hotel, garage and store, situated among the foothills of the Southern Alps, with easy access to ski-fields, salmon/trout fishing, jet boating, golf course, tramping and breathtaking scenery. The house was originally a coal miners' hostel, now converted to a comfortable residence.
There is 1/3 acre of land which I share with 2 friendly dogs, 2 cats, 8 hens and 2 angora goats whose fleeces I shear, spin and knit. I grow all my own vegetables organically and offer good wholesome meals. I am a Scot who emigrated here in 1973 with my 3 children, now all adult and independent. I provide dinner by prior arrangement. Please allow my telephone to ring for some time if booking, preferably after 4:30 pm.
Directions: *My house is situated in Malvern Hills Road, 50 metres off the main Arthurs Pass Road on State Highway 73. Clearly directed by a large sign depicting "Galloway Braes" B & B.*

Coalgate

Homestay
Address: "Gowan Lea",
Whitecliffs Road, Coalgate RD,
Name: Diana and David Bates
Telephone: (051667) 823
Beds: 1 Double 2 Single (2 bedrooms, guest bathroom)
Tariff: B&B Double $55, Single $30, Children half price; Dinner $15
Nearest Town: Darfield 20 km, Christchurch 65 km

Gowan Lea is a hill country farm with a spacious homestead set in a large garden with a backdrop of a native beech reserve.
Our family is now independent and away from home.
We welcome you to stay and share what we enjoy.
There are two guest rooms with two single beds and one double with sole use of bathroom facilities.
You are welcome to join us for dinner by prior arrangement.
Directions: *An hour's drive from Christchurch and 10 km from Glentunnel off Highway 72 at the end of Whitecliffs road you will find us.*

Glenroy
Historic Homestead - Homestay
Address: "Gunyah Historic Homestead", Sleemans Road, GlenroyR.D. 2, Darfield, Mid Canterbury
Name: Rod and Laurie Squires
Telephone: (051666) 800 from July 1992 (03) 318-6800
Beds: 3 Double, 6 Single (6 bedrooms, 3 bathrooms)
Tariff: B&B $50 per person does not include GST, Single supplement $25; Dinner 3 course $25-$35 depending on menu; Campervans $15 power, shower, toilet, laundry, BBQ facilities. Pets - please phone to arrange.
Nearest Town: Darfield 20 mins, Christchurch only 50 mins, Methven 20 mins, Mt Hutt 20 mins

Our spacious historic English style homestead "Gunyah" was built for Wilfred Hall, son of the New Zealand Prime Minister Sir John Hall in 1913. This stately homestead is protected by N.Z. Historic Places Trust on the basis of its historic and architectural significance. Its large drawing room features extensive mahogony panelling, stained glass and leadlight windows and an inviting open fireplace. Tastefully furnished in comfortable antiques, flowing through from a large entry hall, is the formal dining room which seats 14 people around a single rimu table. The adjoining library with its vast collection of readable books is also the smoking and second T.V. room. The 6 upstairs guest rooms occupy the main wing. They are furnished in period style and all have electric blankets, duvets and are temperature controlled, serviced by three modern bathrooms.
The upstairs verandahs overlook the 25 acres of formal gardens, English woodlands, plantations, deer and sheep paddocks. Old rhododendrons and azaleas surround the lawn tennis court and croquet lawn. Large specimen English trees, N.Z. natives, a unique kauri and many other shrubs and spring bulbs enhance this old English garden. Woodland walks have been developed throughout the whole area.

continued over

Further afield you may indulge youself in the many local activities . Golf at the renowned Hororata Golf Club, fish for large salmon in the Rakaia River or Lake Coleridge. Catch trout on the property. Ski Mount Hutt or six other ski fields within one hours drive. Whitewater rafting, jetboating, horseriding, paragliding, tramping, bushwalking or just plain relaxing are right on the doorstep.

At the end of the day a warm welcome awaits you, a hot shower, a gourmet meal featuring the best of Canterbury's game, meat and produce, a complimentary glass of N.Z. wine.

Wake up to the sound of the N.Z. countryside and a substantial English cooked breakfast.

We look forward to welcoming you.

Your hosts,

Rod and Laurie Squires

Directions: *From Christchurch take Route 73 (Arthurs Pass) to Darfield. Turn left through Darfield following the Rakaia Gorge road. Travel through Glentunnel turning left over the Selwyn River. 10 kms from Glentunnel turn left at the small monument at the top of the hill, toward Hororata, then first right into Sleemans Road, past the Baptist camp, across the Hororata River and we are the second driveway on the left. Follow The "Gunyah" signs.*

Rakaia Gorge - Mt Hutt
Farmstay
Address: Rakaia Gorge Homestead, No 12 R.D., Rakaia, Mid Canterbury
Name: Birgitte Richards and Steve Gerard
Telephone: (03) 302-8448
Beds: 2 Double, 2 Single (3 bedrooms)
Tariff: B&B $50 Double, $30 Single, $15 children, $15 Dinner
Nearest Town: Methven 15 kms, Christchurch (1hr 10min East)

Set in the depths of rural Mid Canterbery in the very picturesque Rakaia Gorge, this secluded hideaway sits right on the banks of the Rakaia River. Built in times of rural prosperity in the late 1890's our Homestead features extensive wood panelling, formal dining room, large hallway and sitting room with an open fire. We have park-like surroundings of mature trees and garden.

Originally part of Mt Hutt Station, the farm is now a 600 acre sheep and beef farm.

We have excellent salmon fishing quite literally on our doorstep and trout fishing nearby, we have rods etc. for hire.

Mt Hutt Ski Field is the big attraction during winter (May-Oct) and we're conveniently close. Steve works as a Ski Instructor at Mt Hutt.

Other attractions nearby include: jet boating, scenic walks, an 18 hole gold course, rafting, and during winter heli-skiing and ice-skating at Lake Ida.

Directions: *1 km South of the Rakaia Gorge Bridges on State Highway 72.*

Mt Hutt, Methven

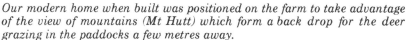

Farmhouse
Address: "Tyrone",
No. 12 RD, Rakaia,
Name: Pam and Roger Callaghan
Telephone: (03) 302-8096
Beds: 1 Double, 2 Single (2 bedrooms, guest bathroom)
Tariff: B&B Double $60, Single $35, Dinner $20

Our modern home when built was positioned on the farm to take advantage of the view of mountains (Mt Hutt) which form a back drop for the deer grazing in the paddocks a few metres away.

As our family have left home we now have two spare bedrooms which we would like to share with guests. These rooms consist of large double bedroom with ensuite and smaller twin with bathroom, all beds have electric blankets.

Included in the gardens are grass tennis court, swimming pool, BBQ and games room with medium size pool table.

The farm is situated between the ski and agriculture service town of Methven and Mt Hutt - Rakaia Gorge area. It consists of three hundred acres running sheep, cattle, deer and some grain crops.

Directions: from Methven follow SH77 towards Highway 72 for 8 kms, farm is on right hand side, name on mailbox or 5 km from Highway 72 towards Methven (refer Christchurch and District map).

Mt. Hutt, Methven

Farmhouse
Address: Pudding Hill Road, SH 72, Methven.
Postal: "Glenview", RD12, Rakaia
Name: Karen and Andrew Hart   **Telephone:** (03) 302-8620
Beds: 1 Double, 2 Single, + cot (2 bedrooms, guest bathroom)
Tariff: B&B Double $70, Single $35, Dinner $15, Children under 13 half price, under 5 free; Campervans $20 up to 4 persons

We are a family of four who live in a large modern farmhouse built for the views, on a 1200 acre sheep and beef farm at the top of the Canterbury Plains. The house, at 450 m (1500 ft) above sea level provides wonderful views, as we look across the plains to Christchurch, directly up into the basin of Mount Hutt Skifield next door, and along the Southern Alps.

Our farm is located on State Highway 72, the picturesque inland road between Christchurch and Southern tourist destinations. You are welcome to join in with or observe any of our farming activities. Bush walks and skifield surround us. A golf course is nearby. Rakaia Gorge, 10 minutes away, offers jet boating and salmon fishing.

Our comfortable house has large flexible open plan living. The spacious guest rooms have their own access from outside, and each bed has an electric blanket. Private bathroom and toilet are close by, with a shower also available. A swimming pool is in the grounds for your use.

Come and join in with our farming family.

Directions: Our 'Farmhouse Accommodation' sign is on State Highway 72, 5 km north of Alford Forest Store (look for the moas!) and 3.5 km south of the Mt Hutt Skifield Road. Our house is the 3rd house, 1.5 km up Pudding Hill Road (toward the hills)

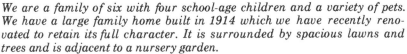

Methven
Homestay
Address: Northfield,
Dolma Street, Methven
Name: Roger and Jane Goldsbrough
Telephone: (03) 302 8622
Beds: 2 Double, 2 Single, Cot (2 bedrooms)
Tariff: B&B Double $75, Single $40, Children under 12 half price; Dinner on request $20 (all plus GST); Campervans $20
Nearest Town: Methven

We are a family of six with four school-age children and a variety of pets. We have a large family home built in 1914 which we have recently renovated to retain its full character. It is surrounded by spacious lawns and trees and is adjacent to a nursery garden.
We have two guest rooms both of which can be family rooms and we can offer a taste of country living. We also have a swimming pool, grass tennis court and trampoline.
We are within very easy reach of skiing at Mt Hutt, fishing, hunting, golfing, jetboat safaris, river rafting and bush walks or you can just enjoy the country air and spend a few relaxing days away from it all.
We are interested in wholefoods and herbs and Roger enjoys making handcrafted furniture and restoring antiques. Jane comes from England and we have travelled overseas as a family and enjoy meeting fellow travellers.
Forward booking would be appreciated.
Directions: *Take the main south road from Christchurch. Once over the Rakaia bridge take the sixth turning on the right (approximately 1 km after bridge), follow the road to Methven and Mount Somers for approximately 32 km, turn left into Dolma Street, we are the third house on the left.*

Ashburton
Farmhouse
Address: "Noumai", No 3 RD, Ashburton
Name: Anne and Norman McConnell
Telephone: (03) 303 7296
Beds: 4 Single (2 bedrooms)
Tariff: B&B Double $50, Single $25, Children half price; Dinner $12
Nearest Town: Ashburton

Our property is a 500 acre irrigation sheep farm. We have an adult family of three – a daughter married and two sons one at home and the other working in Brisbane.
Our home is an older house with spacious bedrooms and generous living areas surrounded by a large garden. There are two guest rooms with twin beds, electric blankets and nearby shower and bathroom.
Family activities include golf and squash and other outdoor activities.
We live on State Highway 1, 12 km north of the turnoff to Mt Cook and the Southern Lakes via Geraldine.
Phone calls welcome anytime.
Directions: *Turn at mailbox over railway line and into driveway.* ⸺

Ashburton
Farmstay
Address: "Carradale Farm", Ferriman's Road, No 8 R.D., Ashburton
Name: Jim & Karen McIntyre
Telephone: (03) 308-6577
Beds: 45 Single (2 bedrooms)
Tariff: B&B $25 Single, children 1/2 price, $15 Dinner, Campervans $20
Nearest Town: Ashburton - 8 km West of Ashburton.

Our modern brick homestead which captures the sun in all rooms is cosy and inviting. It is situated in a sheltered garden where you can enjoy peace, tranquility and fresh country air or indulge in a game of tennis.
Both guest rooms have comfortable twin beds, electric blankets, reading lamps and tea making facilities. They share bathroom, separate shower and separate toilet facilities.
We offer home grown meat, vegetables and fruit.
Our farm is a 220 hectare irrigated sheep farm. You may like to join in farm activities or be taken for a farm tour.
Our 3 adult children have left home although our son who is married lives and works on the farm.
As we have both travelled extensively in New Zealand, United Kingdom and Europe we would like to offer hospitality to fellow travellers. We will meet public transport in Ashburton.
Our hobbies include meeting people, travel, reading, photography, gardening, rugby, cricket and Jim belongs to Masonic Lodge.
Directions: *Turn off State Highway 1 and cross the railway line at Tinwald Tavern, heading west onto Lagmhor Road driving past Tinwald Golf Course. The road then becomes Frasers Road. Travel 6 km to 5 crossroads. Make a left turn onto Ferrimans Road. Our home is the only house on the right side of the road.*

Ashburton
Homestay
Address: 1 Sudbury Street, Ashburton
Name: Pat and Dave Weir
Telephone: (03) 3083 534
Beds: 1 Double, 2 Single (2 bedrooms)
Tariff: B&B Double $50, Single $25, Dinner $15, Children $10, Campervans $5 per person

We are 10-15 minutes walk from town, our comfortable home is situated in a quiet street and we have the added enjoyment of looking out onto a rural scene. The guest accommodation is roomy and comfortable. Your hosts are a middle aged couple with a variety of interests. We welcome the opportunity to meet and greet visitors and wish to make your stay a happy one. We do request visitors not to smoke in our home.

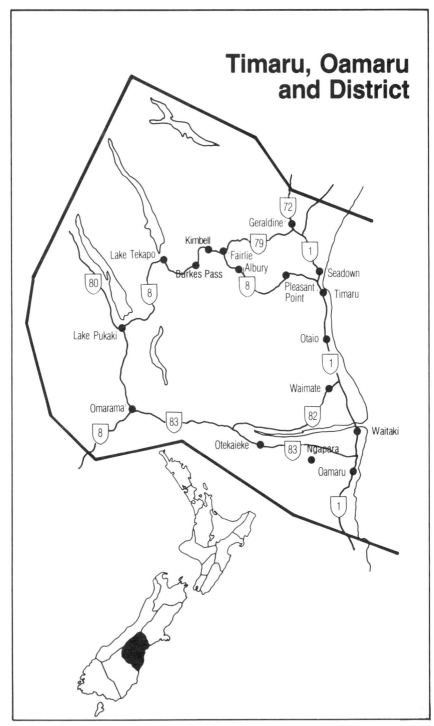

Timaru, Oamaru and District

Geraldine
Guest Lodge
Address: "The Crossing", Woodbury Road, RD 21, Geraldine
Name: Angela and Peter Temple
Telephone: (03) 693 9689
Beds: 3 Double, 2 Single (4 bedrooms, 3 guest bathrooms)
Tariff: B&B Double from $78, Single $41.50, Honeymoon Suite $93, Dinner $20
Nearest Town: Geraldine 3 km

"The Crossing" Guest Lodge is an English gentleman's residence built in 1908. It has been elegantly redecorated and is situated in a park-like setting with a wonderful view of the mountains.
I have recently returned to New Zealand after 33 years spenit n England and Angela has come out to live here.
"The Crossing" opened to the travelling public in October 1989, is a place of food and rest. Accommodation includes a honeymoon suite and twin rooms with luxury ensuites and a further 2 double/single rooms that share. Our dining room is a fully licensed restaurant (where you can meet local clients as well as other travelling guests). Other facilities include guests' lounge and conference room. Our farm provides horse riding, red deer, sheep and peacocks.
"The Crossing" is conveniently situated within 1 hours travelling distance from 5 ski fields, 20 minutes from trekking and scenic walks (Peel forest, Te Moana and Waihi Gorges) and fishing in season. There are also 2 golf courses in Geraldine.
Directions: *Signposted on SH 72/79 Woodbury Road corner 1 km north of Geraldine.*

Geraldine, South Canterbury
Homestay
Address: "Wharepuke Bed and Breakfast", Pye Road, The Downs, RD21, Geraldine
Name: Joan and Peter Larsen
Telephone: (03) 693 8982
Beds: 1 Double 2 Single (2 bedrooms, guest bathroom)
Tariff: B&B Double $60, Single $35; Dinner $15
Geraldine 1 km

The name "Wharepuke" means house on the hill in Maori, and our home is situated in an attractive 1 acre garden setting with magnificent views of mountain and countryside, and adjacent to Talbot Forest Reserve with its numerous bush walks.

We are a middle-aged couple, semi-retired who enjoy the opportunity of meeting visitors to New Zealand and promise you relaxing, comfortable hospitality.

Our spacious old home built about the turn of the century has been renovated to modern standards, with all the atmosphere of the past being retained.

A breakfast of your choice is served at your requested time and an evening meal is available by arrangement if required.

The Geraldine area is very picturesque and day trips to the Gorges and Peel Forest Scenic Reserve 15 km away make a day to remember.

Directions: *At roundabout in main street by Mobil garage turn into Pine Street, left into Jollie Street, right up hill (Totara Street) which runs onto Pye Road.*

"Wharepuke" is second on left

Geraldine, South Canterbury
Farmstay
Address: "Scotsdale",
Coopers Creek, 22 R.D., Geraldine
Name: Aylene & Alex Stalker
Telephone: (03) 696-3874
Beds: 2 Double, 5 Single (4 bedrooms, guest bathroom, 2 toilets, each room has vanity unit.)
Tariff: B&B $60 Double, $35 Single, $20 Dinner
Nearest Town: 10 km North of Geraldine on Highway 72

Experience the serenity of the country in our comfortable, antique studded, spacious home. Our friendly and warm atmosphere attracts many visitors. We are farming 350 acres, running Romney sheep and breeding Hackney ponies to drive in our Gigs.
Our home is set in 2 acres of shrubs, flower gardens and lawn where you may enjoy playing Croquet. Bedrooms open onto balcony featuring breath taking panoramic views of the Southern Alps. Enjoy watching a demonstration of sheep dogs working, view the farm animals and amble along Coopers Creek. There are also many deer farms in our area.
"Scotsdale" is 5 minutes away from Peel Forest Scenic Park with native bush walks and native birds. 3 kms to Rangitata River for Trout/Salmon fishing and rafting. 1 hour to 4 ski fields. 5 minutes to Geraldine. 1 1/2 hours to Christchurch and on main rout to Mt Cook and Queenstown.
A warm welcome awaits overseas and New Zealand visitors alike. We invite you to join us for Dinner and share an evening of relaxation and friendship. We look forward to meeting you.
Directions: *"Scotsdale" is situated at Coopers Creek on Highway 72 at the junction of Peel Forest Road - just 10 kms North of Geraldine.*

Some homes share the bathroom, others have bathrooms
exclusively for guests – they are indicated in the listing.

Kimbell, Fairlie

Self-contained Accommodation & Homestay
Address: State Highway 8, Kimbell, Fairlie
Name: Ron & Kay Collyer
Telephone & Fax: (03) 685-8170
Cottages:
Laurel Cottage: 1 Double, 1 Single
Walnut Cottage: 2 Double, 1 Single
Appletree Cottage: 1 Double, 2 Single
Homestead: 1 Double, 2 Single (2 bedrooms, guest bathroom)
Tariff: per person, cottages from $40, Honeymoon from $60-$67.50, children under 15 from $20. Maid service available. Homestead $40, Dinner $25, Picnic baskets from $20 for 2 people.
Nearest Town: Fairlie 7 km, Skifield 6 km to gate.

Colonial Cottages at Kimbell.
Imagine the rural tranquillity of Kimbell village with a backdrop of snowcapped mountain ranges. Here, set in the privacy of olde worlde cottage gardens, you will find our romantic century old cottages for your exclusive use.
Each with its own character, furnished with antiques of the period with every modern convenience of today. Thoughtfully prepared for your arrival with fresh flowers and special homely touches, the kitchens will be stocked with farm fresh breakfast fare or a very special breakfast for honeymooners.
Skiing, fishing, photography, golf are some things to do or just relax and enjoy the simple pleasure of life.
In Fairlie, there is a choice of eateries from gourmet to take-away or join us for dinner in the homestead.
We promise you an evening of fine fresh food, fun and laughter. We love sharing all the pleasure that we get out of living.
We left the city to look for 10 acres and ended up with 400! So we learnt to be farmers and are now experimenting with heaps of things such as organics and truffles. Book now for a memorable experience.
Directions: *On State Highway 8 - sign at gate.*

Burkes Pass
Homestay
Address: "Stone House",
R.D. 17 Burkes Pass,
South Canterbury
Name: Mark Lahood
Telephone: (03) 685-8316

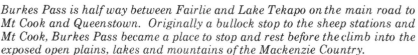

Beds: 2 Double (2 bedrooms)
Tariff: B&B $55 Double, $35 Single, $20 Dinner, Campervans welcome.
Nearest Town: Tekapo & Fairlie

Burkes Pass is half way between Fairlie and Lake Tekapo on the main road to Mt Cook and Queenstown. Originally a bullock stop to the sheep stations and Mt Cook, Burkes Pass became a place to stop and rest before the climb into the exposed open plains, lakes and mountains of the Mackenzie Country.
The early settlers at Burkes Pass built their homes of local materials - stone wood and cob and several still exist today. The owner, with the help of his friends, has continued the tradition and built a lodge of glacial schist and local timbers. The huge stone fireplace and open plan living create an atmosphere which is convivial and relaxing. A perfect place to stop for a few days beside the trickling creek, bordered by an interesting selection of hazlenut trees. For the active there is ski-ing, alpine walks, fishing, para-ponting and hunting in the vicinity.
Directions: *Christchurch to Queenstown and Mt Cook bus stops at Burkes Pass.*

Lake Tekapo
Homestay
Address: Pioneer Drive, P O Box 99, Lake Tekapo
Name: Elizabeth & Brett Shand
Telephone: (03) 6806-703
Beds: 1 Double, 3 Single (3 bedrooms, guest bathroom)
Tariff: B&B $75 Double, $53 Single, $20 Dinner by arrangement
Nearest Town: Fairlie (35 minutes) on Highway 8 from Timaru to Cromwell

Lake Tekapo is on the main highway from Christchurch through to Queenstown, Haast Past or Mt Cook.
When we left our farm to live at our favourite place, looking out over the turquoise blue Lake Tekapo and distant mountains, we added a bedroom wing to our holiday house. This we offer to you with its warm, quiet bedrooms. A non-smoking home.
Lake Tekapo is over 2000 feet above sea level at the edge of the vast Mackenzie tussock plain. The sunshine hours are high. The clear air reveals a night sky to remember.
Enjoy doing nothing or walking, tramping, alpine climbing. Perhaps fishing, skiing, boating. Play squash, tennis or golf. Hunting, fishing and alpine guides are based in our small village.

Lake Tekapo

Homestay + Self-Contained Accommodation
Address: "THE CHALET", Pioneer Drive, Lake Tekapo
Name: Zita and Walter Speck
Telephone: (03) 680 6774
Beds: 3 Double, 3 Single, 4 Bunkbeds in 2 units (1 self-contained unit sleeps 2, 1 self-contained family unit with 4 bedrooms sleeps 10)
Tariff: Accommodation only, Double $60, Single $50, additional person $14. Breakfast: continental $8 per person, cooked $12
Nearest Town: 100 km northwest of Timaru, 230 km southwest of Christchurch; 250 km northeast of Queenstown

Lake Tekapo is a delightful lakeside resort nestled amongst some of New Zealand's most beautiful mountain scenery. It is well-known for the colour of the lake and the Church of the Good Shepherd. It is an ideal stopover place between Christchurch and Queenstown. This region is a great place for people who like the outdoors – walking, tramping, riding, golf, watersports, fishing and hunting are the main summer activities. During the winter months alpine and crosscountry skiing, skitouring and iceskating attract many holidaymakers. Tekapo is also a base for scenic flights over the magnificent Southern Alps.
The scenic splendour in the MacKenzie and the sunsets provide plenty of impressions for painters and keen photographers.
We are a family with two little boys; wir sprechen deutsch, nous parlons français.
Our home is a two-storey building along the lakeshore and close to the famous church. Our guests can stay in a self-contained flatette (sleeps 3) or the bigger self-contained flat (sleeps 10). There is a barbecue area for our guests.
Fishing gear can be hired. It is possible to take our guests for fishing or hunting trips by previous arrangement.
Our aim is to make your stay in Tekapo a memorable and enjoyable part of your holiday.
Directions: *200 m east of the Church of the Good Shepherd.*

Albury
Farmstay
Address: Mount Nessing, RD16, Albury, South Canterbury
Name: Richard and Margaret Hacquoil
Telephone: (03) 685 5739
Beds: 2 Single (1 bedroom)
Tariff: B&B Double $60, Dinner B&B Double $90; Campervans
Nearest Town: Albury 12 km, Fairlie 16 km

We are a family of five with three school-age children.
We live on a sheep and cattle farm in a picturesque setting with mountain views.
Our interests include spinning wool, handcrafts, motorbikes, cars and a Lions Club member.
We live in close proximity to skifields, trout fishing and a golf course is adjacent to our farm.
The room has two single beds and you may join us for a family dinner or have bed and breakfast.
Directions: *on SH 8 Timaru to Fairlie, Albury is 48 km from Timaru and 16 km from Fairlie. When driving from Timaru turn left onto Mount Nessing Road just through Albury township, continue on Mount Nessing Road, take second road on right called Wilfred Road. Our home is third on right, name is on mail box approximately 12 km from Albury township.*

Pleasant Point, Timaru
Farmstay
Address: "Mt Gay", Pleasant Point, RD12, Timaru
Name: Florence and Roger Carter
Telephone: (03 614 7153

Beds: 4 Single (2 bedrooms, guest bathroom)
Tariff: B&B Double $60, Single $40, Children half price; Dinner $20
Nearest Town: Timaru

"Mt Gay" (1000 ft) the family property for over a hundred years, is a sheep, goat and agro forestry farm thirty-five minutes drive from Timaru, two hours from Christchurch and Mt Cook. Bus, train and plane arrivals met at Timaru. There are limestone outcrops with sheltered valleys for walking, Maori drawings, and extensive beautiful views of snow-capped mountains, plains and sea.
In our modern, architecturally-designed home with its pleasant garden surrounds will be found a relaxed atmosphere and good country cuisine which has grown from many years of hosting experience.
One horse for experienced rider or lead-rides for children (no charge). Guns available for rabbit shooting. Five minutes drive to trout fishing river, 30 minutes drive to salmon fishing (tackle available), sixty to ninety minutes to three skifields, thirty minutes to the beach, fifteen minutes to golf, squash, tennis and Olympic pool.
Directions: *Please ring.*

Timaru

Homestay
Address: 16 Selwyn Street, Timaru
Name: Margaret and Nevis Jones
Telephone: (03) 688 1400
Beds: 3 Single (2 bedrooms)
Tariff: B&B Double $55, Single $35,
Children half price; Dinner $15

We are a family of six but with only one child left at home. Our home is a spacious, comfortable, two-storeyed brick house with a grass tennis court in use from October until March.

Situated in central Timaru – 5 minutes walk from the beach and 15 minutes from town, our home is set back from the road in a private garden surrounded by trees.

We have travelled and worked overseas with our four children three and a half years of our married life, and share an enjoyment of meeting people from other countries and feel we have an appreciation of what it is like to be a visitor in a foreign country.

Our main interests centre around music and the theatre in which we are both actively involved. We also play tennis and golf. We enjoy making use of the many walks and opportunities to get into the mountains which are so accessible from Timaru.

Timaru is centrally situated in the South Island – 2 hours from Christchurch, Dunedin, Mt Cook, and five skifields.

Directions: *Please phone.*

Seadown, Timaru

Homestay
Address: Seadown, RD3, Timaru
Name: Margaret and Ross Paterson
Telephone: (03) 688 2468
Beds: 4 Single (2 bedrooms, guest bathroom)
Tariff: B&B Double $55, Single 35, Children half price; Dinner $15; Campervans welcome, but no power.
Nearest Town: Approximately halfway between Timaru and Temuka

We are a mixed cropping farm situated in South Canterbury between Timaru and Temuka, east of State Highway 1.

We grow grass-seed, clover, grain crops and freezing peas and also have 600 sheep.

Our home is an older type home which has been modernised. Electric blankets on all guests' beds. Laundry facilities are available. A swimming pool can be enjoyed in the warmer weather.

Your hostess is interested in spinning, gardening and breadmaking.You are welcome to have your meals with us.

Day trips can be comfortably taken to Mount Cook, Hydro Lakes and skifields. Fishing and golf course a few minutes away; also a walk to the sea coast.

A warm welcome awaits overseas and New Zealand visitors alike.

Directions: *From north approximately 5 km from Temuka to Dominion Road on left. Turn right if travelling from Timaru approx 11 km. To the end of Dominion Road – turn right then left onto Beach Road, till you come to Hides Road on left – first house on left on Hides Road.*

Otaio, Timaru
Farmstay
Address: "Cedar Downs", Otaio, RD1
(Horseshoe Bend Road), Timaru
Name: Mary and Graeme Bell
Telephone: (03 6126-647
Beds: 4 Single (2 bedrooms, guest bathroom)
Tariff: B&B Double $55, Single $35, Children half price; Dinner $15;
Campervans $6 per person (2 campervan points)
Nearest Town: 28 km south from Timaru, 28 km north from Waimate

*"Cedar Downs" is a farm of 600 acres only 1 km from main State Highway
1. Located in a pleasant valley we farm sheep, deer, cattle, and cropping. At
times a demonstration of shearing can be arranged.*

*A comfortable brick home and warm hospitality await you. The two guest
rooms have two single beds in each, all with electric blankets and you have
your own bathroom. There are two campervan power points with shower
and toilet facilities.*

Meals can be provided for live-in or campervan guests if required.

*A swimming pool and barbecue area is set in an attractive garden where
you are welcome to relax. If you prefer you are welcome to join in farm activities.*

Day trips can be comfortably taken to Mt Cook, the lakes and ski fields.

Directions: *28 km south of Timaru or 28 km north of Waimate on
Horseshoe Bend Road (signposted on main road), first farm on left.*

Timaru
Homestay
Address: 5 Watlington Place, Timaru
Name: Russell & Margaret Stuart
Telephone: (03) 684-7503
Beds: 4 Single (2 bedrooms, guest bathroom)
Tariff: B&B $70 Double, $35 Single, children 1/2 price, $15 Dinner
Nearest Town: Timaru

*We are a semi-retired couple, with a grown family of three, who, until recently
were engaged in full-time farming.*

*Our house on the edge of town, is spacious with fine views over the
countryside to the Southern Alps - Mt Cook can be seen in the distance from all
windows.*

*We offer warm comfortable bedrooms with guest bathroom and substantial
meals to suit all tastes.*

We are willing to meet bus, train or plane at small cost.

*Over the years we have enjoyed hosting people from all corners of the world,
and are ready and willing to share our knowledge of our country with our
visitors.*

*Russell is a member of Lions International and Margaret's interests are many
and varied.*

*Timaru is central to the fine trout and salmon fishing areas and to the many
other attractions of South Canterbury.*

We look forward to meeting you and offering our hospitality. ———

271

Lake Pukaki / Mount Cook
Farmstay
Address: Tasman Downs Station, Lake Tekapo
Name: Linda & Bruce Hayman
Telephone: (03) 680-6841
Beds: 1 Double, 2 Single (2 bedrooms)
Tariff: B&B $100 Double, $50 Single, children 1/2 price, dinner included.
Nearest Town: 25 km from Lake Tekapo, halfway between Christchurch and Queenstown.

We are a family of four with a 19 year old son employed on the farm and a 24 year old daughter away from home. Our farm runs sheep and cattle with crops grown for self-sufficiency.

We live in a 15 year old homestead built from natural stone, perfectly located overlooking Lake Pukaki with splendid views of Mount Cook and the Southern Alps. "A place of unsurpassed beauty".

We have a 9 hole mini golf course, trampoline and swing with peaceful surroundings to relax in. Your hosts "have rich pioneering and surprisingly wide experiences".

A great opportunity to experience true New Zealand farm life with friendly hosts.

If you find something missing that you are
accustomed to, simply ask you hosts for it.

Lake Pukaki
Farmstay
Address: "Rhoborough Downs", Lake Pukaki, P.B. Fairlie
Name: Roberta and Logan Preston
Telephone: (03) 435-0509
Beds: 1 Double, 2 Single (2 bedrooms)
Tariff: Dinner, B&B Double $100, Single $50
Nearest Town: Twizel 10 minute drive

Our property of 18,000 acres which carries merino sheep in the MacKenzie country has been in the family since 1919.

We have a family of three grown children occasionally at home.

We are approximately halfway between Christchurch and Queens-town. It is a one hour drive to Mount Cook National Park and Ohau State Forest. Skifields, ice-skating, water sports, fishing and tramping are all handy. Glorious mountain views from the homestead.

I serve delicious New Zealand cuisine, mostly home grown, in quiet and relaxing surroundings.

Twizel township has a bank, doctor, hairdresser, shops, etc. plus golf, tennis and squash facilities.

Directions: *Please phone a day before or preferably earlier as bookings are necessary.*

Omarama
Farmstay
Address: Dunstan Downs, Omarama
Name: Tim and Geva Innes
Telephone: (03) 438-9862
Beds: 1 Double, 3 Single (2 bedrooms)
Tariff: B&B $25 per person, Dinner $25
Nearest Town: Omarama – 17 km west on State Highway 8

Dunstan Downs is a sheep and cattle station in the heart of the South Island high country.
We have two children, both at boarding school.
Our home is full of country warmth and you are welcome to join us for dinner or bed and breakfast.
The Ahuriri River is at our back door, also a lake fishing guide can be arranged at extra cost.
Great tramping nearby in the Ohau and Ahuriri areas. Skiing at Ohau in season only an hour away or 15 min by helicopter (at a price).

Waimate, South Canterbury
Homestay
Address: Wainono Homestead,
RD10 Waimate
Name: Ken and Cynthia Henderson
Telephone: (03) 689 9883
Beds: 1 Double, 2 Single (2 bedrooms, guest bathroom)
Tariff: B&B $35 per person, Children under 13 years half price; Dinner $15
Nearest Town: Waimate

Our two storeyed Edwardian homestead is set in a peaceful 5 acre garden setting and is situated on State Highway 1, midway between Timaru and Oamaru and approximately 2 hours 30 min drive from Christchurch and Dunedin.
There is a choice of guest room, with either a double or single beds and your own bathroom. You have tea making facilities in your bedroom.
The homestead was built in 1910 as a gentleman's residence for Paul Studholme, a son of Michael Studholme, the first white settler in Waimate, and features original leadlight windows and wood panelling..
Enjoy a brief encounter with life as it was in a more gracious era.

273

Waimate

Farmstay
Address: "Te Moana Nui" Willowbridge, RD10, Waimate
Name: Don and Lorna Hayman
Telephone: (03) 689 9837
Beds: 4 Single (2 bedrooms, guest bathroom)
Tariff: B&B Double $60, Single $35, Children half price; Dinner $15;
Campervans $20 up to 4 people
Nearest Town: 44 km south from Timaru, 41 km north from Oamaru,
12 km east from Waimate

*We are midway between Christchurch and Dunedin and have a mixed
cropping and livestock farm situated on the banks of the Waihao river and
bounded on the east by the sea. Fishing, boating and waterskiing within
walking distance.*

*Our attractive home is in a tranquil setting of trees and garden (sheltered
and sunny) with a lovely view of the hills and mountains.*

*Two guest rooms are available, each with twin beds and serviced by a bath-
room and shower room. Ample parking for campervans, power, toilet and
shower room handy.*

*You are assured of warm, friendly hospitality and are most welcome to
have family dinner with us or bed and breakfast if preferred.*

*Waimate has lovely gardens, bush walks, scenic drives, golf, etc. A pleasant
day trip to Mt Cook is possible, or you may prefer to just relax and enjoy our
surroundings. You are very welcome to stay more than one night.*

Directions: *On State Highway 1, 44 km south of Timaru, or 41 km north of
Oamaru, turn into Lucks Road opposite a bright yellow barn, first turn left,
second left, first right into Low's Road, second house on left (5 km from
State Highway).*

Waimate

Homestay
Address: Rattray Place, 138 Queen Street, Waimate, South Canterbury
Name: Alex and Joan Norton
Telephone: (03) 689 7808
Beds: 2 Single (1 bedroom)
Tariff: B&B Double $50, Single $25, Dinner $15
Nearest Town: Timaru 47 km north, Oamaru 47 km south

*We are retired dairy farmers with a family of four, all married. Two
daughters farm with their husbands nearby so if you are interested farm
visits can be arranged.*

*Alex has just retired as Forestry Manager for the local District Council. We
have travelled and enjoy having guests in our home.*

*A warm welcome awaits you at our townhouse-unit, right off the main
street of Waimate, with private parking.*

*You are welcome to have dinner with us, or bed and breakfast of your
choice.*

*We have many interests including gardening, music, sailing, bowling, weav-
ing, and making new friends.*

We request guests not to smoke in our home.

We would appreciate some prior notice of your proposed visit.

Oamaru
Homestay
Address: Gibsons Road,
3 K.R.D., Oamaru
Name: Terry & Glynis Kappely
Telephone: (03) 431-7798
Beds: 1 Double, 2 Single (2 bedrooms, guest bathroom)
Tariff: B&B $50 Double, $25 Single, children 1/2 price, $15 Dinner
Nearest Town: 17 km West of Oamaru on SH83, 35 mins from Kurow

We have a small farm and graze dairy cows, sheep and goats. Some of the sheep and goats will come up so you can pat and feed them.
Our comfortable and spacious home is set in a large garden which we are in the process of developing.
We are not far from Highway 83 which heads past the Hydro Lakes of Waitaki, Avimore and Benmroe then on to Queenstown or North to Lakes Pukaki and Tekapo and Mount Cook.
You are welcome to join our family of four for a quiet night in North Otago. We look forward to meeting you.

Ngapara, Oamaru
Farmstay
Address: "Wallfield", Conlans Ro
6 C.R.D., Ngapara, Oamaru
Name: Bill & Pat Bews
Telephone: (03) 432-6881
Beds: 1 Double, 2 Single (2 bedrooms)
Tariff: B&B $50 Double, $25 Single, $15 Dinner, Campervans $15
Nearest Town: Oamaru 31 kms.

We are third generation farmers on a mixed farm (sheep, cattle, cropping). Our modern home is set in spacious gardens (with swimming pool) creating a peaceful atmosphere which we treasure. We have four children all happily married. Our interests include golf, tramping, gardening, commercial lavender growing, travel and meeting people.
Directions: *Our farm is situated approximately 15 km South of the Waitaki River and 30 km West of Oamaru on Conlans Road which is signposted and about half way between the townships of Ngapara and Tokarahi. Our name is on the gate. The major turnoff points are from Highway One just South of Oamaru and Highway 83 just East of Duntroon (both well signposted). It is just 10 minutes drive to the Tokarahi Golf course which is enroute to the Dansey's Pass - a picturesque drive linking North & Central Otago.* —————

Otekaieke, Oamaru
Farmstay
Address: "Sunny Downs",
Otekaieke, 9k R.D., Oamaru
Name: Kaye & Keith Dennison
Telephone: (03) 431-1741 (after 4.00pm or before 8.00am)
Beds: 2 Double, 1 Single (2 bedrooms)
Tariff: B&B $50 Double, $25 Single, children under 13 1/2 price, $15 Dinner, $20 Campervans (up to 4 people), Sleepout: 2 singles $15 B&B
Nearest Town: Oamaru 60 km East

A warm welcome awaits you at "Sunny Downs" where you will experience the atmosphere of a working farm and enjoy delicious home cooked meals. You will be able to join in farm activities, if you wish, or just relax in our peaceful setting. The house is large, set in spacious grounds with views of the hills and surrounding farmland. Beds have woolrest sleepers and electric blankets.

We are 3 km off HW 83 which is a direct route to and from Mt Cook. The Waitaki River which is internationally known for fishing and jetboating is nearby. Also nearby are facilities for tennis, squash, golf and plenty of places to walk. Ski fields are approx 1 1 /2 hours away.

Comments from our visitors' book include: "A home away from home", "Peaceful", "Relaxing", "Great hospitality", "a warm & friendly family", "we left the best to the last".

Please feel free to call in and see if accommodation is available as sometimes we are outside and don't hear the phone.

Directions: *From Oamaru or Christchurch turn onto SH 83 and continue through Duntroon, take second road on left which is Eastern Road. We are second place on right with "Sunny Downs" on the gate. From Mt Cook Omarama pass through Kurow, take 6th road on right - Eastern Road.*

Waitaki Bridge, Oamaru
Farmstay
Address: Waitaki Kaik, Waitaki Bridge, 5HRD, Oamaru
Name: Mark and Diana Taylor
Telephone: (03) 4313- 868
Beds: 3 Single (2 bedrooms)
Tariff: B&B $25 per person, Dinner $20, Children half price; Campervan facilities
Nearest Town: Oamaru. Christchurch 3 hours, Dunedin 1 hour 30 mins

We farm sheep and grow lucerne for hay. We have a grown up family of 3 who are away from home. Apart from having access to any farming activities you may care to participate in, we also have riding horses available so we can cater for the absolute beginner or the very experienced, as an optional extra, should you be interested. There are ample opportunities for

276

walking, swimming in the river or a round of golf. Should you want to spend a day at the Lakes or go skiing the lakes and mountains are all within easy reach. Oamaru Airport is also just 4 miles away with flights connecting with other centres. Our 1,100 acre farm borders the Pacific Ocean on the one side where there can be good sea fishing. The sea and beach here, unfortunately, are not suitable for swimming. On another boundary we have the internationally famous Waitaki River where every year fisherman spend hours hoping to catch a Quinnat Salmon, or perhaps either a Rainbow or Brown Trout.

Directions: *From Christchurch travelling south on SH 1, after crossing the Waitaki River Bridge, you take the second turning on the left "Kaik Road" and our two storey home is the house on the right at the end approximately two miles. Coming from Dunedin "Kaik Road" is the 1st turning on the right after Oamaru Airport.*

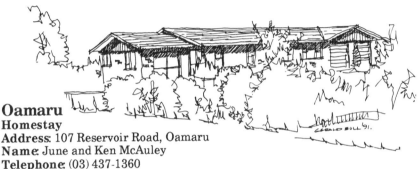

Oamaru

Homestay
Address: 107 Reservoir Road, Oamaru
Name: June and Ken McAuley
Telephone: (03) 437-1360
Beds: 3 Single (2 bedrooms)
Tariff: B&B Double $60, Single $35, Dinner $15, Campervans $20 up to 4 people
Nearest Town: Oamaru 3 kms

We would like to welcome you to our home. We are semi-retired farmers with a married family. We live in a new residential area on Oamaru's scenic drive. On our small farm we have cattle, goats and a friendly sheep dog. Our home is 15 years old, centrally heated, spacious and very comfortable. The guest rooms are twin and single. Beds all have electric blankets. Bathroom and toilet are next to the guest rooms.

We have a great rural, mountain and ocean view. Our interests include Women's Institute, Red Cross work, knitting, sewing, farming activities and developing residential building lots. We enjoy having overseas visitors staying in our home. You are assured of warm friendly hospitality, and are most welcome to have family dinner with us, or just breakfast if you prefer. Non smokers preferred.

Oamaru has lovely public gardens, historic buildings, penguin colony, trout and salmon fishing. A pleasant day trip to Mount cook and lakes is possible.

Directions: *On SH1 at Waitaki Girls High School (7 blocks north of main shopping centre) turn into Ouse Street. Follow white line all the way up Derwent Street and into Reservoir Road. (1.5 kms from SH1). Name and number on letterbox.*

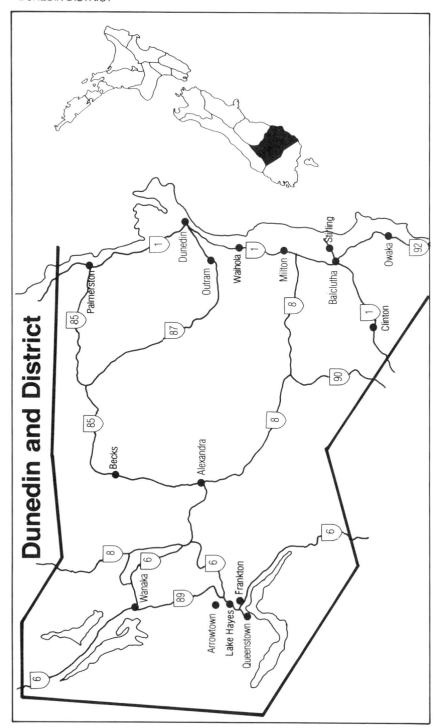

Dunedin and District

Wanaka
Homestay
Address: 75 Tenby Street, Wanaka
Name: Betty & Bill Miller
Telephone: (03) 443-7369
Beds: 1 Double (1 bedroom, guest bathroom)
Tariff: B&B $50 Double, $30 Single
Nearest Town: Wanaka

We are both retired with no family left at home and we enjoy meeting people. We have a modern spacious flat for guests on the ground floor of our home. It has a lounge with TV, a small kitchen with tea-making facilities (tea, coffee and milk for your cup on arrival). There is one double bedroom and a double divan in the lounge if required, bathroom with shower and separate toilet.
We are close to churches, golf course and bowling green and 10 minutes walk from shopping centre and lake.
We would be pleased to meet guests arriving by bus.
We do request visitors not to smoke in our home.
Directions: *Please phone.*

Wanaka
Homestay
Address: 15 Norman Terrace, Wanaka
Name: Shirley and Leighton Jones
Telephone: (03) 4437-135
Beds: 1 Double, 2 Single (2 bedrooms)
Tariff: B&B Double $55, Single $30, School children half price
Nearest Town: Town centre 2 km

Our modern, family home includes a warm visitors flat with twin and double rooms, dinette (tea-making facilities) and bathroom.
Our home is less than 100 m from Lake Wanaka. There is easy access to it through a beautiful lakeside park. From here too there are pleasant lakeside walks.
Wanaka is one of New Zealand`s faster-growing holiday centres. Its opportunity for watersports, its picturesque golf course and proximity to Aspiring National Park have made it a popular summer resort.
Two large skifields are now fully operational with public transport available.
The town offers a variety of good restaurants and activities for visitors.
Shirley and I have just sold our farm and have chosen to reside in Wanaka. We have one son (Scott, 16 years).
Because of the nature of our work we ask anyone arriving before 5.30 to call into the Wanaka Lake Services office and ask for Leighton.
Directions: *From the town centre follow the road west around the lake towards Glendu Bay. Second road on the right (Sargood Drive) leads into Ripponlea subdivision. Norman Terrace is the first road on the right off Sargood Drive. Look for a back section.*

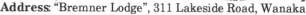

Wanaka
Homestay
Address: "Bremner Lodge", 311 Lakeside Road, Wanaka
Name: Russell and Raylene Nicholls
Telephone: (03) 443 8585, or 443 8286
Beds: 4 Single (2 bedrooms, guest bathroom)
Tariff:,B&B Double $65, Single $45, Dinner $20, Children $35

We call our home "Bremner Lodge", nestled in Bremner Bay on the shore of Lake Wanaka. It is newly built, clad in stone, on a large landscaped section. This is superior accommodation with panoramic views of the lake and mountains and an excellent swimming beach. For winter visitors Wanaka offers two ski fields plus Nordic and heli-skiing, and we have storage space for skis. We have two twin guest rooms and a separate luxurious bathroom, shower and toilet. We also have a large lounge with TV, stereo and library, plus living/dining room. Outdoors a large patio provides peace and tranquility for sunbathing or barbecuing. We can also offer fishing or boating excursions. Dinner available if required. Laundry facilities are available for a small charge.
Wanaka is known for its exceptional scenery in all seasons and you can see it all from our home. Reservations ahead by phone or letter please. Reduced tariff for longer stays.

Wanaka
Homestay
Address: Riverbank Road, P.O. Box 203, Wanaka
Name: Judy and Jonathan Elworthy
Telephone: (03) 443 7968 (home) Fax and phone: (03) 443 7940 (work)
Beds: 1 Double, 2 Single (1 bedroom, guest bathroom)
Tarrif: B&B Double $ 70, Single $45, Dinner $25 p.p.
Nearest Town: Wanaka

Wanaka has been described as New Zealand's best kept secret. The lake and surrounding mountains are spectacularly beautiful and provide a wide range of recreational activities.
Trout fishing, boating, tramping, golf, and horse-trekking are popular during the long hot summer months.
In winter from late June to early October four ski operations offer downhill, Nordic, and heli skiing.
There are several excellent restaurants in the town.
We live in a rural setting, 5 minutes from the lakefront. We have a large garden, grass tennis court and croquet lawn. Fresh fruit and vegetables are aplenty at meals.
We enjoy music, food and wine and outdoor pursuits. Political discussion and debate are a feature of dinner table conversation. The guest room adjoins the house. It is cheerful and spacious. The beds are warm and comfortable. Guests have sole use of a shower and lavatory in the guest wing.
Directions: *Please phone* _____

Wanaka
Homestay
Address: State Highway 6, Makarora
Postal: Private Bag, Wanaka
Name: Barbara & Clinton O'Brien
Telephone: (03) 443-8255
Beds: 1 Double, 2 Single (2 bedroom)
Tariff: B&B $60 Double, $35 Single, children under 13 1/2 price, $20
Dinner by arrangement
Nearest Town: Wanaka 60 km

*Our new open-plan home constructed of natural timbers has 2 guest
bedrooms with their own bathroom. We have lived in the Makarora Valley
for 9 years. Clinton is a National Park Ranger while I run our small Service
Station and tourist shop, during the day.*
*Makarora is a small rural community found at the head of Lake Wanaka.
The Haast Highway, which is the main tourist route from the West Coast to
Otago, passes right through the Makarora Valley.*
*The world famous Mount Aspiring National Park is only a 5 minute drive
from us. Makarora has become the short walks capital of New Zealand.
The National Park also offers excellent fishing, hunting, tramping and
climbing opportunities using Makarora as a base. Alpine flights and jet-
boating can be arranged.*
*Directions: from Wanaka - travel North along State Highway 6 approx 60
km where you will find a Shell Service Station on the left hand side. Other
travelling times - Queenstown 130 km (2 hours), Haast 80 km (1 hr 15 min),
Fox Glacier 186 km (2 hr 30 mins).*

Lake Hayes, Queenstown
Homestay
Address: Lake Hayes, 2 R.D., Queenstown
Name: Clarice & Bill May
Telephone: (03) 442-1430
Beds: 1 Double, 3 Single (guest bathroom)
Tariff: B&B $45 per person B&B, $20 Dinner, full board available
Nearest Town: Queenstown

*Enjoy a relaxed, peaceful holiday in beautiful surroundings on the edge of
Lake Hayes and enjoy unobstructed views of the lake and Coronet Peak
skifield from all rooms. All guest bedrooms have electric blankets, bedside
lamps and heaters.*
*Clarice & Bill are located 15 minutes from Queenstown, 5 minutes from
Arrowtown and 10 minutes from the airport where transport can be
arranged if required.*
*Clarice and Bill moved to this spot when they retired from farming. Bill is a
member of Rotary and Clarice is a retired nurse with hobbies including
patchwork, gardening and gourmet cooking. Treats such as the house
speciality of bran muffins made with yoghurt and bananas, served with lots
of perked coffee, have led to the guest book containing comments such as
"My stomach thanks you for the wonderful food, my heart thanks you for
your warm hospitality" and "They have perfected the art of making folks
feel welcome".*
*They fly the flag of overseas visitors and go out of their way to meet any
special needs.*

Lake Hayes, Queenstown
Homestay
Address: Speargrass Lodge, Speargrass Flat Road, Lake Hayes RD1 Queenstown
Name: Denis and Jenny Jenkins
Telephone: (03) 442-1411 Call collect within the South Island
Beds: 1 Double, 7 Single (4 bedrooms, 3 guest bathrooms)
Tariff: B&B Double $80, Single $50, Children under 13 half price; Dinner $25
Nearest Town: Queenstown 15 minutes, Arrowtown 5 minutes

Our home is known as Speargrass Lodge, set in 11 acres of landscaped garden and meadow amidst the beautiful mountain scenery that this area is so famous for.

We are a busy household with two schoolage children, an assortment of friendly farmyard animals and we enjoy opening our home to visitors from all over the world.

Guests are invited to relax in the peaceful, rural environment yet be within short driving distance of the many tourist and recreational activities that Queenstown has to offer.

Accommodation for up to 9 guests is spacious and comfortable and includes ensuite facilities, large living area with huge open fireplace, games room, barbecue area and children's trampoline.

As qualified chefs we take pleasure in cooking memorable meals for our guests from light summer dishes to hearty apres ski dinners.

Our home is in a central location to four major snowfields so skiing plays an important part of our southern winters. We also own and operate the "Flower Barn" on our property which is a year-round tourist attraction well-known for its displays of dried flowers and country cottage crafts.

Directions: *Speargrass Lodge is easy to find. Heading north on the main Cromwell highway from Queenstown turn left to Arrowtown after passing Lake Hayes. Then it is first left along Speargrass Flat Road. AA signage at the intersection. Heading south to Queenstown from Cromwell turn right to Arrowtown on first sight of Lake Hayes then again first left along Speargrass Flat Road.*

Please let the hosts know if you have to cancel.
They will have spent time preparing for you.

Queenstown
Health Retreat
Address: Bush Creek Health Retreat, Bowen Street, Queenstown
Name: Mrs Ileen Mutch
Telephone: (03) 442-7260
Beds: 1 Double, 5 Single (4 bedrooms)
Tariff: B&B Double $70, Single $35, Children half price; Campervan facilities
Nearest Town: Queenstown 1.5 km

I offer bed and breakfast service in a very relaxed and beautiful atmosphere set in 3 acres. Guests delight in the magical sounds of native birds, cascading waterfall and the impressive glowworms.

I assure a comfortable stay with thermostat heating, electric blankets, feather duvets, woolrest underlays - all the extra home comforts.

Bathroom, shower, toilets upstairs and down. Guest lounge and sundecks. Bedrooms open onto balcony with mountain views of Coronet Peak and skifields. Tea and coffee making facilities are provided and breakfast arrangements are flexible.

My family have all left the nest.

Such a good feeling emanates from the cascading water. Being soothed and lulled to sleep and awakening really refreshed. Lovely water - tastes as pure as it can come, straight off my mountain.

I have a natural healing practice and I am a nutritionist.

Queenstown is rich with every kind of eating to suit your taste and I can direct you right to the gem spots.

Bush Creek Health Retret is signposted and easy to find on Gorge Road heading towards the skifields.

Let the phone ring for a long time when telephoning.

Queenstown
Homestay
Address: 6 Oregon Drive,
Kelvin Heights, RD2, Queenstown
Name: Audrey & Kathie Galbraith
Telephone: (03) 442-9665
Beds: 1 Double, 2 Single (2 bedrooms, guest bathroom)
Tariff: B&B $35 per person, Dinner optional extra with advance notice $25

From a history of pioneering families in New Zealand, we are two sisters who have "been there, done that" overseas before settling in Queenstown.
Our home is a modern two-storeyed colonial style with panoramic views of majestic mountains and across Lake Wakatipu to Queenstown centre. This area, Kelvin Heights, takes the accolades for the highest sunshine hours in Queenstown.
The two guest rooms are on the ground floor and serviced with own bathroom / toilet facilities. Bathroom is cosily carpeted and heated.
Queenstown is known as an international tourist resort and offers excellent dining, 7-day-week shopping, and activities for the adventurous and less adventurous.
Driving times are Queenstown centre 15 minutes, airport 10 minutes, golf course 2 minutes. Not forgetting the southernmost winery in the world for wine production and tasting, just 20 minutes away.
We request guests not to smoke in our home.
Directions: *Please phone before 9 am or after 4.30 pm.*

Queenstown
Homestay
Address: 22 Brecon Street, Queenstown
Name: Shirley & Noel Jackson
Telephone: (03) 4429-542
Beds: 1 Double, 2 Single (2 bedrooms)
Tariff: **B&B** $60 Double, $35 Single, $20 Dinner, children negotiable
Nearest Town: Queenstown - 3 minute stroll to Mall

Our home overlooks the town centre and has a fantastic view of the surrounding area, especially the rugged mountain range - "The Remarkables". Although so close to the centre of a very popular tourist resort we can offer a comfortable and peaceful stay. We offer 2 guest rooms, one with 2 single beds, the other with a double bed. All have electric blankets, warm bedding and are very comfortable. Bathroom facilities shared with hosts. Smokers welcome.
Breakfast either continental or cooked - your choice. We offer a nourishing 3 course dinner with wine. Being a tourist town, Queenstown has seven day shopping and many fine restaurants catering for most tastes. Plenty to do both summer and winter.
Directions: *Please phone before 8:00am or after 2:00pm. Look for the hill with the gondola's, find the street that takes you there. We are the black house, 2nd on the left.*

New Zealand's
Federation of Bed &
Breakfast Hotels

Queenstown
Guest house
Address: Melbourne Guest House, 35 Melbourne Street, Queenstown
Name: Celia & Les Walker
Telephone: (03) 442-8431
Beds: 12 Double, 5 Single - guest bathrooms
Tariff: B&B $45 per person
Nearest Town: Queenstown

The Melbourne Guest House has long been Queenstown's most popular choice for trampers and holiday makers alike. Cis and Les Walker know exactly what their guests require, a delicious continental and cooked breakfast to start the day. All the comforts of home such as fresh hot spa, showers, bath, television, coffee and tea facilities are available for your use at your own leisure. For those who prefer a touch of luxury and elegance, private facilities are also available. Some have their own kitchens. We are only 3 minutes walk to the town centre. We know your holiday will be an enjoyable one to remember and look forward to your arrival.

Queenstown
Homestay
Address: No. 2 Boyce Crescent, Frankton, Queenstown
Name: Lois and Ivan Lindsay
Telephone: (03) 442-3162
Beds: 4 Single (2 bedrooms, guest bathroom) Separate unit accommodation if required
Tariff: B&B Double $60, Single $35, Dinner $20; Children half price
Nearest Town: Frankton 1 km, Queenstown 6 km

Our home, which is in a sunny situation overlooking Lake Wakatipu, has guest rooms with electric blankets, bedside lamps, and heaters. Also separate guest bathroom, laundry facilities, and a sunny conservatory overlooking flower gardens. Morning and afternnon teas provided when required.
We are retired sheep and grain farmers with a family of six all married. We have been hosting tourists for six years and offer warm and friendly hospitality, taking a special pride in our meals which we share with our guests. (wine is served with dinners.)
We are at the base of the Remarkable Mountains where excellent skiing is available. Arrangements can be made for guests going to Milford Sound and you can be picked up and returned to our gate at night.
There is a shopping centre in Frankton with airport, coach-stop, golf, tennis, walking tracks, water sports, bungy jumping coach and coach and plane transport to and from Milford Sound, all within 1 km of our home. Horse riding can be arranged for those interested. For those arriving by coach transport can be arranged to and from Queenstown where many more tourist attractions are available.
Directions: *Turn into McBride Street by Mobil service station, Frankton. Proceed to end of street where our home with the archway will be easily recognised.*

Queenstown
Homestay
Address: 17 Brisbane Street, Queenstown
Name: Gordon & Isobel McIntyre
Telephone: (03) 442-9251
Beds: Double in 'Stable', 3 singles in Garden Room, 1 single in Lake Room, 2 guest bathrooms
Tariff: B&B $75 Double, $45 Single, $25 Dinner
Nearest Town: Queenstown (5 mins stroll through the park and along the lakeside to town centre)

A 125 year old stone stable which is listed by the New Zealand Historic Places Trust, shares a private courtyard with our home, both providing convenience and comfort with fantastic lake and mountain views. Our home is in a quiet cul-de-sac and set in a garden abundant with rhododendrons and native birds. It is less than 100 metres from the beach where a small boat is available for guests' use. The beautiful Kelvin Heights Golf Course is close and tennis courts, bowling greens and ice skating rink are in the adjacent park. We are within easy walking distance from all tourist, dining and shopping facilities.
A courtesy car is available to meet public transport. We enjoy organising local sightseeing trips with Isobel's picnic lunches a speciality. Our air conditioned 4 wheel drive is suitable for accessing the 4 local ski fields and many gold mining and historic sites.
Those who choose to dine with us will enjoy silver-service 3 course dinners served with New Zealand wines. The choice includes lamb, venison, fresh fish and chicken. The long summer evenings make barbecues a pleasant option. Breakfast is often served in the courtyard.
Our combined interests include: local history, cooking, yachting and weaving. We have farmed in Southland, bred Welsh ponies, and have travelled extensively overseas.
Directions: *Follow State Highway 6 (Franklon Road) to where it veers right at the Kingsgate hotel. Continue straight ahead. Brisbane Street ("no exit") is 2nd on left. Phone if necessary.*

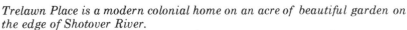

Queenstown
Country Home Accommodation
Address: "Trelawn Place",
Arthurs Point, Queenstown
Name: Nery Howard
Telephone: (03) 442 9160
Beds: 1 Double, 2 Single (2 bedrooms, 2 guest bathrooms)
Tariff: B&B from $35 per person, enquire when booking
Nearest Town: Queenstown 4 km

Trelawn Place is a modern colonial home on an acre of beautiful garden on the edge of Shotover River.
Although only 4 km from the Post Office, we are surrounded by farmland and mountains making it a tranquil retreat from busy Queenstown.
There are double and twin bedded rooms each with private bath and shower. The house is big enough for your stay to be as sociable or private as you wish. There are open fires and an outdoor hot tub, and laundry.
We have travelled extensively and enjoy welcoming guests.
As well as natural beauty and great walks, Queenstown and Fiordland are the centre for many exciting outdoor activities which we have tried, so can help you choose what suits you best and take care of bookings. Most tourist companies pick up guests at the gate. Michael is a keen fly fisherman and can take you on picnic safaris to some of NZ's best fishing rivers.
Directions: *At the end of Highway 6A in Queenstown turn right towards Arthurs Point "Trelawn Place" B&B is signposted 4 km out of Queenstown. Courtesy pickup if required.*

Queenstown
Homestay
Address: "Maison",
80 Lordens Place,
Fernhill, Queenstown
Name: Mark and Edie Whetu
Telephone: (03) 442-6345
Beds: 3 Double, 2 Single (4 bedrooms, guest bathroom)
Tariff: B&B Double $60, Single $35, Dinner $15
Nearest Town: Queenstown, 2 km from Queenstown PO

"Maison" is a large family home, recently renovated, with breathtaking views of Lake Wakatipu and The Remarkables from the spacious living room and the bedrooms.
The house is set on a hill amongst big trees, and it is a peaceful retreat just 2 km from the busy resort of Queenstown. It is close to all the activities Queenstown has to offer. Fishing, skiing, climbing, rafting, trekking, jetboating, golf are available nearby. We are happy to assist you with arrangements for these activities.
Mark is the local mountain guide and Edie runs the ski schools at Coronet

Peak and The Remarkables. We have lived and worked overseas and enjoy meeting visitors from New Zealand and overseas.
There are separate bathroom and toilet facilities available for guests. There is a spa and a sauna. A good base for your tramping or skiing holiday, or simply a relaxing retreat. We welcome you to have dinner with us or if you prefer only bed and breakfast. We ask you not to smoke in the house.
Directions: *Telephone after 4 pm for booking and directions.*

B&B hosts do it because they enjoy meeting people.
It is a friendship business.

Queenstown
Self-contained Accommodation
Address: "Braemar House", 56 Panorama Terrace, Queenstown
Name: Ann & Duncan Wilson
Telephone: (03) 442-7385
Beds: 2 Single (1 bedroom, guest bathroom) + 2 divans in lounge
Tariff: B&B from $35 per person (enquire other options when booking).
Nearest Town: 1.5 km from Queenstown town centre

This apartment on the middle floor of our home is fully self-contained and private if guests want it that way, but our personal hospitality is always available.
"Braemar House", now 5 years old, is situated on a steep Queenstown hill section but with easy access from roadways, provides magnificent panoramic views of lake and mountains, and as guests will realise, our interest include gardening with many varieties of native trees and plants. Other activities which could interest visitors are tramping (hill walking), ski-ing, golf, photography and local history.
For travellers with their own transport, we have off-street parking, but a courtesy car is available for others. Transport and Guiding services are also available to out-of-town locations.
We have travelled extensively at home and overseas, and believe we fully understand the requirements of visitors to Queenstown.
Directions: *Turn up Suburb Street off Frankton Road, then first right into Panorama Terrace.*

Arrowtown
Guest House
Address: "Postmaster's Guest House", 50 Buckingham Street, Arrowtown
Telephone: (03) 442-1204 Fax (03) 442 1408
Beds: 2 Double, 2 Single (3 bedrooms, guest bathroom)
Tariff: B&B $65 Double, $45 Single
Nearest Town: Queenstown, 15 mins from Arrowtown

*Postmaster's Guest House is an historical home (Historic Places Trust "C"
category). Right on the Main Street of Arrowtown, two minutes walk to all
the shops, restaurants, hotels, museum, library. Public bus service to the door.
We take up to 6 guests and offer full laundry, TV lounge, on-site parking. We
also hire Gold Detectors, gold pans, mountain bikes. We are only 2 minutes
walk from the Arrow River (1870 richest aluvial gold river in the world)
where there is recreational mining for the public. Very comfortable, warm
house.*

Arrowtown

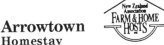

Homestay
Address: 12 Argyle Place, Arrowtown
Name: Joycelyn & Murray Potter
Telephone: (03) 442-1267
Beds: 4 Single (2 bedrooms, guest bathroom)
Tariff: B&B $60 Double, $35 Single, children (under 12) 1/2 price, dinner by arrangement
Nearest Town: Arrowtown - 19 km from Queenstown, 12 km from Frankton Airport

We are retired from farming and welcome guests to share our comfortable modern bungalow in historic Arrowtown. Our guest rooms have electric blankets on each bed, bed lamps and heaters. From both bedrooms there is easy access to the guest bathroom.

The main street, close to the Arrow River, with restaurants, bistros, Post Office, Lake's District Museum, shops etc, is just five minutes walk away.

Arrowtown is twenty minutes from Queenstown and ten minutes from Frankton Airport and under fifteen minutes driving time from activities such as bungy jumping, jet boating, white water rafting, horse-riding etc. It has a local bowling green and 18 hole golf course (clubs can be hired). Te Anau and Milford Sound are an easy day trip from here. In winter we are centrally placed for Coronet Peak, Remarkables and Cardrona ski-fields.

Our joint interests include sports, gardening, knitting and travelling.
Directions: *Please phone for bookings and directions.*

Arrowtown

Farmstay - Self-contained Accom
Address: "Taranga", Arrow Junction,
R.D. 1, Queenstown
Name: Mrs Suzie Wood
Telephone: (03) 442-1438
Beds: 1 Double, 2 Single (2 bedrooms, guest bathroom)
Tariff: **B&B** $60 Double, $35 Single, chidren 1/2 price, $22 Dinner, Campervans $20
Nearest Town: Arrowtown

"Taranga" is a small farm 4 km from Arrowtown, 17 km from Queenstown beside the Arrow River. My new home has superb views of farmland and mountains. It has a large living-room with open fire and pool table. There is a guest bathroom. Self-contained accommodation is also available in my weaving studio set apart from the house (2 single beds plus 2 folding beds if required) and in a 6 berth caravan with fridge, stove, water and heating. Tariff is $45 per night for 2 people, $10 for each extra person. Linen is availabe for a small charge.

Merino sheep and angora goats supply me with fibre for spinning and weaving. There is a barbeque area among pine trees. On-farm activities include pony riding (two ponies), gold panning (guests really do find gold), walking and river swimming. Future plans include a four hole golf-course. A riding stable, the Arrowtown Golf Course and excellent walks are within easy reach.
Directions: *Please phone.* _____

291

Arrowtown

Homestay
Address: 20 Wiltshire Street,
Arrowtown, Central Otago
Name: Mrs Cynthia Balfour
Telephone: (03) 4421-326
Beds: 1 Double, 2 Single (2 bedrooms guest bathroom)
Tariff: B&B Double $80, Single $45; Dinner $20, $25 with wine; Child $15
Nearest Town: Arrowtown, 19 km from Queenstown

I am a semi-retired businesswoman, well travelled with a variety of interests including gardening, cooking, arts and crafts and skiing. I welcome the opportunity of offering hospitality to visitors to New Zealand.
My attractive colonial-style home is located in the historic centre of Arrowtown, an old gold mining town in Central Otago.
The area offers both summer and winter activities. Queenstown, an international tourist resort, is about 20 minutes away.
My warm, comfortable home has two guest rooms. I prefer non smokers. Interesting home cooking is a speciality. I like 24 hours notice for dinners. Skiers are welcome from approximately mid-June to mid-October depending on the season. Rates negotiable.
Comments from guests you can see in my visitors book include
"Wonderful hostess. Warm friendly visit and great breakfast."
"Lovely cottage and flowers. Great accommodation."
"A top Bed and Breakfast"
—join these satisfied travellers.
Reservations ahead by phone or letter please.

Becks

Farmstay
Address: Becks, RD2, Omakau, Central Otago
Name: Earl and Pam Harrex   **Telephone:** (03) 447 3609
Beds: 1 Double, 1 Single (2 bedrooms)
Tariff: B&B $28 p. p. Children half price; Dinner $15; Campervans $15
Nearest Town: Alexandra 45 km

We farm sheep and deer at Becks in Central Otago. Guests are always welcome to take part in the everyday running of the farm. We are a family of five - two schoolage children and one at university.
We have recently renovated our older-style homestead, set in picturesque grounds with a swimming pool and barbecue area. A large open fire, plus central heating provides a cosy home during the winter months.
Our family interests include gardening, swimming, fishing, patchwork, music, summer and winter sports including curling - a traditional winter sport unique to Central Otago. We are two hours from four major ski-fields.
We offer guests motorbike rides, horseriding, short trips to nearby historical St Bathans and other nearby goldmining ghost towns.
We really enjoy showing visitors our quiet, peaceful rural setting with magnificent views of the vast openness of Central Otago.
Directions: *From Alexandra take State Highway 85 to Becks Hotel. First left turn to St Bathans. Our farm is 2 km from turnoff - named motor gate. From Palmerston take State Highway 85 for 120 km to Becks School. Right turn to St Bathans.*

Palmerston
Farmstay
Address: "Centrewood", No.1 RD Palmerston, Otago
Name: Wendy and Jim Preston
Telephone: (03) 465-1295
Beds: 1 Double, 4 Single (3 bedrooms, guest bathroom)
Tariff: B&B Double $35 per person, Dinner by arrangement
Nearest Town: Palmerston 11 km

"Centrewood" is a sheep and cattle farm situated on the coastline north of Dunedin, 11 kms from Palmerston. the farm was first settled by hosts great grandfather in 1857.
We welcome the opportunity to meet guests from overseas and to share our large colonial homestead set in native bush. The guest wing is very comfortable, one double bedroom, two twin bedrooms, electric blankets on all beds. Private bathroom and games room. We also have a tennis court
The sea forms the Eastern boundary, there you can enjoy private beaches. The rare yellow eyed penguins nest on our coastline, also there is a seal colony. Sheep and cattle wander over the undulating land and you are welcome to join in farm activities.
We both enjoy playing golf and I am interested in all crafts but currently enjoying patchwork and quilting, making quilts and wall hangings for my home. We provide fine New Zealand meals featuring farm killed meat and fresh vegetables. Afterwards we could play a hand of bridge.
We suggest two nights stay to get the feel of the local scene and Dunedin has much to offer and only 40 minutes away.
Directions: *Please phone*

Kew, Dunedin
Homestay
Address: 24 Easther Crescent, Kew, Dunedin
Name: Mrs Betty Anderson
Telephone: (03) 4557-637
Beds: 1 Double with ensuite bathroom, 2 Single (2 bedrooms)
Tariff: B&B Double $60, Single $35,

Our modern home is situated on a rise and offers a wonderful view of the harbour and surrounding hills. The double room has an ensuite and both bedrooms have heating and electric blankets and sun all day. The twin room shares the host's bathroom. A large lounge and living room are available to guests with washing machine and dryer also available. An excellent hotel is situated within five minutes walk away and offers first class meals six days a week and very reasonably priced. It is only four minutes away to public transport and seven minutes by car from city centre. Golf courses, bowling greens, tennis courts and most sports are nearby. I'm retired and involved several organisations in our city.
Although a short distance from a main thoroughfare I am situated at the end of a private road.

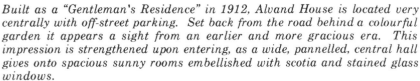

Dunedin

Guest house
Address: Alvand House,
3 Union Street, Dunedin
Name: Farah Jamali
Telephone: (03) 477-7379
Beds: 3 Double, 4 Single (4 bedrooms, guest bathroom)
Tariff: B&B $65 Double, $45 Single, children 1/2 price, Dinner $18

*Built as a "Gentleman's Residence" in 1912, Alvand House is located very
centrally with off-street parking. Set back from the road behind a colourful
garden it appears a sight from an earlier and more gracious era. This
impression is strengthened upon entering, as a wide, pannelled, central hall
gives onto spacious sunny rooms embellished with scotia and stained glass
windows.*
*A skillful blend of contemporary furniture and modern conveniences provides
present day comfort in period surroundings. The location ensures a quiet
night's sleep, while it is only a five minute walk to the main shopping area, the
University of Otago and the Otago Museum. An additional ten minutes will
take you to the Early Settlers' Museum or to Olveston (a home of the same era
on a very grand scale), all of which warrant a leisurely visit. For the
convenience of our welcome guests, we have full laundry facilities. Allergy
sufferers need not be concerned about pets.*

Dunedin

Homestay
Address: 6 Kiwi Street, St Leonards, Dunedin
Name: Shirley and Don Parsons
Telephone: (03) 4710-690
Beds: 2 Double, 1 Single (2 bedrooms)
Tariff: B&B Double $60, Single $35, Children half price; Dinner $15–$18
Nearest Town: 5 km from Dunedin

*We live in a quiet suburb 10 minutes from the city centre. Our home over-
looks the lovely Otago Harbour and is within easy reach of many of the
local attractions – Larnach Castle, Olveston, the Albatross colony and
Disappear-ing Gun, Portobello Aquarium and harbour cruises.*
*Dunedin is a lovely city situated at the head of the Otago harbour with
many interesting and historic stone buildings to view.*
There are also many lovely bush walks within easy reach of the city.
*We have a family of five who have all left home so we have two rooms
available, one double with a cot and one with a double and one single bed.
Children are very welcome. The bathroom facilities are shared.*
*We have a generous amount of living space and you may have an evening
meal with us or if you prefer only bed and breakfast.*
Directions: *From the Dunedin Railway Station follow Anzac Avenue onto
Ravensbourne Road. Continue down the harbourside approximately 5 km
until you reach St Leonards. Turn left at the church into Pukeko Street then
left into Kaka Road then straight ahead to Kiwi Street and turn left.
Courtesy car available.*

Dunedin
Homestay
Address: Magnolia House,
18 Grendon Street, Maori Hill, Dunedin
Name: Joan & George Sutherland
Telephone: (03) 4675-999
Beds: 1 Double, 3 Single (3 bedrooms, guest bathroom)
Tariff: B&B $65 Double, $35 Single
Nearest Town: Dunedin city centre 2 km

We live in a superior suburb on half and acre of land, one third of which is native bush with wood pigeons, tuis, bellbirds and fantails. The rest is in lawn and attractive gardens.
Our 1913 house is spacious with a large dining room and drawing room, and a more intimate sitting room.
The double room has its own large balcony looking out on lawns and bush. The guest rooms are airy and have antiques. Guests' bathroom with shower and tub. There is central heating.
Two nights in Dunedin is a must. We are very close to Otago Golf Club and can supply clubs and bag. Also nearby is Olveston stately home and Moana Olympic-size swimming pool. The Otago peninsula is a wonderful day's sightseeing.
We have two cats, a courtesy car, bus nearby and no smoking.
Directions: *Please phone* ─────────────

Dunedin
Homestay
Address: 431 Pine Hill Road, Dunedin
Name: Eli & Lindsay Imlay
Telephone: (03) 473-0247
Beds: 1 Double (Queen), 2 Singles, (2 bedrooms, guest bathroom)
Tariff: **B&B** $75 Double, $40 Single, children (under 12) 1/2 price, $20 Dinner
Nearest Town: Dunedin (4 kms to centre)

Relax in the comfort of our cozy home with tranquil rural setting where native birds are frequent visitors. Enjoy our sheltered patio and cottage garden which we love. Absorb the peacefulness of our surroundings - views shared by all living and bedroom areas. It's like living in the country yet only a few minutes by car from the city centre. Public transport nearby, courtesy car available and ample off-street parking.
Comfortable tasteful furnishings ensure a homely atmosphere. Guest tea/coffee facilities are provided in a small lounge area, but we enjoy meeting people and welcome visitors to share our home and informal lifestyle. Eli, who has lived in Dunedin for over 20 years is Norwegian, and offers a unique blend of Scandinavian and New Zealand hospitality. Children of all ages most welcome.
Directions: *Please phone. If greeted by "Insolscreen", don't panic! We run our small business from home. If we are temporarily unavailable you may leave a message on our answerphone.* ─────────────

Dunedin

Homestay
Address: 84 London Street, Dunedin
Name: Bruce and Val Duder
Telephone: (024) 778-638
Beds: 1 Double, 4 Single (3 bedrooms, guest bathroom)
Tariff: B&B Double $80, Single $45, Children half price; Dinner $20

We offer the unique experience of staying in one of Dunedin's historic mansions (B Classification from NZ Historic Places Trust), seven minutes walk to the Octagon, and near the special attractions in central Dunedin.

The house is full of French polished mahogany, beautiful stained glass windows, and original brass fittings. Despite its grandeur, it is a very comfortable home.

Our guest rooms are upstairs, with superb views of the city. The main guest room has a queen-size bed and a single, and a vanity unit. There is a twin bedded room and a single room. There are two bathrooms, one solely for guests, the other shared with us. Also upstairs is a "galley" where guests can make a cup of tea or coffee anytime, plus a small reading room.

We share our living room, which has a beamed ceiling and an inglenook with an open fire, with our guests. We do provide dinner, with a little notice, using good New Zealand produce. Special diets can be catered for given 24 hours notice. Breakfast can be as substantial as you choose.

Allergy sufferers should note we have three cats.

Send for free map and brochure.

The standard of accommodation in The New Zealand Bed and
Breakfast Book ranges from homely to luxurious but you can
always be sure of superior hospitality.

Dunedin

Guest House
Address: 342 High Street, Dunedin
Name: Janet Yiakmis
Telephone: (03) 477 9053
Beds: 2 Double, 4 Single (3 bedrooms, guest bathroom)
Tariff: $B&B Double $80, $70, $50, Single $50, $40, $30,
Children welcome, Dinner by arrangement

*Our 100 year old home was formerly the Manse for a prominent inner city
Presbyterian Church and was the home of Rutherford Waddell, a prolific
writer, compelling preacher and noted social reformer.*
The house is well designed, spacious, sunny and comfortable.
*The conservatory, garden and a separate lounge are available to guests.
Browsing in the bookshelves is encouraged and so are piano playing,
laughter and conversation. We cater for non-smokers.*
*Deacons Court is 3 blocks (uphill) from the central business area and has 10-
15 good restaurants available within 5 minutes walk. Light evening meals
are available on request (morning please). If guests are staying more than 2
nights and supply us with a list of their interests we are happy to organise a
dinner party on the premises for up to 8 people inviting guests from the
local community who have similar professional and/or personal interests.
The charge for this is modest and should be discussed with the proprietor on
arrival. Vegetarian dining is a specialty.*
Guided special interest tours can be arranged.

Outram, Dunedin

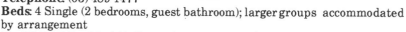

Farmstay
Address: "Lee Ridges",
Hindon, RD2, Outram
Name: Bruce and Nola Dick
Telephone: (03) 489 1477
Beds: 4 Single (2 bedrooms, guest bathroom); larger groups accommodated
by arrangement
Tariff: B&B Double $60, Single $45; Dinner $15
Nearest Town: 40 km west from Dunedin, Mosgiel 25 km

*Our 560-acre sheep farm offers you the opportunity to experience
"everyday" rural New Zealand. At 1300 ft above sea level we have a
panoramic view of surrounding countryside.*
*Our near-new home has a guest bedroom and games room upstairs. Electric
blankets and heaters in all rooms. A warm welcome awaits you.*
*Bruce always willing to take interested people around the farm. Nola accus-
tomed to cooking for guests – "Lee Ridges lamb" a speciality. Wine or non-
alcoholic drinks served with dinner. We have two daughters at university, a
son at boarding school, and a daughter at home. Also a variety of pets,
including one indoor cat.*
Directions: *Travelling south from Dunedin turn off State Highway 1 into
Mosgiel and towards Outram on State Highway 87. Cross over Taieri River
(1 km before Outram), at end of bridge turn right into George King
Memorial Drive. Continue on tar-sealed road 15 km. We are second house
on left after Lee Stream Gorge.* _____

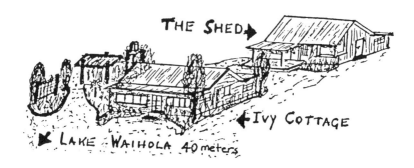

THE SHED→

←Ivy COTTAGE

LAKE WAIHOLA 40 meters

Waihola
Homestay
Address: "Ivy Cottage", Waihola, Otago 9150
Name: Bryan & Robin Leckie
Telephone: (03) 417-8946
Beds: 1 Double, 3 Single (2 bedrooms, guest bathroom)
Tariff: **B&B** $55 Double, $35 Single, children 1/2 price, $20 Dinner
Nearest Town: 40 km South of Dunedin on SH1

"Ivy Cottage" is only 30 minutes drive south of Dunedin. The driveway entrance is on State Highway 1. Our property has commanding views as well as walking access to Lake Waihola.

Our main guest accommodation is detached from "Ivy Cottage" in an eye-catching building affectionately known as "The Shed". This unit has one double (ground floor), one single (mezzanine), ensuite, heaters, TV, tea, coffee, fridge, clothes washing and drying facilities. In "Ivy Cottage" we offer 2 single beds with share facilities. All beds have electric blankets.

We are retired Restauranteurs, and continue our interests in food and wines. Other interest include, power boating, sailing, fishing, bird watching, golf, bowls, travelling, gardening, crafts, bridge, and keeping in touch with our extended family.

Lake Waihola and the waterways are well known for their birdlife and fishing. The waterways extend to the Sinclair Wetlands, a wildlife reserve, Waipori Lake and the Taieri River down to the sea at Taieri Mouth. We have a 5 metre cabin boat and, with prior notice, exploring these magnificent waterways can be arranged. The lake is also extensively used in the summer for water sports i.e. swimming, rowing, sailing, skiing etc. Windsurfers, canoes, ski bikes and yachts are available for hire.

Good bush walks, tramping areas and sightseeing drives are only minutes away.

We enjoy hosting people and look forward to sharing the warmth of "Ivy Cottage" with future travellers. We would appreciate a few hours prior notice from guests who require dinner.

Directions: *Please phone. Transport can be arranged from the Airport or Bus/Train terminals.*

Waihola
Homestay
Address: Sandown Street, Waihola, South Otago
Name: Lillian and Trevor Robinson
Telephone: (03) 417-8218
Beds: 1 Double, 2 Single (2 bedrooms, guest bathroom)
Tariff: B&B Double $45, Single $25, Dinner $15; Campervans $20
Nearest Town: 16 km north of Milton, 40 km south of Dunedin

Waihola is a small country town situated on SH1 40 km south of Dunedin (15 km from airport). Lake Waihola is suitable for fishing, boating and swimming. There is an outdoor bowling green, bush walks and 10 minutes drive to golf course.
We have a very comfortable home with a view of the mountains, lake and township.
Our double bedroom has ensuite with shower, handbasin, toilet, also tea making facilities. All beds have electric blankets.
We enjoy meeting people and ensure you a pleasant stay.
Directions: *Please phone, the night before where possible.*

Milton
Guest House
Address: "Garvan Homestead",
SH1, Lovells Flat, RD2, Milton
Name: Judy and Doug Anderson
Telephone: (030) 417-8407
Beds: 2 Double, 3 Single (3 bedrooms, guest bathroom)
Tariff: B&B Double $80, Single $60, Dinner $25
Nearest Town: Half way between Milton and Balclutha

"Garvan Homestead" is a large historic Tudor style home set amid 16 acres of gardens, parks and woodlands, and a most restful stop-over for travellers. The homestead has been completely refurnished and decorated with period furniture - a step back in time for your indulgence. We operate a morning/afternoon tea rooms and will serve you an enjoyable evening four course meal of traditional NZ fare. Summer travellers can also enjoy outdoor BBQ's, a swim in our pool or a game of tennis or just plain laze about on any one of our balconies or patios. Guest bathrooms are situated on both floors and bedrooms have tea making facilities for your convenience.
Garvan is an experience you will long remember and as a family run business we look forward to being your hosts. Keen fishermen are only 12 km from the Clutha River and only 1 hour's drive to the beautiful Catlins and Southern scenic coast.
Directions: *We are situated on SH1 approximately 13 km south of Milton, and opposite the historic "Old Sod Cottage". We are well sign-posted, but would apprecite a telephone call prior to your arrival. Sorry, but we are closed on Mondays. Non-smoking!*

Balclutha

Guest House
Address: Rosebank Guest House, 5 Keithmore Road, Balclutha
Name: Alastair and Pam Gilchrist
Telephone: (03) 418-2148
Beds: 4 Single (2 bedrooms, guest bathroom)
Tariff: B&B $35 per person, Children $20, Dinner $15
Nearest Town: 5 minute drive to town centre

Our guest house includes a guest lounge with tea and coffee making facilities. A continental breakfast will be served. Dinner is available by arrangement only.
Your hosts - a young couple with their daughter Anna have wide ranging interests and enjoy providing hospitality for New Zealand and overseas visitors. We do request visitors not to smoke or drink alcohol in our house.
Directions: *Coming from south from SH1 - turn right into Wilson Road, veer right at Francis Street, then left into Keithmore Road.*
Coming from north from Clyde Street - travel past the shopping area. Turn left into High Street, right into Francis Street, left into Armstrong Street, then right into Keithmore Road.

Stirling

Farmstay
Address: "Rotoiti", Main Road, Stirling, South Otago
Name: Crawford & Janet Anderson
Telephone: (03) 418-0588
Beds: 4 Single (2 bedrooms)
Tariff: **B&B** $50 Double, $30 Single, $15 Dinner
Nearest Town: Balclutha

We live in a comfortable 85 year old farm house with modern facilities. (Our adult family have all left.) It is surrounded by a woodland garden. We have two guest bedrooms. Two single beds in each with innersprung mattresses on firm bases, electric blankets, heaters. Guests share bathroom and laundry facilities.

The Clutha River providing good fishing bounds the farm on three sides. Our son sharemilks on the farm which has been farmed by the Anderson family for 100 years. It is a modern dairy farm with rotary milking shed for 230 Friesian cows, supplying nearby Otago Cheese Company. We have 160 Drysdale ewes which graze floodbanks and pond paddock which is a refuge for ducks and a variety of wading birds.

The farm is one hours drive from Dunedin, 30 minutes from Nugget Point Lighthouse where there are yellow eyed penguins and a colony of fur seals. The farm is a comfortable stopover for travellers to Stewart Island or the Lakes District. A good road follows the Clutha River - an attractive route to Central Otago.

Directions: *We will meet guests off bus or trains at Balclutha or from Momona airport (50 kms). Please phone ahead for booking.*

Owaka – (The Catlins)

Farmstay + Self-Contained Cottage
Address: "Greenwood", Tarara, RD2 Owaka, South Otago
Name: Alan and Helen-May Burgess
Telephone: (03) 4158-259 (if no reply, phone after 6 pm)
Beds: 4 Single (2 bedrooms)
Tariff: B&B Double $55, Single $40; Dinner $15, Lunch if required; Campervans $20; Self contained house at Papatowai beach (sleeps 8) $50 per night (4 persons), $10 each extra person
Nearest Town: Owaka 14 km

We farm in the Catlins district our homestead situated within walking distance from the beautiful Purakaunui Falls (features on the front cover of Wild New Zealand book).

Our home which is set in a large garden offers warm, comfortable accommodation for up to four persons. The main guest bedroom walks through to a furnished day-room with vanity unit (hand basin), giving you private living facilities and this opens to the outdoors. The bathroom, toilets and shower room are shared.

A three-course dinner may be provided.

Our 1500 acre farm is hilly to rolling country, farming sheep, cattle and deer. Alan enjoys taking people around the farm.

Our district features many beautiful scenic drives and walks through native forest and beaches. Trout, salmon or rock fishing may be enjoyed.

Directions: *Take State Highway 92 to Owaka from Balclutha or Invercargill. From Owaka follow the signposts to Purakaunui Falls for 14 km. Our name and farm name is on the gate entrance (just before you reach the falls).*

Owaka
Farmstay
Address: Glenomaru, RD1, Balclutha
Name: Bruce and Kathryn Wilson
Telephone: (03) 4158-282
Beds: 4 Single (2 bedrooms, guest bathroom)
Tariff: B&B Double $25 per person, Children half price; Dinner $12; Campervan off-street parking
Nearest Town: Balclutha 22 km, Owaka 11 km

We are a family of six – three daughters and a son. Our son lives at home and is leasing an adjoining property.
We live on a 900 acre mixed farm running beef, sheep and deer. Guests may be taken on a farm tour.
We are near Kaka Point, renowned for beach, lighthouse and yellow-eyed penguins.
The guest room has two single beds and shares our bathroom.
You may have family dinner with us or if you prefer only bed and breakfast. Guests can be collected off public transport from Balclutha free of charge.
Directions: *Take Highway 92 from Balclutha towards Owaka, first turn right past sawmill. From Owaka turn left beside sawmill up gravel road.*

Tell other travellers about your favourite homes.

Owaka
Farmstay
Address: "Tarara Downs", RD2 Owaka, South Otago
Name: Ida and John Burgess
Telephone: (03) 415 8293
Beds: 1 Double, 2 Single (2 bedrooms); Sleepout for 3
Tariff: B&B Double $55, Single $35, Children half price;
Dinner $15 (3-course), $10 (2-course); Sleepout $10 per person
Nearest Town: Owaka 16 km

Our 1325-acre farm is situated in an area renowned for its bush and coastal scenery. Also the beautiful Purakaunui Falls are within walking distance.
The farm runs sheep, cattle and deer and we also have horses to ride and riding instruction available.
Many farm activities may be seen and participated in, eg sheep shearing and dogs working. Fishing trips and bush walks may be arranged. Our pets love people and attention!
We live in a comfortable New Zealand farmhouse and enjoy eating our own produce and local delicacies.
Children very welcome.
Directions: *Follow State Highway 92. Approximately 1 1/2 hours drive from Invercargill or Dunedin on a scenic, coastal road, follow signposts to Purakaunui Falls – we are the closest house to them.*

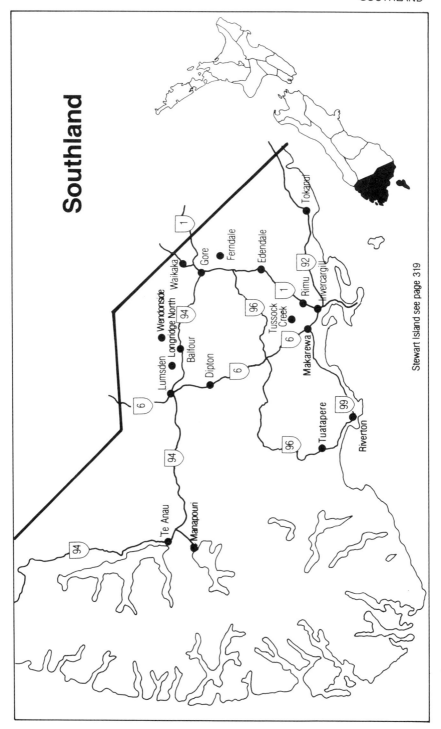

Southland

Stewart Island see page 319

Te Anau
Farmstay
Address: Sinclair Road, RD1, Te Anau
Name: Teresa Hughes
Telephone: (03) 249-7581
Beds: 2 Single (1 bedroom, guest bathroom)
Tariff: B&B Double $60, Single $40
Nearest Town: Te Anau 5 km

*My husband, Dave, and I, and our three teenage children live on a deer farm
overlooking Lake Te Anau.*
The guest room has a beautiful view of the Lake and mountains.
*Te Anau is the centre of all tourist attractions in Fiordland. We would suggest
a stay of more than one night to allow more time to enjoy them, e.g. a day trip
to Milford Sound (116 km) or a visit to Doubtful Sound – a very relaxing day.
There are also many interesting bush walks and the lakes and rivers have
excellent fishing.*
As I teach during the day please ring before 8 a.m. or after 6 p.m.
We can assure you of a very warm and friendly stay.
Directions: *Continue through Te Anau on road to Milford Sound for about
5 km, turn right at Sinclair Road and continue for 1 km. We are the second
house on the left – our name is on the letterbox.*

Te Anau
Homestay
Address: Corner of Manapouri and Waiau Roads, Te Anau
Postal: P O Box 58, Te Anau
Name: Ian & Claire Collie
Telephone: (03) 249-7388 (home), or (03) 249-7308 (bus)
Beds: 4 Single, (2 bedrooms)
Tariff: B&B $60 Double, $40 Single, children 1/2 price, $15 Dinner
Nearest Town: Te Anau

*Our home is situated at the southern end of Lake Te Anau, just 4 kms from the
town's main street.*
*We have a five acre property with a rural atmosphere. From our home we
offer you superb views of Lake Te Anau and surrounding mountains.*
*A good golf course is 2 kms away. During the summer evenings golf or a
leisurely stroll to the Wildlife Centre, the Lake or a well planted park are all
achievable.*
*For the keen fisherman, Te Anau offers good fishing. Naturally you will want
to experience what Fiordland National Park has to offer. We are willing to
assist you with plans to see the area. If you intend doing any tramps we can
store any gear you don't require with you.*
We both have interests in gardening and tramping and enjoy meeting people.
We assure you of a warm welcome.

Te Anau
Farmstay
Address: Kakapo Raod, R.D. 2, Te Anau,
Name: Brian and Joy Pinnell
Telephone: (03) 249-7897
Beds: 1 Double, 2 Single (2 bedrooms)
Tariff: **B&B** $65 Double, $40 Single, $16 Dinner
Nearest Town: Te Anau 9 km

Our farm is set in rolling country. From it there are beautiful views of Lake Te Anau and the surrounding mountains. We farm deer and you are welcome to drive or walk among them at most times of the year, or watch them from the comfort of our lounge. During winter feel free to help feed them.
From Te Anau you can drive or bus to Milford Sound and arrange trips to many attractions in the area. There are walks close to the town, good fishing within easy distance, and an 18 hole golf course. Brian plays golf and enjoys fishing and hunting. Joy spins and likes gardening. We enjoy our lifestyle and would like to share it with you.
Directions: *Turn off SH94 onto Kakapo Road on Mossburn side of Te Anau. Our farm is on the left, just over the top of the hill, 4 1/2 km from the turnoff.*

Te Anau
Farmstay
Address: "Hillend Farm", Kakapo Road, (P O Box 69), Te Anau
Name: Naomi & David Hughes
Telephone: (03) 249-7126 or (03) 249-7081
Beds: 2 Single (1 bedroom)
Tariff: **B&B** $70 Double, $45 Single, $18 Dinner
Nearest Town: Te Anau (8 kms on sealed road)

Welcome to Hillend Farm. From our home overlooking Te Anau, the incredible 360 degree lake and mountain panorama never fails to impress our guests.
Deer, sheep and goats graze our 80 acres. Naomi keeps a colourful garden, nice for relaxing in after a busy day's sightseeing.
Our 13 year old daughter, Freda is the only one of our five children remaining at home - she has two cats, Tuti and Jaws! The West Highland Terrier's called Abby.
David, besides farming, is developing a small-group Tour business "Trips 'n' Tramps" involving guided walks, Milford Sound Tours and scenic rafting on Fiordland's clear trout-filled rivers.
We enjoy sharing our Fiordland experience with our guests and can assist with information, sightseeing and reservations to ensure your Fiordland holdiay is a memorable event.
Directions: *Turn off SH94 onto Kakapo Road, 4 km on Mossburn side of Te Anau. Our place (name on letterbox) is on the left, on top of the hill, 4 kms from the turnoff.*

Te Anau

Farmstay
Address: "Anak Downs", Takitimu R.D. 1, Te Anau
Name: Noeline & Ken Adam
Telephone: (03) 249-8573
Beds: 4 Single (2 bedrooms)
Tariff: **B&B** $55 Double, $35 Single, children 1/2 price, $15 Dinner
Nearest Town: Te Anau 40 km, Manapouri 20 km

Our farm is at the foot of the Takitimu mountains situated in the Te Anau Basin, with our comfortable farmhouse in a garden setting. Bathroom and toilet facilities to be shared with family. We offer friendly rural hospitality which includes a tour of our sheep and beef property, and a working dog demonstration.
The Fiordland area offers much to the traveller. Milford Sound, Doubtful Sound, Milford, Kepler and Routeburn walking tracks plus many shorter bush and lakeside walks. For the fisherman there are Lakes Te Anau and Manapouri and excellent rivers. The Mararoa River forms part of our boundary. There is a beautiful 18 hole golf course in Te Anau.
Directions: *Coming from either Queenstown or Gore, highway 94, 32 km from Mossburn, lefthand turn off signposted Clifden, drive in 14 km. Our house on lefthand side of road, name on mailbox.*

Te Anau

Farmstay
Address: please phone
Name: Dorothy & Donald Cromb
Telephone: (03) 249-5805
Beds: 4 Single
Tariff: **B&B** $40 per person, $20 Dinner
Nearest Town: Te Anau, 20 km

You are surrounded by "million dollar" views while enjoying the luxury of our large family home (2 teenage daughters). We are situated in a very handy position close to the main road, 40 km after Mossburn, 20 km before Te Anau making an excellent base for your sightseeing trips to magnificent Milford and Doubtful Sounds. We recommend you spend two nights so that you can enjoy a relaxing trip to the Sounds, as well as a look over our 279 Hectare (700 acres) farm which carries 3000 sheep and 100 cattle. Guests are welcome to join in farming activities that are in progress at the time of your visit. Some of New Zealand's best fishing rivers within a few minutes drive as are the finest walking tracks in the world, golf courses etc.
Personal attention and service assured.
Directions: *Please phone.*

Te Anau
Guest House

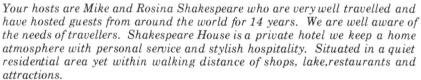

Address: 10 Dusky Street, Te Anau
Name: Shakespeare House
Telephone: (03) 249-7349, **Fax:** (03)249-7629
Beds: 3 Double, 7 Single (6 bedrooms, all with private facilities or own shower & h,c water
Tariff: B&B Double $78-$80, Single $60-$66, Dinner $20

Your hosts are Mike and Rosina Shakespeare who are very well travelled and have hosted guests from around the world for 14 years. We are well aware of the needs of travellers. Shakespeare House is a private hotel we keep a home atmosphere with personal service and stylish hospitality. Situated in a quiet residential area yet within walking distance of shops, lake,restaurants and attractions.
Milford and Doubtful Sound Tours pick up at the gate. 10% discount can be arranged for these tours. When you return from your tours you can enjoy Rosina's dinner, which is cooked and presented with flair and style, then relax with tea or coffee which is available 24 hours. All our rooms are ground floor, each with own shower and handbasin.
We offer peace and quiet with no young children. Smoking is not allowed in dining or bedrooms but you may feel free to do so in the conservatory. Vehicle and baggage can be stored for guests. Walking tracks in our World Heritage Park. A courtesy car is available from the travel centre for guests arriving by plane or bus. Mike and Rosina (yes they are related to William) look forward to offering you B&B AS YOU LIKE IT.

Te Anau
Farmstay + Self-Contained Accommodation
Address: Please phone
Name: Ross and Joan Cockburn
Telephone: (03) 249-7082
Beds: 4 Single (2 bedrooms, guest bathroom)
Tariff: B&B Double $70, Single $45; Dinner $18; Self-Contained Farm Quarters $40 (up to 4 persons, $6 each other person, max 10, linen available $4 per person);
Nearest Town: Te Anau 18 km

We live on a rolling, hill country sheep, cattle and goat station, situated 18 km from Te Anau and offer walks / tramping, native bush and horse riding. Also swimming and trout fishing in the Whitestone river.
You are welcome to join in with the daily working of the property or use us as a base for day trips to all Fiordland. A two night stay is more restful.
We have three teenagers who are usually away at school or university. As a family we enjoy meeting and entertaining people.

Te Anau
Farmstay
Address: Sinclair Road, R.D. 1, Te Anau
Name: Alan & Gayle Todd
Telephone: (03) 249-7195
Beds: 1 Double (1 bedroom with guest bathroom)
Tariff: B&B $55 Double, $35 Single, children 1/2 price, $15 Dinner
Nearest Town: Te Anau

We are a young family with four children aged from 4 to 10 years old. We live on a deer farm with a lovely view of Lake Te Anau and the surrounding mountains. We are ideally situated to all the tourist attractions of the Fiordland National Park.
Our guest room is very comfortable and has a private bathroom beside.
Phone us anytime for a reservation.
Directions: *Carry on through Te Anau towards Milford Sound for about 5 km, turn right at Sinclair Road. We are the first house on the left with our name on the letterbox.*

Manapouri
Self-Contained Accommodation
Name: Ruth and Lance Shaw
Telephone: (03) 249 6664
Beds: 1 Double, 2 Single (2 bedrooms, guest bathroom)
Tariff: Accom only, Double $55, Single $35, Children half price; Meals provided if required, breakfast $7.50, packed lunch $9.50, dinner $15
Nearest Town: Te Anau

Lance and I live in a small town on the perimeter of Fiordland National Park, only 3 minutes walk from Lake Manapouri. This is geographically an ideal place for you to use as a base from which to see Fiordland.
Our home is surrounded with mature trees and many birds. A warm, homely

*flat with off-street parking. will make your stay comfortable. Television, an
open fireplace, cooking facilities and privacy guarantee you a restful stay.
We are in our mid 40s, both have an interest in photography, sailing, diving
and the environment. Lance works as a skipper on the Department of
Conservation research vessel. This work includes marine studies, underwater
photography and environmental conservation.
I am a freelance writer, work as a youth social worker and as I am a
vegitarian we have a vegetable garden
We have both travelled widely and with our local knowledge we will be able
to help you plan an enjoyable stay. We can organise anything you want to do,
sit and chatter for hours, or just let you rest awhile.
We really look forward to your company.*

Manapouri
Self-Contained Accommodation
Address: House 8 Te Anau-Manapouri Highway
Name: Ron and Phyllis MacGibbon
Telephone: (03) 2496-873
Beds: 1 Double, 2 Single (guest bathroom)
Tariff: B&B Double $60, Single $35, Dinner $18
Nearest Town: 21 km south of Te Anau

*We are a retired, non-smoking couple and enjoy meeting people, our family
having grown up and left home. Our interests include organic gardening
both glasshouse and outside, allowing us to serve fresh high quality fruit and
vegetables in our home cooked meals. We have available solely for guests a
fully serviced all electric flat to sleep up to four people. This flat of 1,000
square feet is on the upper floor of our own home. We are situated 21 km
south of Te Anau on the highway between Te Anau and Manapouri overlooking Lake Manapouri with its clean safe sandy beaches and the beautiful
mountains of Fiordland National Park, with approximately two hours driving
time to Milford Sound. There are boat trips, walking tracks, fishing trips and
farm tours by arrangement. Altogether an ideal relaxed holiday situation for
all visitors.*

Manapouri

Guest House
Address: Grand View House,
Murrell Ave, Manapouri
Name: Jack and Klaske Murrell
Telephone: (03) 249 6642
Beds: 2 Double, 4 Single (4 bedrooms, 3 with private bathrooms)
Tariff: B&B Double $100-$120, Single $60-$70, Dinner by arrangement $30
four courses
Nearest Town: Te Anau

*Murrells in their historic Grandview House, through three generations have
provided over 100 years of hospitality to visitors.*
*The house is set in its own extensive grounds which slope down to Lake
Manapouri on one side, and the Waiau River on the other. Pet deer roam in
half the grounds.*
*The grounds set behind tall hedges consist of spacious lawns and old
fashioned cottage gardens offering peace and seclusion.*
*Built in 1889, this large rambling house features wide verandahs, spacious
picture lined passages and a cosy sitting room complete with open fireplace
and overflowing bookshelves.*
*Guest rooms are furnished with comfortable colonial antique furniture, cosy
quilts, fresh flowers and a welcoming bowl of fruit. Meals are served in the
Victorian Dining room, Grandma's menu is the speciality of the house.*
*This is a perfect base for any day excursions to Milford sound, Doubtful
Sound, or any of the adventure treks available through Fiordland National
Park. Dinghies and canoes are available and a number of half or whole day
walks begin right here.*
Directions: *Situated off Main Road, take Murrell Ave opposite store and
garage, behind hedges. Bookings advisable, please phone ahead.*

Lumsden

Farmstay
Address: State Highway 6, Josephville, Lumsden
Name: Annette and Bob Menlove
Telephone: (03) 248-7114
Beds: 4 Single (2 bedrooms, guest bathroom)
Tariff: B&B Double $55, Single 30; Dinner $15
Nearest Town: 9 km south of Lumsden, Invercargill 80 km

*We live on a 480 hectare farm on State Highway 6 'to the lakes'. Our home is
warm and of modern design. We enjoy meeting people and would like to have
you to stay with us.*
*We have a large garden and lawn tennis court which you are welcome to
enjoy. also we enjoy hiking in the mountains.*
*We live beside the Oreti River well-known for its trout fishing. Our farm has
got sheep, cattle, deer and goats.*
Included in your visit is a four-wheel-drive trip around the farm.
*You would be welcome to have the family meal with us or if you prefer bed
and breakfast.*
Our house is on the right at the foot of the hill 9 km south of Lumsden.

Balfour
Farmstay
Address: "Hillcrest", No. 1 R.D., Balfour
Name: Ritchie and Liz Clark
Telephone: (03) 201-6165
Beds: 2 Single (1 bedroom)
Tariff: B&B Double $55, Single $35, Children under 12 half price; Dinner $12; Campervans $15
Nearest Town: Lumsden 16 km, Gore 40 km

We welcome you to join us on our farm. We are a family of four with three young boys and as a family enjoy working together, meeting people and enjoy playing social tennis and squash. I am fond of cooking and welcome you to share our family dinner or if you prefer only bed and breakfast.
On our 650-acre farm we run 2,500 ewes, a few cattle and some cropping. From our semi-detached guest room you can enjoy views of surrounding farm lands and mountains.
A complimentary farm tour is included.
Extra beds available on request, and children welcome.
Our farm is situated 3 km from Balfour which is a popular stopover, being on the main tourist route from the lakes to Dunedin via Gore. We are only minutes from some of the top trout fishing rivers.
Directions: *When arriving at Balfour crossroads, take the road to Waikaia, then the first turn to the left before transport depot and travel 2.5 km, we are on the right. Please phone. If no reply please try again.*

Balfour
Farmstay
Address: Longridge North, No. 6 R.D., Gore
Name: Ivor and Margaret Black
Telephone: (03) 201-6090
Beds: 4 Single (2 bedrooms)
Tariff: B&B Double $50, Single $25, Campervans welcome
Nearest Town: Lumsden 15 minutes, Gore 35 minutes north-east

We live in a beautiful farmland valley surrounded by majestic mountains. We are on the main tourist route to Milford Sound, Lakes Te Anau and Manapouri and Queenstown. Our home is comfortable and warm.
Our family are grown up and away from home. We have travelled and we enjoy meeting and having people to stay.
We farm sheep, deer and cattle and are very fortunate to be only ten minutes from one of the most famous trout fishing rivers in the world, the Mataura River, with two others close by. So, if it is fishing, farming or just relaxing in our tranquil surroundings, we will enjoy sharing it with you.
Lake Te Anau gateway to Fiordland and the famous Milford Track 1 hour away, Lake Manapouri (New Zealand's loveliest lake) and Doubtful Sound 1 hour, Queenstown and Invercargill 1 hour 15 mins.
Directions: *From Gore (30 mins) you turn right at Balfour crossroads then second turn left (signpost) follow tarseal, we are fifth house on left hand side (5 min). From Lumsden you take the road to Gore, just out of Lumsden at signpost you keep left and follow tarseal over hill. We are fifth house on right hand side (15 min). Please phone.*

Dipton
Farmstay
Address: "Bilberry Oak", Dipton R.D.
Name: John and Judy Buchanan
Telephone: (03) 248-5228 (booking essential please)
Beds: 1 Double, 2 Single (2 bedrooms)
Tariff: B&B Double $50, Single $25, Children under 13 half price; Dinner $15 per person
Nearest Town: Lumsden 24 km, Invercargill 70 km

Our farm is situated on one of the main roads from Invercargill through to the attractions of Te Anau, Milford Sound and Queenstown so it is a convenient stopover point during your travels.
Our comfortable farmhouse is set in a large garden which includes a covered swimming pool and a barbecue area which we use a lot during the summer months.
We welcome you to have dinner with us or just bed and breakfast, the choice is yours. We also offer the use of our laundry facilities if you so desire.
John is always very willing to take folk about the property, explain about the New Zealand way of farming and if at all possible, let you see at close hand such activities as shearing. Our is mainly a sheep farm with a little cropping and a few cattle. We also have a Hampshire Sheep Stud.
We are interested in most sports and if you feel like a day's break from sight-seeing, a game of squash or golf or a few hours fishing on the Oreti River could be easily arranged. I am a keen knitter and often have a selection of sweaters and other knitted articles for sale – no ridiculous mark-ups added here! Please ask if you are interested.
Directions: *Take the Dipton–Castlerock road (west side of Oreti river), turn on to Boundary Road, second house on right.*

Wendonside
Farmstay
Address: "Ardlamont Farm",
Church Road, Wendonside, No 7RD, Gore
Name: Lindsay and Dale Wright
Telephone: (03) 202-7774
Beds: 1 Double, 2 Single (2 bedrooms)
Tariff: B&B Double $60, Single $40, Dinner with wine $20, Children welcome
Nearest Town: Riversdale 15 km, Balfour 12 km

We invite you to spend some time with us on our 4th generation 1200 acre mixed sheep and beef property which spreads from the flat river plains to steep rolling and tussock hills offering panoramic views of the surrounding area.
We are happy to show you over the farm, and related activities.

We have three young children and our interests include spinning and weaving, computers, Toastmasters, squash and golf. Having travelled widely we enjoy contact with other travellers.
Recent renovations have greatly enhanced the warmth and spaciousness we offer you in our large 80 year old farmhouse. Quality meals are a speciality, catering to specific tastes with one day's notice.
Situated half way between Queenstown and Dunedin (15 minutes off S.H.94), we are also ideally placed for day trips to Te Anau and Milford Sound.
Local attractions include two of New Zealand's best trout fishing rivers, the Mataura and Waikaia.
We assure you a visit will be worth your while. Please phone.

Waikaka
Farmstay
Address: Blackhills, RD3 Gore, Southland
Name: Dorothy and Tom Affleck
Telephone: (03) 207 2865
Beds: 2 Single (1 bedroom)
Tariff: B&B Double $50, Single $30, Children under 13 half price; Dinner $15
Nearest Town: Waikaka township, Gore

We are a family of six with four teenage children. Our fifty-year-old home, recently renovated to give generous comfortable living area, is situated on our 360 ha intensive sheep farm on a ridge above Waikaka River.
The guest room has two single beds (other beds may be available).
You may have dinner with us or if you prefer only bed and breakfast.
Our interests include family, farm, church, Masonic Lodge, sport and music. A warm welcome to couples and families.
Venture off the main road and enjoy warm hospitality, superb views and the refreshment of a quiet rural visit.
Directions: *Turn off State Highway 1 just north of Gore, onto State Highway 90. Turn left at Waikaka Valley corner, marked by church and windmill, follow signposts to Waikaka until T corner (approx 10 km). At T corner turn left, then first right onto gravel Nth Chatton Road. Proceed 4 km veering right at each intersection. We live on Robertson Road, the last kilometre a steep hill - 20 minutes from State Highway 1.*

Tokanui
Farmstay
Address: Progress Valley, R.D. 1,
Tokanui, Southland
Name: June & Murray Stratford
Telephone: (03) 246-8843
Beds: 1 Double, 2 Single (2 bedrooms)
Tariff: B&B $30 per person, children special rates, $15 Dinner, campervans welcome.
Nearest Town: Invercargill 1 hour, Dunedin 2 1/2 hours

Welcome to our place, just off the Southern Scenic Route of State Highway 92. We are ideally situated to spend a few days exploying this unique are of The Catlins.
There are many unspoilt beaches, petrified forest, yellow eyed penguins, waterfalls, bushwalks and caves all within 20 minutes drive from our home. Nearby is an excellent craft shed, local pottery and museum.
Our home is set in a large garden with tennis court, it has central heating and an open fire in the lounge. All beds have electric blankets.
The farm is 1000 acres with 3600 stock units of sheep, cattle and deer. 2 working dogs help with stock management. Guests are most welcome to join in farm or community activities.
We have a grown up family and enjoy meeting people, our interests range from rugby and most sports to music and gardening.
Our favourite menus consists of a local seafood for entree, followed by home grown meat and fresh veges from the garden, followed by homemade desserts.
Directions: *From Invercargill follow SH92 and 20 km past Tokanui take a right turn to Progress Valley. We are first house on right. From Dunedin go to Balclutha on to SH92 through Owaka and Catlins Forest until sign post to Progress Valley. Turn left, we are first house on right.*

The standard of accommodation in The New Zealand Bed and
Breakfast Book ranges from homely to luxurious but you can
always be sure of superior hospitality.

Ferndale, Gore
Farmstay
Address: Ferndale, RD2, Gore
Name: Lorna and Colin Dickie
Telephone: (03) 203-8335
Beds: 1 Double, 1 Twin Room
Tariff: B&B Double $55, Single $35; Dinner $15
Nearest Town: Mataura 7 km

Our home is 2,000 square feet, 10 years old, has large lounge-dining room and a pool room.
We are a middle-aged, semi-retired couple living on a 100-acre farmlet. We have sheep and thoroughbred horses.
We have a motorboat and are keen on camping and fishing. We are only abut 4 km from Mataura river, one of the world's greatest fishing rivers.
Our house is situated in a very quiet and peaceful area.
Directions: *Coming south, turn off State Highway 1 at Clinton Hotel, proceed south 37 km towards Mataura. Going north, turn through Mataura, past paper mills, 7 km up Ferndale Road.*

Rimu, Invercargill
Farmstay
Address: Rimu, No. 1 R.D., Invercargill
Name: Margaret and Alan Thomson
Telephone: (03) 230-4798
Beds: 4 Single (2 bedrooms, guest bathroom)
Tariff: B&B Double $55, Single $35; Dinner $20
Nearest Town: Invercargill 13 km 4 km from SH 1

Our home is approximately 30 years old, warm and comfortable with a sunny aspect, all rooms overlooking a colourful garden, with the farm beyond.
We run breeding ewes, a few very quiet Angora goats, and also have a licensed meat processing factory on our property. The beautiful city of Invercargill is only 13 km away and the choice of trips by sea or air easily arranged to wonderful Stewart Island. Te Anau, Queenstown and Dunedin only 2 hours' travel away.
You may have dinner with us and share an evening of relaxation and friendship or if you prefer only bed and breakfast. We can provide the breakfast of your choice with all home grown products. Stay as many nights as you wish, a 'welcome' is always assured.
Directions: *Take State Highway 1, travel approximately 8 km from Invercargill P.O. (towards Dunedin), turn right (towards large green building with red roof), turn left, then right over railway line. Travel straight ahead for 4 km, we are on your left, A. J. Thomson on the mail box. Travelling from Dunedin on State Highway 1 take Rimu turnoff on left, turn right at crossroads, we are 1 km from there, on your right.*

Invercargill
Private Hotel
Address: 240 Spey Street, Invercargill
Name: Montecillo Travel Lodge
Telephone: (03) 2182-503, Fax (03) 2182-506
Beds: 4 Double, 6 Single, 6 bedrooms
Tariff: B&B Double $79 Single $59; Dinner $23; Campervans $25

We are Aileen and James Horn. Our Bed and Breakfast Hotel is in a quiet street and close to the centre of Invercargill (10 minutes walk to all shopping). The main building is some 90 years old and we have returned it to its original state of large rooms and ensuite facilities, providing the best in beds and bedding.
We provide a full cooked breakfast – for the early starters or late sleepers – up to 9 am. A home-style three course roast dinner is available at 6 pm.
You can walk to the park and museum in five minutes.
A golf course is ten minutes walk, as well as a number of historic buildings.
Your comfort and a restful stay in Invercargill is our business.
We can arrange trips to Stewart Island and ensure that your next stop is booked and suitable. Free call to next B&B
Our guests recommend a two-night stay to at least find out about Invercargill, Bluff and Stewart Island. Four nights to see it all well, and have a well deserved rest.

Invercargill
Farmstay +
Self-Contained Accommodation
Address: "Lorneville Lodge",
6 R.D., Lorneville, Invercargill
Name: Bill and Pauline Schuck
Telephone: (03) 2358-031, 2358-762
Beds: 2 Single, 2 Double, 1 child's cot (2 bedrooms, guest bathroom)
Tariff: B&B Double $70, Single $35; Dinner $22; Children under 13 half price;
Campervans $8.50 per person
Self-contained tourist cabins, 12 beds, $15 per person
Nearest Town: Invercargill 14 km

We are situated 3 km from the main highway which takes you to Queenstown and Te Anau.
We are a family who have moved out of town to enjoy the "good life" on a 17-acre farmlet. Our main interest is goat farming.
We have sheep, hens, two cats, a dog and thoroughbred horses.
Our home has had extensive renovations so that we can provide the most comfortable accommodation possible. All beds have Sleep Well matresses, electric blankets and sheepskin overlays. You have a private bathroom if requested.
You may wish to spend time with us helping with chores and walking around the paddocks or perhaps you want to sit and relax to take time out from your busy itinerary.

Safe playing area for children.
If you are travelling by bus or plane we are happy to meet you.
You may have a family dinner with us or if you prefer only bed and breakfast.
All meals are prepared from farm fresh produce and our vegetables come from our own organic garden. I enjoy cooking and can promise you a delightful meal.
Invercargill has a beautiful park, interesting shops and friendly people.
Boat and plane leave Invercargill for Stewart Island.
Directions: *Travel north on State Highway 6 from Invercargill for 10 km. Turn right at Lorneville garage on to Lorne–Dacre highway, proceed for 3.5 km.*

Tussock Creek, Invercargill
Farmstay
Address: Sherwood Farm, Channel Road, Tussock Creek, No. 1 R.D., Winton
Name: Pat and Derek Turnbull
Telephone: (03) 221-7270
Beds: 4 Single (2 bedrooms, guest bathroom)
Tariff: B&B $25 per person, Dinner $15; Campervans $20
Nearest Town: Invercargill

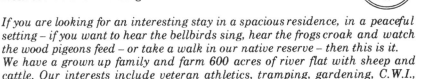

If you are looking for an interesting stay in a spacious residence, in a peaceful setting – if you want to hear the bellbirds sing, hear the frogs croak and watch the wood pigeons feed – or take a walk in our native reserve – then this is it.
We have a grown up family and farm 600 acres of river flat with sheep and cattle. Our interests include veteran athletics, tramping, gardening, C.W.I., and genealogy. We have travelled extensively.
We are suitable for a base as all southern tourist attractions are within easy daily reach. Having another 400-acres at Stewart Island enables us to arrange connections and accommodation there if required.
Directions: *Coming from either Invercargill or Queenstown/Te Anau, turn into Tussock Creek Road from Wilsons Crossing corner (midway between Invercargill & Winton) and proceed east for 11.5 km on bitumen and gravel., past the radio mast, cross the Makarewa River and our gateway is by the bridge.*
Coming from Gore, travel on highway 96 to beyond Hedgehope and turn left into Channel Road towards Tussock Creek. Please phone first.

Makarewa
Homestay
Address: 1953 Main Invercargill Queenstown Highway, Makarewa
Postal: Post Office, Makarewa, Southland
Name: Robert and Valerie Anderson
Telephone: (03) 235-8352
Beds: 1 Double, 2 Single (2 bedrooms)
Tariff: **B&B** $50 Double, $25 Single, children 1/2 price, $15 Dinner
Nearest Town: Invercargill is 10 km South from Makarewa

Our home is situated on State Highway 6, main Invercargill Queenstown Highway. We welcome you to our home which has a peaceful garden setting. All beds have electric blankets.
We are only a short distance from many activities - golfing, fishing and tramping etc. Invercargill has many interesting places to visit.
We are interested in meeting people, golf, music and crafts. Our property is run as a Commercial Horticultural Venture and Organic Gardening is one of our main interests.
You may have dinner with us or if you prefer bed and breakfast.
Directions: *1953 Main Road, Makarewa. Please phone.*

Tuatapere
Farmstay
Address: Riverbend Farm, Pukemaori Road, Tuatapere,
Name: Bob & Nancy Marshall
Telephone: (03) 225-5849
Beds: 4 Single (2 bedrooms)
Tariff: **B&B** $50 Double, $25 Single, $12-20 Dinner, children 1/2 price
Nearest Town: 7 km from Tuatapere on Southern Scenic Route, 80 km from Invercargill on tarsealed roads.

We are a family of four, our two daughters have both left home to join the workforce.
Our farm has a variety of animals and we have access to all types of farming - deep, goat, rabbit etc.
Our home is 14 years old - a colonial, brick, modern, convenient home surrounded by trees and gardens and captures the sun in all rooms. The guest rooms have twin single beds with electric blankets if required. Both rooms are spacious and share bathroom facilities, two toilets.
You may have dinner with us or, if you prefer, only bed and breakfast. We will provide breakfast of your choice.
The farm is picturesque with a river flowing through and therefore has some interesting walks.
Te Anau is 90 km away so can be a base for travelling to Fiordland. Tuatapere is popular for all outdoor activities like hunting, fishing and tramping.
Warm and friendly hospitality assured.
Directions: *Travel State Highway 99 which is also part of the Southern Scenic Route from Invercargill to Tuatapere. Travel from Tuatapere to Riverbend Farm by Orawia Road. We are 7 km away from Tuatapere. From Te Anau turn left at junction in Tuatapere and the drive 7 km to Riverbend Farm.*

Riverton
Farmstay
Address: Otaitai Bush, No.3 RD, Riverton, Southland
Name: Ian and Elaine Stuart
Telephone: (03) 234-8460
Beds: 2 Single (1 bedroom)
Tariff: B&B Double $50, Single $30, Dinner $15; Campervans $20 (4 people)
Nearest Town: 5 km from Riverton on Southern Scenic Route, 40 km from Invercargill

We are a family of five, our three sons all in the work force.
Our sunny and well heated house is surrounded by flower and vegetable gardens. The guest room has twin beds with electric blankets if required, share bathroom facilities, two toilets. View of Foveaux Strait and Stewart Island from lounge window. You may share dinner with us or if you prefer just bed and breakfast.
Our sheep farm is situated on the Southern Scenic Route 5 km from Riverton. Riverton is one of the oldest settlements in NZ, a fishing port with safe swimming beaches.
We enjoy sharing our home with visitors and a friendly stay assured.
Directions: please phone.

Halfmoon Bay, Stewart Island
Homestay
Address: "The Nest",
Halfmoon Bay, Box 88, Stewart Island
Name: Lorraine Squires
Telephone: (03) 219-1310, or 219-1185
Beds: 2 Double, 1 Single (2 bedrooms guest bathroom)
Tariff: 24 hour stay, 3 meals $65 per person

We are a commercial fishing family and we invite you to share our home as you explore "Rakiura", Isle of the Glowing Skies.

Beautiful island, we know so well
Where freedom, love and peace do dwell
Haven of refuge in time of strife
Heavenly place to enjoy sweet life
　　　A. von Tunzelman

All meals included in tariff.
We are a non-smoking household.

319

The NZ B&B Book
Comment Form

In order to maintain our high standard of hospitality we welcome your comments and suggestions.

Did you stay at any B&Bs especially deserving of praise?
Did you stay at B&Bs where the hospitality or amenities were less than you expected?
Do you have any comments?

Where did you get your *New Zealand Bed and Breakfast Book*?

How many of our B&Bs have you stayed at?

May we quote your comments?

Name..

Address..

....

Post to: The New Zealand Bed and Breakfast Book
27 Marine Drive, Mahina Bay,
Eastbourne, New Zealand

Order Form

The Australian Bed and Breakfast Book and *The New Zealand Bed and Breakfast Book* are comprehensive guides to B&B those countries. They describe homes, farms and guest houses offering warm, friendly hospitality. The charges are modest and the hospitality is genuine.

Price List
In New Zealand
The books are available from bookstores and information offices for $14.95. Or post your cheque using the form below. We will pay delivery costs.

In Australia
The books are available from bookstores and information offices for $12.95. Or post your cheque (Aussie $) using the form below. We will pay delivery costs.

Overseas Orders
You may order by simply sending your personal cheque in your own currency. Payment includes airmail postage

Either Book	**Both Books**
US$16.95	US$28.95
CAN$19.95	CAN$34.95
GB£9.95	GB£16.95
JP2230 Yen	JP3790 Yen
GER29.95 Dm	Ger49.95 DM

Please send me by airmail
The New Zealand Bed and Breakfast Book ....

The Australian Bed and Breakfast Book ....

Here is my cheque for............................

Name..

Address..

....

Post to: Moonshine Press
                  27 Marine Drive, Mahina Bay
                  Eastbourne, New Zealand

Index

NOTES